MONTGOMERY, R. A.

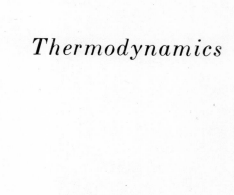

Thermodynamics

Thermodynamics

Franklin P. Durham

LOS ALAMOS SCIENTIFIC LABORATORY

SECOND EDITION

Prentice-Hall, Inc.

ENGLEWOOD CLIFFS, N. J.

1959

Library of Congress Catalog Card Number: 59-12679

Printed in the United States of America
91489

PREFACE

Courses in undergraduate thermodynamics have obtained an almost universal reputation as being among the most difficult in engineering curricula. This is unfortunate since the subject is so basic to engineering and is a necessary tool for later application courses such as steam power, gas turbines, internal combustion engines, heat transfer, refrigeration, aerodynamics, and gas dynamics. It is the author's belief that one difficulty encountered by the reader on first coming in contact with thermodynamics is the book itself.

Although many available books are judged to be excellent by an instructor who is familiar with the subject, these same books may be inadequate as judged by the reader who is unfamiliar with the subject. The author has used several of the most widely adopted thermodynamics texts in recent years and found none of them to be satisfactory from the standpoint of the students. Two of the most common objections are that the material is not written at a level that is suitable for the average student and that nowhere in the hundreds of formulas developed is a pattern given that summarizes and stresses the use of the important basic relations from which the more specialized formulas are derived. A third objection, common to most engineering books, is the lack of a system in the use of symbols which would aid the reader in learning the language of the equations. It was further noted by the author that most of the current elementary thermodynamics texts do not introduce the concept of stagnation conditions in steady flow systems. The concept of stagnation conditions is basic in the experimental measurements of high speed flows and simplifies the general energy equation without neglecting kinetic energy. It will be of increasing importance to engineers in the fields of steady flow power-plants.

With these factors in mind the writing of this book was undertaken with the following specific aims:

1. To develop the basic theory in terms of a minimum number of simple equations. This eliminates the necessity of memorizing a large number of specialized equations and focuses the reader's attention on the *important* relations. The fundamental relations are summarized in Chapter Seven, where they are divided into two groups: those that

apply to any thermodynamic medium and those that apply to the ideal gas.

2. To present simply the requirements for and necessity of reversible processes in the analysis of ideal thermodynamic processes.

3. To introduce the concept of entropy early in the book and to integrate this concept throughout, along with the treatment of irreversible processes.

4. To introduce the concept of stagnation conditions in steady flow processes and to stress the importance of their use.

5. To use a set of symbols incorporating a *system* for the distinction between entire and specific quantities, molar quantities, and quantity rates—with no double meanings or ambiguities.

Since the presentation has been simplified throughout, the instructor may go into more detail, in the classroom, in areas he wants to stress, and still the student has a text for home study that is easy to follow.

The first six chapters develop the basic theory which is summarized in Chapter Seven. Chapters Eight through Twelve are specific applications of the basic theory and may be studied in any desired order except that Chapter Eleven should not precede Chapter Eight. Chapter Thirteen on gas dynamics and Chapter Fourteen on heat transfer have been included for use in curricula where no special courses in these subjects are taught. An illustrated glossary of thermodynamic terms will be found in the Appendix.

The basic material in the text was developed and used in classes at the University of Colorado prior to publication.

The author wishes to thank Professor B. T. Arnberg for his help with the symbols and for his constructive criticism of the first six chapters; and Mrs. Kay Benson for her enthusiasm and help in preparing the manuscript.

Additional credit is gratefully given to the thermodynamics staff of the U. S. Military Academy at West Point, for suggesting the glossary and many of the changes included in the second edition.

FRANKLIN P. DURHAM

Los Alamos, New Mexico

CONTENTS

Appendix Charts   *320*

Glossary of Thermodynamic Terms   *322*

Index   *345*

Chapter I

FUNDAMENTALS

1.1 Thermodynamics

Thermodynamics is the physical science that deals with the study of energy, energy transfer, and the media employed for the transfer of energy. It is one of the most fundamental of the tools of engineering and is basic to the study of such fields as internal combustion engines, gas turbines, steam power plants, jet engines, aerodynamics, fluid mechanics, refrigeration, and heat transfer. The material in this book is designed to supply a necessary background for the study of the above fields, with primary emphasis on work and heat and the flow of gases and vapors.

1.2 Force, mass, and weight

A proper understanding of the dimensions and units is necessary for a working knowledge of thermodynamics. Much confusion exists over the units of force, mass, and weight in the British "gravitational" system based on pounds, feet, and seconds. The following paragraphs are presented in an effort to clarify these units and their use.

1.3 Force

The basic force unit in the British system is the pound force (lb). The pound force is defined as the force required to support the "standard pound body" (a certain mass of platinum preserved at the Standards Office in Westminister, London) against a standard gravity acceleration of 32.174 ft/sec².

1.4 Mass

Mass is a quantity of matter, and its magnitude is independent of the forces acting on it. The engineering unit of mass in the British system is the slug.

A slug is defined as that quantity of matter which, when acted on by a force of one pound, will undergo an acceleration of one foot per second per second.

1

From Newton's Second Law, that force is equal to mass times acceleration, a slug of mass under the acceleration of gravity would be acted on by a force in pounds numerically equal to the acceleration of gravity in feet per second per second. The "standard" acceleration due to gravity at the earth's surface is taken as

$$32.174 \text{ ft/sec}^2$$

(Use 32.2 ft/sec² for sliderule work.)

Another unit of mass, the pound mass (lb_m), is widely used and is the source of considerable confusion. While the pound mass is basic in that it is the mass of the standard pound body previously referred to, it must be used with care. If a slug is divided into 32.174 equal parts, each of these parts is a pound mass. Thus

$$w = 32.174m \quad \text{where} \quad w = \text{mass, } lb_m, \quad m = \text{mass, slugs} \quad (1.2)$$

It should be noted that the number 32.174 in Eq. (1.2) is simply a conversion factor relating two mass units. This is analogous to the relation between feet and inches; that is, 12 inches is equal to 1 foot. This conversion factor is sometimes called the gravitational conversion factor and is given the symbol g_c. From Eq. (1.2) and the definition of a slug, the following dimensions may be given to the conversion factor:

$$g_c = 32.174 \frac{lb_m}{lb} \text{ ft/sec}^2 \quad (1.3)$$

1.5 Weight

Weight is the force exerted on a measuring device, such as a set of scales, by a mass at rest acted upon by the acceleration due to gravity. The unit of weight in the British system is the pound, and since weight is a force, this unit is the pound force.

From Newton's Second Law, the following relation exists between weight, mass, and the acceleration due to gravity,

$$wt = mg = \frac{w}{g_c} g \quad (1.4)$$

where wt = weight, lb
      m = mass, slugs
      g = acceleration due to gravity, ft/sec²
      w = mass, lb_m

Thus, at a location where the acceleration due to gravity is 32.174 ft/sec², one slug of mass would weigh 32.174 lb and one pound mass would weigh 1 lb.

Frequently, in engineering literature, mass and weight in pounds are used interchangeably. While no numerical errors should result from such careless use of the pound mass unit and the pound force unit as long as the acceleration due to gravity is approximately 32.2 ft/sec², the two units are not dimensionally equal. Therefore, in order to avoid confusion, the term "weight" will not be used in this book to refer to a quantity of matter.

1.6 Thermodynamic media

Since thermodynamics is the study of energy transfer to and from a medium or media, the nature of the medium or media chosen for a thermodynamic process is important. The medium used for the transfer of energy in the steam power plant is water, both in liquid and in vapor form. The media used in the internal combustion engine are air and fuel vapor, which unite chemically to form combustion products. The medium used in many refrigeration plants is ammonia. The media used in some rocket motors are liquid oxygen and alcohol.

All these media are chosen for the specific applications because of some property or properties particularly suited to the given process. It is thus evident that a study of the behavior and properties of thermodynamic media is necessary.

1.7 Basic coordinates

It has been found experimentally that a knowledge of the pressure, temperature, and specific volume (P, T, and v) of a medium is sufficient completely to describe the state or condition of the medium. Further, it has been found, for any medium, that it is usually possible to write a mathematical expression for one of these characteristics as a function of the other two.

For example, it has been found for gases, such as air near atmospheric conditions of pressure and temperature, that the following equation describes the state of the gas,

$$Pv = RT \qquad (1.5)$$

where R is a constant, called the gas constant. This equation will be treated in greater detail in later sections.

Although other coordinates may be used to describe thermodynamic media, the basic coordinates are pressure, specific volume (or its reciprocal, density), and temperature.

1.8 Pressure

Pressure is defined as force per unit area. The most common unit of pressure in the British system is the pound per square inch. In many thermodynamic equations, however, it is necessary to use square feet rather than square inches in order to maintain a dimensional balance. In this case, the unit of pressure is the pound per square foot. Other common units of pressure are inches of mercury, inches of water, and atmospheres.

Atmospheric pressure is exerted on all objects in the earth's atmosphere. At the earth's surface, atmospheric pressure is equivalent to the weight of a column of air of unit cross section extending from the earth's surface vertically to outer space, where there are no air molecules. This pressure is called barometric pressure, since it is determined by a barometer and is usually measured in terms of inches of mercury. So-called "standard," or average, atmospheric pressure at sea level is taken as 29.92 in. mercury (14.7 lb/in.², or 2117 lb/ft²). The pressure exerted by standard atmosphere is called one atmosphere of pressure. Thus

$$1 \text{ atm.} = 14.7 \text{ lb/in.}^2$$

A column of mercury 1 in. high and 1 in.² in cross section weighs 0.491 lb and, hence, exerts a pressure of 0.491 lb/in.² per inch of height. Hence, the pressure exerted by a column of mercury of any cross section can be converted to pounds per square inch by the following relation:

$$1 \text{ in. mercury} = 0.491 \text{ lb/in.}^2$$

A column of water 1 in. high and 1 in.² in cross section weighs 0.0361 lb and, hence, exerts a pressure of 0.0361 lb/in.², or 5.2 lb/ft². The pressure exerted by a column of water of any cross section can be converted to pounds per square inch or pounds per square foot by the following relation:

$$1 \text{ in. water} = 0.0361 \text{ lb/in.}^2 = 5.2 \text{ lb/ft}^2$$

Pressure in a liquid or a gas acts equally in all directions and may be measured directly by a variety of pressure-sensing devices or gages. Most pressure-sensing instruments are acted on by atmospheric pressure, which opposes the pressure to be measured, and, therefore, measure the pressure of a fluid above or below atmospheric pressure. Such pressure readings are called "gage pressure," and the entire force per unit area exerted by the fluid is obtained by adding atmospheric pressure to the gage pressure. The resulting pressure is called the absolute pressure and must be used wherever pressures (not pressure differences) occur in thermodynamics.

Absolute pressure = gage pressure + barometric pressure

An example of a common pressure measuring device is the U-tube or manometer shown in Fig. 1.1. The tube contains a liquid more dense than the medium being measured. The pressure in the pressure vessel is exerted on one end of the column and atmospheric pressure on the other. The pressure in the vessel is then supporting the column of liquid plus the pressure of the atmosphere.

Some pressure gages read absolute pressure directly rather than the pressure that exceeds or is less than atmospheric pressure. Examples are mercury and aneroid barometers, aircraft manifold pressure gages, and altimeters.

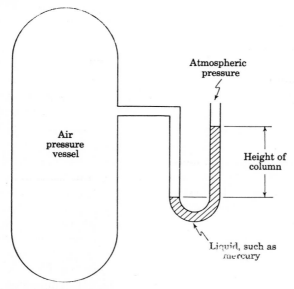

Fig. 1.1. Manometer used for pressure measurement.

Unless otherwise specified, all pressures used throughout this text will be absolute pressures.

1.9 Specific volume and density

The specific volume of a medium is defined as the volume per unit mass. The reciprocal of the specific volume is called the density and is the mass per unit volume. Common units for specific volume are ft^3/lb_m. Common units for density are lb_m/ft^3 or $slugs/ft^3$.

The specific volume of any homogeneous medium can be determined by first measuring the volume of a liquid displaced by a quantity of the medium and by determining its mass from its weight. The weight of a solid or liquid may be measured directly. The weight of a gas may be determined from application of buoyancy principles.

1.10 Temperature

The concept of temperature, of "hot" and "cold" objects, is an everyday experience. A precise definition of temperature, however, is difficult. An operating furnace is hot. A block of ice is cold. The thermal state of a furnace is greater than that of the human body. Therefore, a furnace feels hot. The thermal state of a block of ice is less than that of the human body. Therefore, a block of ice feels cold.

Temperature is a property of a medium that represents its thermal state or level. Two bodies are at the same temperature if there is no change in the properties of either when they are brought in contact. Two bodies at different temperatures when brought in contact will come to equilibrium if they remain in contact for a sufficient time. In this case, the temperature of the hotter body is reduced and the temperature of the colder body is increased.

Temperature cannot be measured directly but must be determined by a comparison of thermal equilibria. A temperature indicator, when placed in boiling water, will come to equilibrium with the water, and its reading will indicate a thermal level equivalent to that of boiling water. The same indicator, when placed in ice, will come to equilibrium with the ice, and its reading will indicate a thermal level equivalent to that of ice. The range between the boiling and freezing points of water under standard atmospheric conditions can be used as the basis of a temperature scale. The centigrade scale is such a scale. The range between boiling and freezing is divided into 100 divisions, and each of these divisions is called one degree centigrade. Zero for the scale is chosen as the freezing point, and the boiling temperature becomes 100 degrees centigrade (100C).

A similar scale is the Fahrenheit scale, where the range between boiling and freezing is divided into 180 divisions. The original zero for this scale was chosen as the freezing point of an ice-salt mixture, so that the freezing point of water is 32 units above zero and the boiling point is 212 units above zero. The conversion from centigrade to Fahrenheit is then

$$\text{degrees Fahrenheit} = \tfrac{9}{5}\ \text{degrees centigrade} + 32$$

The conversion from Fahrenheit to centigrade is

$$\text{degrees centigrade} = (\text{degrees Fahrenheit} - 32)\tfrac{5}{9}$$

Both the centigrade and Fahrenheit scales have been developed from the freezing and boiling points of water under standard atmospheric conditions. Neither of these scales is adequate for a thermodynamic temperature scale, since their zeros were arbitrarily chosen. If the freezing and boiling points of ammonia, for example, had been chosen for the basis of temperature scale and divided in the same way as the Fahrenheit or centigrade scales, the resulting numerical temperatures would represent a totally different thermal level. If mercury had been chosen instead of water, still another thermal level would be represented by any given temperature. Obviously, a more basic temperature scale is necessary for thermodynamics, which must deal with the behavior of many fluids, gases, and solids.

The thermodynamic scale of temperature is, therefore, based on a zero that is the same for all substances. This is the so-called absolute zero and is the lowest temperature that is possible of attainment.† This temperature has been determined experimentally by extrapolation of the results of tests of a constant volume gas thermometer to be $-459.69F$ or $-273.16C$. The absolute scale in the centigrade system is called the Kelvin scale and is abbreviated by the letter K. The absolute scale in the Fahrenheit system is called the Rankine scale and is abbreviated by the letter R. Thus

$$\text{degrees Kelvin} = \text{degrees centigrade} + 273.16$$

$$\text{degrees Rankine} = \text{degrees Fahrenheit} + 459.69$$

† Further justification of an absolute thermodynamic temperature scale will be given in a later section.

The unit of temperature used throughout this text will be the degree Fahrenheit and the temperature scale used, unless otherwise specified, will be the absolute, or Rankine, scale.

Temperature may be measured by a variety of instruments. Among the most common are liquid column thermometers (mercury and alcohol), vapor pressure thermometers, thermoelectric pyrometers (thermocouples), and optical pyrometers.

1.11 Thermodynamic systems

The analysis of most problems of thermodynamics requires the definition of a thermodynamic system. A thermodynamic system may refer to any space or to any matter or group of matter that is separated from its surroundings by a real or fictitious boundary. Examples of systems are a gas turbine engine and its instantaneous contents of flowing gas, the combustion chamber of this engine, the gaseous contents of a cylinder of an internal combustion engine, and the entire engine and its instantaneous contents.

Although thermodynamic boundaries are arbitrarily chosen, the choice of these boundaries and the resulting system directly affect the analysis of the energy involved. Consider, as an example, the motor-generator set shown in Fig. 1.2. If the system is defined by boundary A, electrical energy is supplied to the system and mechanical shaft work is obtained from the system. If, on the other hand, the system is defined by boundary B, there is no shaft work external to the system and the only energy crossing the boundary of the system is electrical energy input and the electrical energy output.

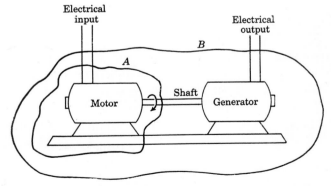

FIG. 1.2. DIAGRAM OF MOTOR-GENERATOR SET, SHOWING BOUNDARIES.

As another example, consider the cylinder and piston shown in Fig. 1.3, where the cylinder is filled with high pressure gas and is pushing the piston to the right. If the system is defined by the cylinder walls and piston face, boundary A, the external work leaving the system is the force exerted on the piston by the gas times the distance through which the piston moves. If the system is defined by boundary B, the external work leaving the system is that which the connecting rod performs on the shaft. The external work for system B is less than that for system A, since some of the energy imparted to the piston is absorbed by the friction of the piston rings acting against the cylinder wall and does not reach the connecting rod.

1.12 Reversible processes

In the field of thermodynamics, physical laws are reduced to mathematical statements or equalities. In order to perform mathematical operations on these equalities, such as differentiation and integration, the relation between all the thermodynamic variables, such as pressure, temperature, and volume, must be known. One requirement for such a relation is that the medium under consideration be at or infinitesimally near a condition of equilibrium throughout any process in which energy transfer takes place. Such equilibrium must be with regard to either time or location, but not necessarily with regard to both time and location. Only in this way will the variations among the thermodynamic properties be predictable and capable of being expressed as simple mathematical functions.

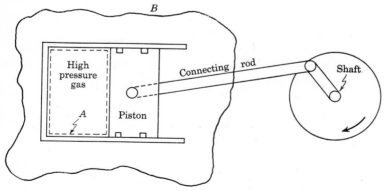

FIG. 1.3 DIAGRAM OF CYLINDER AND PISTON, SHOWING BOUNDARIES.

No such equilibrium can exist within a medium for any actual thermodynamic process owing to such phenomena as friction, (viscosity), conduction of heat, and imperfect elasticity. This difficulty has led to the concept of an ideal, or "reversible," thermodynamic process which may be used to approximate any actual process and which may be treated mathematically without resorting to statistical methods.

In addition to the necessary requirement for equilibrium it is desirable to be able to treat a general class of thermodynamic processes as mathematical functions that can progress equally well in either direction, that is, as functions that are not restricted as to direction.

The usual definite integrals of elementary calculus behave in this way. Consider the simple differential equation

$$dy = f(x) \, dx$$

where $f(x)$ is a simple, single-valued function of x. If no restrictions are placed on this function, the equation implies that integration in the positive x direction from x_1 to x_2 will give a result equal in magnitude but opposite in sign to the value obtained when the integration takes place in the negative x direction from x_2 to x_1. That is, interchange of the limits does not alter the magnitude of the integral. Thus

$$\int_{y_1}^{y_2} dy = \int_{x_1}^{x_2} f(x) \, dx = -\int_{x_2}^{x_1} f(x) \, dx$$

To satisfy the above requirement, a further restriction is placed on the ideal thermodynamic process, namely, all energy transfers in a process that is progressing in one direction must be equal and opposite in sign to all energy transfers that would take place if the process were made to go in the opposite direction. The "sign" here refers to energy transfer into or from the system rather than the direction of a physical displacement. Thus, if one type of energy transferred into the system is considered positive, the same type of energy transferred from the system would be negative.

The above process must be truly reversible. This requirement for a reversible process forbids the existence of friction from the process since the force of friction always acts opposite to the direction of motion and "negative" friction, or friction force that acts in the direction of motion, when the motion is reversed, is physically impossible.

In general, the existence of friction within a fluid medium also eliminates the possibility of equilibrium. However, it is possible to conceive of a mechanical process in which rubbing friction is present that takes place so slowly that the system is essentially in equilibrium throughout. Such a process would not be reversible even though it satisfied the necessary conditions for equilibrium.

The requirements of a reversible process, as indicated above, may be summarized as follows:

1. The process takes place in the absence of fluid friction or friction of any type.

2. The system departs from equilibrium by no more than an infinitesimal amount.

3. The process may proceed in either direction, and the system must be returned to its exact initial state by traversing the original process in the reverse order.

The primary requirement for a reversible process is that it be frictionless. Thus, "reversible" and "frictionless" may be used synonymously for all practical purposes.

Reversible processes of the above type are frequently termed "internally reversible." A somewhat more restricted reversible process involving the relation of the system to its surroundings, and known as an "externally reversible" process, will be discussed later in connection with the Second Law of Thermodynamics. Since this book will in general be concerned with internally reversible processes, such processes will be referred to as reversible and the more restricted type will be called externally reversible. In this text an internally reversible process is assumed in all problems unless stated otherwise.

1.13 Intensive and extensive quantities

A useful concept in the study of thermodynamics is that of intensive and extensive quantities, or properties. An intensive quantity is a quantity that is not related to the mass of the matter with which it is associated. An extensive quantity is a quantity that is directly proportional to the mass of the matter with which it is associated.

If the matter in a given condition is divided into two equal parts by mass, the values of the extensive properties will become half of the original values and the values of the intensive properties will be unchanged. In addition, all specific properties are intensive properties.

Pressure and temperature are examples of intensive quantities. Volume is an example of an extensive quantity.

For the purpose of consistency it is desirable to work in terms of a unit mass for all energy balances. Quantities per unit mass are called "specific" quantities. For example, specific volume is cubic feet per pound mass in the English system of units. Only extensive quantities can be stated on a specific basis. Intensive quantities are complete in themselves and cannot be stated on a specific basis. Obviously pressure per pound mass and temperature per pound mass do not have quantitative significance.

1.14 Notation

The notation used throughout the text is listed in Table 1 of the Appendix. This list of symbols and units has been adopted to reduce the amount of memorization and confusion on the part of the student in regard to double meanings and ambiguity. A system suggested by B. T. Arnberg is employed to distinguish specific, molar, and entire quantities and their time rate.

Where quantities are often used on a specific or per unit mass basis and time rates of the quantities are also commonly used, the following rules have been adopted:

1. Lower-case letters refer to specific properties (quantity per pound mass). Two exceptions exist.

$$m = \text{entire mass, slugs}$$
$$w = \text{entire mass, lb}_m$$

2. Capital letters Q and W refer to energy in transition on a specific basis. That is,

$$Q = \text{heat flow, B/lb}_m$$
$$W = \text{work, ft-lb/lb}_m$$

3. Letters with a bar over them indicate molar quantities (quantity per pound mole). For example

$$v = \text{specific volume, ft}^3/\text{lb}_m$$
$$\bar{v} = \text{molar volume, ft}^3/\text{mole}$$

4. Letters with a curve (tilde) over them indicate entire quantities (the product of the entire mass and the specific quantity). For example,

$$u = \text{specific internal energy, B/lb}_m$$
$$\tilde{u} = wu = \text{internal energy, B}$$

Entire quantities will be little used, as it is more convenient to work in terms of specific quantities. The entire quantity for any problem can be found by multiplying the specific quantity by the mass involved.

5. Letters with a dot over them indicate the time rate of the quantity. For example,

$\dot{w}$ = mass rate of flow, lb_m/sec

$\dot{v}$ = volume rate of flow, ft^3/sec

$\dot{W}$ = $\dot{w}W$ = work rate (power), ft-lb/sec

$HP = \dfrac{\dot{w}W}{550}$ = horsepower

Presented along with this list are the corresponding symbols adopted by the American Standards Association that frequently appear in engineering literature. It will be noted that 35 ambiguities, or multiple meanings, exist in the American Standards Association symbols, while none exist in the symbols adopted for this text.

Unless otherwise stated with regard to a specific problem, the units associated with all quantities will be those given in the Appendix.

PROBLEMS

1. A body weighs 2065 lb at a point on the earth where the acceleration due to gravity is 32.1 ft/sec². What is its mass in pounds and in slugs?

2. A body weighs 2065 lb at a point on the moon where the acceleration due to gravity is 5.35 ft/sec². What is its mass in pounds and in slugs?

3. A body has a mass of 80 lb_m and is accelerating uniformly at 10 ft/sec. What is the force acting on the body?

4. A force of 10 lb is acting horizontally on a body whose mass is 20 lb_m. In the absence of friction what will be the acceleration of the body?

5. A body has a mass of 8.5 slugs and is accelerating uniformly at 30 ft/sec². What is the force acting on the body?

6. An external force of 10 lb is acting vertically upward on a body whose mass is 0.3 slug. The acceleration due to gravity is 32.16 ft/sec². In the absence of friction is the body rising or falling, and what is its acceleration?

7. A vacuum gage reads 27 in. of mercury. What is the absolute pressure in pounds per square inch if the barometric pressure is 29.3 in. of mercury?

8. The absolute pressure in an evacuated tank is 1 lb/in.² What would a mercury manometer connected to the tank read if one side is vented to the atmosphere with a barometric pressure of 760 mm of mercury?

9. A water pressure gage reads 150 lb/in.² The barometric pressure is 24.5 in. of mercury. What is the absolute pressure at the gage?

10. The absolute pressure in a steam line is 206 lb/in.² Barometric pressure is 30 in. mercury. What would a pressure gage connected to the line register?

11. A water manometer connected to a wind tunnel and vented to the atmosphere has a positive reading of 2 in. What is this pressure in pounds per square inch? If the barometer reads 30 in. of mercury, what is the absolute pressure in inches of mercury?

12. Change the following temperatures to degrees absolute on the centigrade scale (Kelvin): 0C, 50F, 300F, 300C, −20F.

13. Change the following temperatures to degrees absolute on the Fahrenheit scale (Rankine): 0C, 27F, 300F, −10C, −10F.

14. Change the following to degrees centigrade: 120R, 120K, 92K, −13F, 2010R.

15. Change the following to degrees Fahrenheit: 120R, 120C, 120K, 520R, 2000R, 1800K.

16. What is the specific volume of a liquid in a cylindrical tank 1 ft long and 1 ft in diameter if the weight of the liquid is 40 lb under standard gravitational conditions?

17. A cylindrical tank 5 ft long and 10 in. in diameter contains 1 lb$_m$ of air. What is the specific volume?

18. The specific volume of water is 0.0162 ft³/lb$_m$. What is the mass of a volume of water occupying a spherical container 10 in. in diameter?

19. If the specific volume of a gas is 13 ft³/lb$_m$, what mass of the gas would be contained in a room $8 \times 10 \times 20$ ft?

20. Why is a process in which friction occurs not a reversible process?

21. Which of the following processes most nearly approach reversibility: air escaping from a tire; water flowing from a pipe into a tank; compressing a spring; steam expanding through a nozzle; the flow of mercury in and out of a barometer tube?

Chapter II

TYPES OF ENERGY

2.1 Energy classification

Thermodynamics is a study of energy, primarily with regard to heat and work. It is, therefore, necessary to identify and define heat and work and other related types of energy that will be of importance in this field.

Two broad classifications of energy are those which may be described as equilibrium state properties of a thermodynamic medium, sometimes referred to as point functions; and those which are defined as energy in transition, sometimes referred to as path functions. Of the first category some examples are pressure, temperature, volume, internal energy, potential energy, and kinetic energy. Any property of a medium is a point function, and vice versa. In the second category are work, heat, chemical energy, electric energy, and atomic energy. One of the distinguishing features of a path function is its transitory nature. These functions occur only during a change of state. Once the change is completed they no longer exist.

It is convenient where possible to work in terms of the energy per unit mass of a thermodynamic medium, that is, in terms of specific quantities. The entire quantity of energy involved can be found by multiplying the specific quantity by the mass of the medium under consideration. For this reason the discussion of energy types will be directed toward specific quantities.

2.2 Internal energy

Internal energy is the energy a medium possesses as a result of its thermal state and is caused by the internal molecular activity and molecular bonding forces of the medium. It is energy stored within the medium. The primary evidence of internal energy is the temperature of the medium although, in some cases, it is necessary also to know the pressure or volume to completely determine internal energy. The symbol to be used for specific internal energy is u and the conventional units of u are B/lb_m.

It is easily appreciated that water at the boiling point has more internal energy than water at the freezing point. In order to change the state of water from boiling to freezing, it is necessary to remove energy from the water. In the same although somewhat less apparent way, a gas, such as air, at high temperature has more internal energy than the same gas at low temperature.

It is not necessary to know the absolute value of internal energy of a medium since only differences in internal energy are involved in thermodynamic relations. It is convenient in tabulating properties of a medium to assign some arbitrary zero value to internal energy.

2.3 Potential energy

Potential energy is the energy a medium possesses as a result of its elevation relative to some arbitrary datum. It is equivalent to the energy necessary to lift the medium from the arbitrary datum to its elevation in the absence of friction.

The force necessary to lift a substance under the action of gravity is equivalent to the weight of the substance. The energy necessary to lift the substance a distance y is the product of the force times the distance, if the distance is not so large as to cause a variation in gravitational attraction. Thus, for a substance of mass m, where m is in slugs, the force acting is

$$F = mg \tag{2.1a}$$

The force acting on one pound mass, from Eq. (1.3), is then

$$F = g/g_c \tag{2.1b}$$

and the specific potential energy is

$$\text{specific potential energy} = gy/g_c \tag{2.1}$$

Potential energy has no absolute value but is always taken relative to some arbitrary datum. It can thus be either positive or negative with respect to that datum.

2.4 Kinetic energy

Kinetic energy is the energy a medium possesses as a result of its motion. It is the energy that could be recovered in bringing to rest a medium that is in motion, in the absence of friction.

Consider a medium of mass m traveling with a speed V. Referring again to Newton's Second Law, as the medium slows down, with negative acceleration dV/dt, the net force acting on the medium is

$$F = -m\frac{dV}{dt} \tag{2.2a}$$

In coming to rest, the medium will traverse a distance x, and the differential element of energy recovered in distance dx is

$$F \, dx = -mV \, dV \qquad (2.2b)$$

Since $$dx = V \, dt \qquad (2.2c)$$

Thus the energy recovered in bringing the medium to rest is

$$\text{kinetic energy} = \int_0^x F \, dx = - \int_V^0 mV \, dV = \frac{mV^2}{2} \qquad (2.2d)$$

Making use of the relation between the pound mass and the slug, Eq. (1.3), the specific kinetic energy is

$$\text{specific kinetic energy} = \frac{V^2}{2g_c} \qquad (2.2)$$

2.5 Work

Work is, by definition, the energy resulting from a force having moved through a distance. It is energy in transition and not a property of a thermodynamic system. The common unit for work is the foot-pound. The symbol for specific work is W and for an entire quantity of work is $\tilde{W}$.

For work to take place, a force must act through a distance. If the force, F, acting in the direction of x is variable with the distance, x, the work performed may be evaluated as

$$\tilde{W} = \int_0^x F \, dx \qquad (2.3)$$

This equation is derived from the definition of work and is not a reversible relation except in the absence of friction. It is simply the summation of the products of the force and the differential element of distance in the direction from 0 to x. Only if the process is frictionless (reversible) will interchange the limits result in the same magnitude of work when the direction of the process is reversed. Nevertheless, Eq. (2.3) allows the evaluation of work in physical processes in which the force is constant or the relation between force and distance is known.

Equation (2.3) implies that the following relation exists:

$$\tilde{W} = \int_0^{\tilde{w}} d\tilde{W}$$

This is, of course, not possible, since work is not a property of a medium or of a thermodynamic system. A system at rest possesses no work and a system cannot progress from an initial work to a final work, with the net work being the difference between the two. Work may be evaluated only for energy in transition, and then its value depends on the way in which the energy is transmitted.

For these reasons the differential of work is an inexact differential and will be defined by the following relation,

$$\tilde{W} = \int_c d\tilde{W} \tag{2.4}$$

where the integral is evaluated for the particular process through which the work takes place. With Eq. (2.4) as the definition of differential work it is now possible to write

$$d\tilde{W} = F\, dx \tag{2.5}$$

A familiar example of work is the energy necessary to compress a spring.

Example 2.1:

A coil spring has a spring constant (force necessary per inch of compression) of 20 lb/in. Determine the work necessary to compress the spring 3 in.

Solution:

In this case the relation between F and x is

$$F = 20x$$

Substituting this value in Eq. (2.3), supplying limits, and integrating gives

$$\tilde{W} = 20 \int_0^3 x\, dx = 90 \text{ in.-lb}$$

2.6 Work for a thermodynamic medium

Most work is transferred to or from some thermodynamic medium whose condition can be expressed by a relation between the coordinates pressure, specific volume, and temperature. In the case of work performed by or absorbed by a homogeneous medium, it is convenient to express the work in terms of the pressure and volume rather than in terms of force and distance. This is best illustrated by visualizing a piston and cylinder arrangement as shown in Fig. 2.1, where the system undergoes no changes in potential energy.

Imagine the cylinder fitted with a piston that develops no friction between itself and the cylinder walls. The cylinder is filled with 1 lb_m of a gas that is compressed under the action of a force that moves the piston to the left. The piston moves so slowly that the gas is infinitesimally close to equilibrium throughout the compression process and no internal friction is developed. Since the cylinder contains 1 lb_m of gas, the volume, at any instant, is equal to the specific volume.

As the piston moves through a distance dx, an amount of work equal to $F\,dx$ is supplied to the gas. That is,

$$dW = F\,dx \tag{2.6a}$$

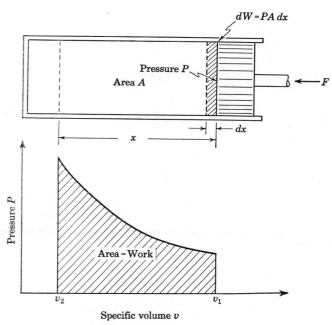

FIG. 2.1. WORK FOR A THERMODYNAMIC MEDIUM.

The pressure exerted on the piston is uniform and the force acting is equal to the product of the pressure and the area, PA. Thus

$$F = PA \tag{2.6b}$$

and

$$dW = PA\, dx \tag{2.6c}$$

However, the product $A\, dx$ is equal to the differential volume dv, so that the above relation becomes

$$dW = P\, dv \qquad \text{(reversible)} \tag{2.6}$$

The work supplied in compressing the gas from an initial volume v_1 to a final volume v_2 is then

$$W = \int_{v_1}^{v_2} P\, dv \qquad \text{(reversible)} \tag{2.7}$$

which can be integrated if the functional relation between pressure and volume is known. Equation (2.7) indicates that work can be evaluated as the area under the pressure-volume curve as shown in Fig. 2.1.

The requirements for the above development are that the medium be essentially in equilibrium, with the piston moving very slowly, thus eliminating the possibility of internal (viscous) friction. Since these are the requirements of a reversible process, Eqs. (2.6) and (2.7) apply to reversible processes. Other derivations of Eq. (2.6) can be made in which P is defined as the pressure at the piston face rather than the pressure throughout the medium. In this case, equilibrium and, hence, reversibility are not required. However, from the practical standpoint, a fixed relation between the pressure and volume must exist throughout the medium in order to integrate Eq. (2.7), and the process must be considered reversible.

In any actual engines employing cylinders and pistons, fluid and mechanical friction will exist, and equilibrium is not possible throughout the medium. In many cases, however, the actual process can be closely approximated by a reversible process. The relative simplicity of the mathematical treatment justifies the approximation.

Equations (2.6) and (2.7) were developed on a specific, or unit mass, basis. If more or less than a unit mass is involved, the equations may be written

$$d\tilde{W} = wP\, dv = P\, d\tilde{v} \tag{2.8}$$

and

$$\tilde{W} = w \int_{v_1}^{v_2} P\, dv \tag{2.9}$$

Example 2.2:

Determine the work required to compress 0.1 lb$_m$ of a gas under reversible conditions if the relation between the pressure and specific volume for the process is

$$Pv = 30{,}000 \text{ ft-lb/lb}_m$$

and the initial and final specific volumes are 14 ft^3/lb$_m$ and 3 ft^3/lb$_m$.

Solution:

Solving the above expression for P in terms of v,

$$P = \frac{30{,}000}{v}$$

Substituting this relation in Eq. (2.7) and integrating,

$$W = 30{,}000 \int_{14}^{3} \frac{dv}{v} = 30{,}000 \ln \frac{3}{14}$$

$$= -46{,}300 \text{ ft-lb/lb}_m$$

For 0.01 lb$_m$ the work becomes

$$\tilde{W} = wW = -4630 \text{ ft-lb}$$

The negative sign here indicates a decrease in volume or a compression process in which work is transferred to the gas.

2.7 Shaft work

Shaft work is the energy delivered by or absorbed by a mechanism, such as a turbine, air compressor, or internal combustion engine. It is the type of energy that is the object or desired result of heat engines, since, in heat engines, heat is developed for the purpose of performing work. Shaft work can always be evaluated from the basic relation for work, Eq. (2.3), where the force and distance refer to the mechanism that is developing or absorbing work.

In the preceding derivation for work performed on a thermodynamic medium the shaft work supplied to compress the medium was equal to the work done on the medium since no mechanical friction was present and the system itself was not in motion nor was there any change in potential energy. For this type of process, called a nonflow process, the shaft work is equal to the work of the medium. It will be shown later that for other types of process the shaft work is not equal to the work of the medium.

2.8 Flow work

Flow work is a classification of energy that occurs only when fluid flows into or out of a thermodynamic system. It is the energy the upstream fluid delivers to the downstream fluid in forcing fluid into or from a system. A mathematical statement for flow work can be made simple only when fluid is entering or leaving a system at a constant rate and when the pressure is constant across the boundaries of the system that the fluid is crossing.

Consider the fluid flowing steadily into the system shown in Fig. 2.2. The boundary of the system is at the left, and the pressure P is constant across the area of the boundary A. The fluid to the left of the boundary is expending energy in forcing the fluid into the system. The force acting is the product of the pressure and area, PA. An increment of volume of the fluid dv then moves through a distance dx in entering the system. The differential of work is then, as before,

$$F\ dx = PA\ dx = P\ dv \qquad (2.10a)$$

since

$$dv = A\ dx \qquad (2.10b)$$

The energy necessary to force one pound mass into the system is then

$$\text{Specific flow work} = \int_0^v P\ dv = Pv \qquad \text{(ft-lb/lb}_m) \quad (2.10)$$

It should be noted that any homogeneous medium at rest has a pressure and a specific volume; hence, the product Pv can be evaluated. However, in such a case, the product does not represent energy since no flow occurs. The product Pv represents energy only in steady flow processes in which the pressure at a boundary of the system is constant.

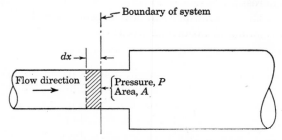

Fig. 2.2. Diagram of system for steady flow work.

The concept of flow work is often a difficult one for the beginner to grasp. Let us consider another example in an attempt to clarify flow work.

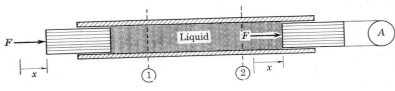

Fig. 2.3.

Fig. 2.3 represents a cylinder of constant cross-section, A, filled with an incompressible liquid. The cylinder is closed at both ends by movable pistons. During a given time interval a constant force, F, causes the piston on the left to be displaced a distance x. In the absence of friction the force F will be transmitted undiminished, to the piston on the right which, in turn, will be displaced by the incompressible fluid a distance, x. From Eq. (2.5) the work done on both pistons is seen to be

$$\tilde{W} = Fx$$

The work done on the piston on the left has been transmitted to the piston on the right. In this example the liquid which connects the pistons has acted as a conductor of work. The work which is conducted through a fluid in this manner is called *flow work*. In this particular case, it is equal to Fx. To evaluate this work in terms of the properties of the fluid at section 1, we can express the above equation as follows:

$$\tilde{W} = Fx\left(\frac{A}{A}\right) = \left(\frac{F}{A}\right)(xA)$$

In this expression (F/A) is recognized as the pressure at section 1 and (xA) as the volume of fluid which passes section 1 during the given time interval. This results in

$$\tilde{W} = P\tilde{v}$$

which, when divided by the mass in pounds passing section 1, gives the specific flow work as Eq. (2.10): Specific flow work $= Pv$.

In this simple example the flow work passing section 1 equals the flow work passing section 2. If, however, there are energy gains or losses between sections or a change in the diameter of the cylinder, the flow work changes in magnitude from one section to another. At a given section, where the rate of flow and the pressure are constants, the flow work will always be equal to Pv.

2.9 Heat

Heat is thermal energy in transition. It is the energy transmitted between two bodies or media that have different temperatures. Heat flows from the high-temperature body into the low-temperature body. The removal of energy from the high-temperature body lowers its temperature, and the flow of energy into the low-temperature body raises its temperature. If the bodies remain in contact for a sufficient period of time, they will reach the same temperature, thermal equilibrium will exist, and there will be no further flow of heat between them. A temperature difference, even though infinitesimally small, is necessary for heat to flow.

Heat is not a property that is possessed by a substance, just as work is not a property possessed by a substance. Heat exists only when thermal energy is in transition, and the amount of heat depends on the type of process involved. The differential of heat, therefore, is an inexact differential and is defined in the same manner as the differential of work. That is,

$$\tilde{Q} = \int_c d\tilde{Q} \tag{2.11}$$

where the integral is evaluated for the process through which the heat is transferred.

The unit of heat energy in the British system is the British thermal unit (B), which was originally defined as the amount of heat necessary to raise the temperature of one pound of water one degree Fahrenheit under standard atmospheric conditions. It has been determined experimentally that this amount of energy is equivalent to 778.13 foot-pounds of mechanical energy.

Since thermodynamics deals with energy balance and both heat and work units are used, it is frequently necessary to employ a conversion factor, called the energy conversion factor, or the mechanical equivalent of heat. This conversion factor is given the symbol J and is

$$J = 778 \text{ ft-lb/B} \tag{2.12}$$

The distinction between heat and internal energy is frequently troublesome to students new to thermodynamics. If heat is transferred to a substance at rest in the absence of mechanical work, the internal energy of the substance is increased. A familiar example is the heating of a pan of water on a stove. Heat is transferred from the high-temperature flame or electric coil to the water. This flow of energy into the water raises its temperature and increases its internal energy. When the pan is removed from the stove, heat no longer flows from the burner to the water. The water does not possess more heat after it has been heated (heat is not a property of a substance), even though it is said to be "hot." It does have more internal energy after it has been heated. In this case, heat has been converted into internal energy. It is also possible to convert work into internal energy, as will be shown later.

Once the pan of water is removed from the stove, heat will flow from the water to the surrounding atmosphere, which is at a lower temperature. This flow of energy from the water will reduce its internal energy and increase the internal energy of the atmosphere. In this case, internal energy of the water has been converted into heat, which, in turn, is reconverted to internal energy in the atmosphere.

Heat may be evaluated in thermodynamics by several methods, although the definition of heat does not serve as a basis for its evaluation as does the definition of work. One method of evaluating heat is by an energy balance, as will be discussed in later sections. Other methods of evaluating heat are based on the definition of the heat capacity of a medium or specific heat and on the concept of a thermal property called entropy.

2.10 Specific heat

The heat capacity, or specific heat, of a medium is defined as the quantity of heat necessary to increase the temperature of a unit mass of the medium by one degree. It has been found experimentally that the specific heat of a medium is a function of both the temperature and the pressure of the medium as well as the process used for the heat addition. Mathematically, this may be stated as

$$c_n = \frac{Q}{(T_1 + 1) - T_1} \tag{2.13}$$

where the subscript n refers to the type of process used for the heat addition. The two most common processes used for the evaluation of specific heat are constant pressure processes, for which $c_n = c_p$, and constant volume processes, for which $c_n = c_v$. It will be shown later that these two specific heats are not necessarily equal. The practical importance of specific heat for other types of process is slight although the definition of specific heat may be applied to processes other than constant pressure or constant volume.

If the specific heat is a function of temperature, as it is with many engineering media, Eq. (2.13) will define the specific heat for only one temperature, T_1. In this case, the limiting value of Eq. (2.13) is more useful and is

$$c_n = \frac{dQ}{dT} \qquad (2.14)$$

Equation (2.14) can be used to evaluate the heat flow for a given reversible process if the specific heat is known and if the relation between specific heat and temperature is known. For a constant pressure process, Eq. (2.14) can be integrated to give

$$Q = \int_{T_1}^{T_2} c_p \, dT \qquad \text{(reversible constant pressure)} \qquad (2.15)$$

And, for a constant volume process, Eq. (2.14) can be integrated to give

$$Q = \int_{T_1}^{T_2} c_v \, dT \qquad \text{(reversible constant volume)} \qquad (2.16)$$

The most common units for specific heat are B/lb_m F, although it is frequently stated as B/Mol F, where Mol stands for the molecular weight in pounds. The entire heat flow can be found by multiplying the heat per unit mass by the total mass involved.

Example 2.3:

Determine the heat required at constant pressure in raising the temperature of 2 lb_m of methane gas from 40F to 540F if the specific heat at constant pressure is given by

$$c_p = 0.282 + 0.00046T$$

Solution:

The Rankine temperatures corresponding to 40F and 540F are 500R and 1000R. From Eq. (2.15) the heat flow for one pound mass is

$$Q = \int_{500}^{1000} (0.282 + 0.00046T) \, dT = 313.5 \; B/lb_m$$

The total heat flow is then

$$\tilde{Q} = wQ = 2(313.5) = 627 \; B$$

The definite integrals of Eqs. (2.15) and (2.16) indicate that the heat flow for a reversible process can be represented as the area under the curve of specific heat versus temperature. This is shown schematically in Fig. 2.4 for an arbitrary function $c_p = f(T)$. For small temperature ranges for most thermodynamic media the specific heat may be considered constant. In this case, integration of Eqs. (2.15) and (2.16) gives

$$Q = c_p(T_2 - T_1) \qquad \text{(constant pressure constant specific heat)} \qquad (2.17)$$

$$Q = c_v(T_2 - T_1) \qquad \text{(constant volume constant specific heat)} \qquad (2.18)$$

2.11 Mean specific heat

For processes in which the temperature range is so large that the specific heat cannot be considered constant, a useful concept is that of a mean specific heat. The mean specific heat for a process is defined as that value which, when multiplied by the temperature difference for the process, would give the same heat flow as though the actual variation in specific heat had been considered. The mean specific heat for the process from T_1 to T_2 in Fig. 2.4 is shown in the same figure. It will be seen that this constant value gives a rectangular area equal to

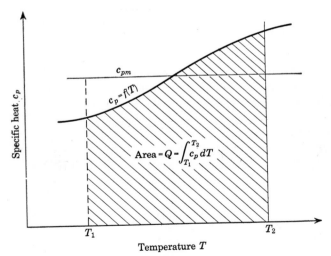

FIG. 2.4. HEAT AS AN AREA.

the area under the specific heat curve for the limiting temperatures T_1 and T_2. The mean specific heat is thus defined by the relation

$$c_{pm} = \frac{\int_{T_1}^{T_2} c_p\, dT}{T_2 - T_1} \qquad \text{(constant pressure)} \qquad (2.19)$$

$$c_{vm} = \frac{\int_{T_1}^{T_2} c_v\, dT}{T_2 - T_1} \qquad \text{(constant volume)} \qquad (2.20)$$

Example 2.4:

The relation for specific heat at constant volume for air is given by

$$c_v = 0.258 - \frac{120}{T} + \frac{40,000}{T^2} \text{ (B/lb}_m \text{ F)}$$

Determine (a) the amount of heat necessary to raise the temperature of 1 lb$_m$ of air from 40F to 600F at constant volume; (b) the mean specific heat for the process.

Solution:

The Rankine temperatures for the process are 500R and 1060R. From Eq. (2.16) the heat flow per pound is

$$Q = \int_{500}^{1060} \left(0.258 - \frac{120}{T} + \frac{40,000}{T^2} \right) dT = 96.2 \text{ B/lb}_m$$

The mean specific heat, from Eq. (2.20), is

$$c_{vm} = \frac{96.2}{1060 - 500} = 0.\ 172 \text{ B/lb}_m \text{ F}$$

Specific heat may be used to evaluate heat flow for constant pressure or constant volume processes in which the medium does not undergo a change in phase such as freezing or boiling. There are many processes, however, for which the specific heat is not known or for which the specific heat is infinite and cannot be used to evaluate heat.

The specific heat of water between freezing and boiling at atmospheric pressure is approximately 1 B/lb$_m$ F. However, water boils at a constant temperature under constant pressure conditions. Thus, heat is added to the water with no change in temperature, and Eq. (2.15) cannot be used to evaluate the heat added. Similarly, when water freezes, it gives up heat at constant temperature under constant pressure conditions and again Eq. (2.15) cannot be used. Compression of a gas under constant temperature conditions is another example of the inadequacy of the specific heat relation for evaluating heat flow. In all constant temperature processes, the specific heat may be considered infinite but cannot be used to evaluate a quantity of heat.

2.12 Entropy

Another method exists for determining the heat flow that can be used for any reversible process. This method is based on the use of a thermal property of a medium called "entropy." A fundamental definition of entropy will be reserved for a later article. The concept of entropy, however, is useful in the evaluation of heat and is introduced here for that reason.

Work is defined for a fluid medium as the product of an intensive or forcing coordinate, the pressure, and the change in an extensive or quantitative coordinate, the volume. With regard to heat flow, temperature is an intensive coordinate, and entropy is an extensive coordinate. The symbol for specific entropy is s. For the present, then, entropy will be defined as a coordinate that satisfies the following relation for a reversible process

$$dQ = T\,ds \qquad\qquad \text{(reversible)} \quad (2.21)$$

Making use of this equation, heat flow for a reversible process can be evaluated as the area under the curve of temperature versus entropy, just as work is evaluated as the area under the curve of pressure versus volume. For a constant temperature process only, integration of Eq. (2.21) results in a rectangular area

$$Q = T(s_2 - s_1) \qquad\qquad \begin{array}{c}\text{(reversible constant} \\ \text{temperature)}\end{array} \quad (2.22)$$

For any heating process other than a constant temperature process, the relation between temperature and entropy must be known before the integration can be accomplished.

The specific entropy is a property of a medium just as is specific volume. A knowledge of the absolute value of entropy, however, is not necessary since only changes in entropy are involved in thermodynamic processes. For this reason, the zero value of entropy may be arbitrarily chosen when it is desirable to tabulate the properties of a thermodynamic medium.

Example 2.5:

Determine the heat required to convert 1 lb_m of water to steam under standard atmospheric conditions if the entropy for water at the boiling point is 0.3120 B/lb_m R and for 100 per cent steam at the same temperature is 1.7566 B/lb_m R.

Solution:

Boiling water at constant pressure is a constant temperature process. The absolute temperature corresponding to 212F is 672R. From Eq. (2.22) the heat per pound is

$$Q = 672(1.7566 - 0.3120) = 970 \text{ B}/lb_m$$

This quantity is the latent heat of water.

In many thermodynamic processes, it is desirable to determine the change in entropy rather than evaluating the heat flow. In this case, Eq. (2.21) may be rearranged to give

$$ds = \frac{dQ}{T} \qquad \text{(reversible)} \qquad (2.23)$$

While this equation for the evaluation of entropy change is valid only for reversible processes, entropy is a property of a medium and does not depend on the type of process leading from one state to another. Therefore, in integrating Eq. (2.23) the actual process involved may be replaced by one or more fictitious reversible processes. All that is necessary is that the initial and final states of the real and reversible processes be coincident.

Example 2.6:

Determine the entropy change for 1 lb_m of water when it is heated from the freezing point at 32F to the boiling point at 212F under standard atmospheric pressure. The specific heat of water may be taken as 1 B/lb_m F.

Solution:

The absolute temperatures for the process are 492R and 672R. From Eq. (2.14)

$$dQ = c_p \, dT = (1) \, dT$$

Substituting this value in Eq. (2.23) and integrating,

$$s_2 - s_1 = \int_{T_1}^{T_2} \frac{dT}{T} = 0.312 \text{ B/lb}_m \text{ R}$$

This entropy change corresponds to the entropy given for water at 212F in the preceding example. Obviously, the zero value of entropy in that example was arbitrarily chosen as 32F. The processes for Examples 2.5 and 2.6 are combined on a temperature-entropy diagram in Fig. 2.5.

2.13 Adiabatic processes

In addition to processes in which heat is transferred, many processes in thermodynamics involve no heat flow and are termed "adiabatic" processes. An adiabatic process is defined as a process in which there

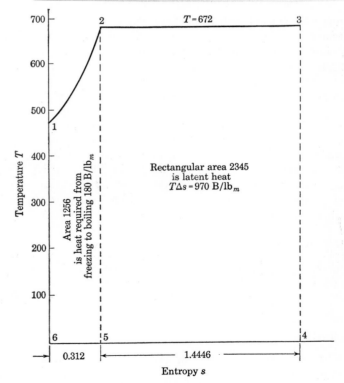

FIG. 2.5. T–s DIAGRAM FOR WATER.

is no heat transfer across the boundaries of the system. Such a process can be imagined for a system that is perfectly insulated.

2.14 Other types of energy

In addition to heat and work, other types of energy in transition are chemical energy, electrical energy, and atomic energy. The study of these types of energy is beyond the scope of this book, and they will be mentioned here only briefly.

Chemical energy is the energy liberated or absorbed when two or more substances react chemically to change their composition. Reactions which liberate energy are termed exothermic reactions, and those which absorb energy are termed endothermic reactions. Chemical energy is usually energy in transition within a thermodynamic system rather than energy that crosses the boundary of a system. The study of chemical energy is complex and is covered in the field of chemical thermodynamics. For the purposes of this text, chemical energy will be treated as heat that originates within the system and does not cross the boundaries of the system.

Electrical energy is the energy resulting from the flow of electrons in electrical circuits. It may be converted into either work or heat, depending on the apparatus involved. In general, in thermodynamic processes involving work and heat, electrical energy may be satisfactorily handled if it is treated as work.

Atomic energy is energy in transition that results from nuclear reactions. It is different from all other types of energy in that mass is converted into energy, whereas the mass of all other energy systems remains constant with energy transfer. The treatment of atomic energy requires a different perspective from that of simple thermodynamic processes and will not be necessary in this book.

PROBLEMS

1. A vertical cylindrical tank 8 ft high and 3 ft in diameter is filled to within 1 ft of the top. The base of the tank is 10 ft from the level of the ground. What is the potential energy of the water in the tank with respect to the ground?

2. How much work would be required to fill the tank in Prob. 1 from a pump located at the ground level?

3. A pump delivers 10 ft³/min of water to a tank located 30 ft above its inlet. What is the power developed by the pump?

4. The tank in Prob. 3 is 1 ft high and 2 ft in diameter. What is the difference in work required to fill the tank from the bottom compared to filling the tank from the top?

5. A ball weighing 0.61 lb is dropped from a tower 200 ft tall. Neglecting resistance of the air, what is the energy absorbed when the ball strikes the ground?

6. A ball weighing 0.5 lb is thrown vertically and reaches a height of 50 ft. Neglecting air resistance, what was the initial velocity?

7. An automibile having a mass of 3250 lb_m is traveling on level road at 60 miles per hour. The brakes are applied, and the car stops in 260 ft. What is the energy dissipated in bringing the car to rest? In what form will this energy be after the car has stopped? If the deceleration is constant, what is the stopping force?

8. What would be the stopping force in Prob. 7 if the initial velocity was (a) 30 miles per hour?; (b) 90 miles per hour?

9. A gas expands reversibly at a constant pressure of 80 lb/in.^{2} from an initial volume of 1 ft^3 to a final volume of 7 ft^3. What is the work done by the process?

10. A gas having a specific volume of 13 ft^3/lb_m under goes a reversible constant pressure process at 50 lb/in.^{2} to a specific volume of 5 ft^3/lb_m . What is the work required for 0.1 lb_m of the gas?

11. A gas in the amount of 3 lb_m is compressed reversibly at a constant temperature of 100F. The equation of state for the gas is given by Eq. (1.5). The gas constant R is 53.3 ft-lb/lb_m R. The initial and final pressures are 14 lb/in.^{2} and 20 lb/in.^{2} What is the work required to perform the compression?

12. A gas is expanded reversibly at a constant temperature of 500F, performing 10,000 ft-lb/lb_m of work. The equation of state for the gas is given by Eq. (1.5), and the gas constant is 35 ft-lb/lb_m R. The initial pressure is 200 lb/in.^{2} What is the final pressure?

13. The relation between the pressure and specific volume for a certain reversible process for a gas is $Pv^n = C$, where n and C are constants. Determine the work involved if the process undergoes a change from P_1 , v_1 , to P_2 , v_2 in terms of P_1 , P_2 , v_1 , v_2 , and n.

14. A liquid having a constant specific volume of 0.016 ft^3/lb_m enters a pump under steady flow conditions at 10 lb/in.^{2} and leaves

the pump at 300 lb/in.^{2} If the rate of flow is 10 ft^3/min, what is the specific work delivered to the liquid and the horsepower absorbed?

15. A water pump absorbs 10 horsepower in compressing water in a reversible steady flow process from 2 lb/in.^{2} to 400 lb/in.^{2} The specific volume of the water is constant and is 0.0162 ft^3/lb$_m$. What is the mass flow rate?

16. The variation in specific heat with temperature for a substance is given by

$$c_p = 0.1 + 0.00004T \text{ (B/lb}_m \text{ R)}$$

What is the heat required and change in entropy when 1 lb$_m$ of the substance is heated from 45F to 300F? What is the mean specific heat?

17. The specific heat of hydrogen is given by

$$c_p = 2.85 + 2.89(10^{-4})T + 10(T)^{-1/2}$$

What is the heat required to heat 0.06 lb$_m$ of hydrogen from 80F to 480F? What is the change in entropy?

18. The specific heat at constant pressure for a gas is given by

$$c_p = A + BT + CT^2$$

where A, B, and C are constants. A reversible constant pressure process takes place between two temperatures, T_1 and T_2 . Express the heat flow and entropy change for the process in terms of these temperatures and the constants.

19. The constants in Prob. 18 are $A = 0.282$, $B = 0.46(10^{-4})$, $C = -0.2(10^{-8})$. What is the mean specific heat for a process acting between 0 and 600F?

20. Heat is added at constant pressure to a piston and cylinder containing 0.05 lb$_m$ of air in a reversible process. The initial temperature, pressure, and specific volume are 500R, 14.7 lb/in.^{2}, and 12.5 ft^3/lb$_m$. The final temperature is 800R, and the final specific volume is 20 ft^3/lb$_m$. The specific heat for air is 0.24 B/lb$_m$ F. What are the work done and the heat added? What is the change in entropy? Sketch P–v and T–s diagrams for the process.

21. A closed rigid container contains a gas whose specific heat at constant volume is 0.1715 B/lb$_m$ F. There is added 100 B/lb$_m$ of heat, and the initial temperature is 40F. What are the final temperature and the change in entropy?

Chapter III

PROPERTIES OF THERMODYNAMIC MEDIA

The various types of energy of importance in engineering thermodynamics have been described in the preceding chapter. Before these types of energy can be treated in other than general terms, the properties of the thermodynamic medium for a process under consideration must be known, or some relation between the properties must be known. It has been previously stated that the thermodynamic coordinates, pressure, temperature, and specific volume, fix the state of a medium. For a given pressure and temperature the following properties are of interest: specific volume, internal energy, and entropy.

3.1 Enthalpy

Another quantity that combines the properties internal energy, pressure, and specific volume has been found to be very useful and is called "enthalpy." Enthalpy is, by definition, the sum of the internal energy and the product of pressure and specific volume expressed in consistent units. That is,

$$h = u + \frac{Pv}{J} \tag{3.1}$$

In processes involving flow work the term Pv represents energy, and in such processes enthalpy is the sum of two energy terms and is itself an energy term. In processes involving no flow work the term Pv does not represent energy but is simply the product of two properties, the pressure and the specific volume. Therefore, even though specific enthalpy carries the units of energy (B/lb_m) by definition, it is nothing more than a combination of properties and may be thought of as a property of a medium.

The specific properties of a substance are related to the form or phase of the substance, and some knowledge of the various forms of a substance is necessary before the properties of the substance can be discussed intelligently.

3.2 Forms of matter

Thermodynamic media may be in the form of a solid, a liquid, or a gas. The following definitions of these forms are commonly accepted:

A solid is a form of substance that possesses a definite shape independent of any container. A liquid is a form that will conform to the shape of a container but will present one free surface if it does not fill the container. A gas is a form that will conform to and fill a container. A gas near the condensation point is called a vapor.

Pure thermodynamic media are capable of existence in all three forms or phases. The form or phase of a substance represents the state of its molecular aggregation. The molecules in a liquid are not so closely spaced as those in a solid at the same pressure and have more freedom of movement. The molecules in a gas are not so closely spaced as those in a liquid at the same pressure and have more freedom of movement. The internal energy of a medium is closely associated with the degree of molecular activity within the medium, and the form of a medium determines to some extent its energy level. Energy is required to change the state of molecular aggregation, and this energy is termed "latent heat."

A familiar example of phase change of a substance is the conversion of ice into water and water into steam by the addition of heat. When a substance undergoes a change in phase, heat is added or removed with no change in the temperature of the substance.

Consider heating 1 lb$_m$ of ice at atmospheric pressure from some temperature below the freezing point of water. As heat is added, the temperature increases to the temperature at which ice melts. This is

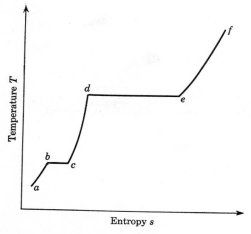

Fig. 3.1. Temperature-entropy diagram for water at constant pressure.

shown as line a–b in Fig. 3.1, which is a temperature-entropy diagram. It will be recalled that the area under a temperature-entropy curve is equivalent to the heat transmitted for a reversible process. The area under line b–c represents the heat addition required to melt the ice. The area under line c–d represents the heat addition to raise the temperature of the water from the freezing to the boiling point. At point d the entire quantity of water is at the boiling point and is termed "saturated liquid." Further addition of heat from d to e causes the water to boil and change phase from liquid to gas. At point e the entire quantity is in the form of steam and is termed "saturated vapor." Further addition of heat from e to f increases the temperature, and steam in this region is termed "superheated steam."

3.3 Critical conditions

If a higher pressure than atmospheric were chosen for the above discussion the line d–e would be above that shown in Fig. 3.1 and shorter. The locus of the points d–e for all pressures is called a saturation curve and is shown in Fig. 3.2. As shown in Fig. 3.2, a pressure

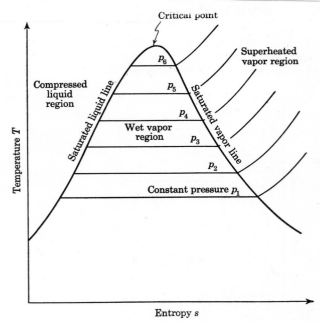

Fig. 3.2. Saturation curve for water.

and temperature are finally reached where the latent heat of vaporization is zero and the saturated liquid and saturated vapor lines meet at a point. This condition is termed the "critical point." This pressure is termed the "critical" pressure, and the temperature is termed the "critical" temperature. At and above the critical point no well-defined distinction exists between the liquid and gas phase. Table 3.1 lists the critical conditions for several common substances.

Diagrams similar to Fig. 3.2 can be constructed for any thermodynamic medium, such as carbon dioxide or ammonia. Water has been chosen for this discussion since it is a familiar fluid.

3.4 Phase diagrams

Phase changes may be from solid to liquid, called melting; from liquid to vapor, called boiling; or from solid to vapor, called sublimation. In addition to these phase changes there are several distinct solid phases that are identified by the crystalline structure of a solid substance. Only one solid phase will be considered here, and that is the solid phase that changes to liquid with the addition of heat.

These phase changes may be shown on a single diagram, called a phase diagram, which relates the pressure and temperature at which phase changes take place. Such a diagram for water is shown in Fig. 3.3. As shown in Fig. 3.3, the sublimation curve, fusion curve, and vaporization curve meet at a point called the triple point. The vaporization curve terminates at the critical point, as previously discussed.

The sublimation curve terminates at the triple point, and sublimation for most substances will occur only at very low pressures. An exception is dry ice, CO_2, which sublimes readily at atmospheric pressure and temperature.

TABLE 3.1

CRITICAL CONDITIONS

Substance	Critical Temperature Fahrenheit	Critical Pressure lb/in.^{2}
Helium......................	−450	34
Hydrogen....................	−400	291
Nitrogen....................	−233	500
Oxygen......................	−182	735
Water.......................	705	3205

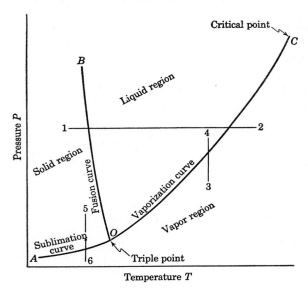

FIG. 3.3. PHASE DIAGRAM FOR WATER.

Triple point data for several common substances are presented in Table 3.2.

Process 1–2 in Fig. 3.3 represents a constant pressure heating process above the triple point in which ice first transforms to liquid water and then to steam. Process 3–4 represents a constant temperature compression in which steam is transformed into liquid water. Process 5–6 represents a constant temperature expansion in which ice is transformed directly from ice to steam. It will be noted from Table

TABLE 3.2

TRIPLE POINT CONDITIONS

Substance	Triple Point Temperature Fahrenheit	Triple Point Pressure lb/in.²
Carbon dioxide	−70	75
Helium	−455	0.748
Hydrogen	−434	0.995
Nitrogen	−346	1.862
Oxygen	−361	0.039
Water	32	0.088

3.2 that the final absolute pressure for the last process must be less than 0.088 lb/in.^{2}

3.5 Quality

By quality (symbol, letter X) is meant that per cent of mass of a boiling liquid that has vaporized. The quantity $(1 - X)$ is called the moisture, or the percentage moisture. Water at the saturated vapor condition has a quality of 100 per cent; at the saturated liquid condition, zero quality. Quality has no significance in the superheated vapor or compressed liquid regions; it applies only in the wet vapor region and to the liquid-to-vapor phase change.

Since both pressure and temperature can remain constant while a substance is undergoing a phase change, this pressure and temperature do not define the condition of the substance. In the wet vapor region the pressure (or temperature) and the quality will define the condition of the substance if the properties of the saturated liquid and saturated vapor are known.

3.6 Vapor tables

Much experimental and analytical work has been done to determine the properties of thermodynamic media such as water, carbon dioxide, and ammonia in the wet vapor and superheat regions. These properties have been tabulated for many substances. Condensed tables of the properties of saturated liquid and saturated vapor for water are given in Tables 2 and 3 of the Appendix. Table 4 gives the properties of superheated water vapor.

Table 2 is based on saturation temperatures, and Table 3 is based on saturation pressures. Both pressures and temperatures are necessary to determine the properties in the superheat region and are used in Table 4. The properties listed in these tables are specific volume, enthalpy, and entropy. No values for internal energy are given. Internal energy values can be easily calculated, however, from the values of enthalpy, specific volume, and pressure by making use of the definition of enthalpy, Eq. (3.1).

It is conventional in tabulating properties in the saturated vapor region to use the subscript f to indicate the saturated liquid condition and the subscript g to indicate the saturated vapor condition. For example,

$$v_f = \text{specific volume of saturated liquid}$$

$$v_g = \text{specific volume of saturated vapor}$$

It has also been found convenient to tabulate the change in properties in the phase change from saturated liquid to saturated vapor. The subscript $_{fg}$ is used to indicate this change. For example,

$$v_{fg} = v_g - v_f$$

$$= \text{change in specific volume during phase change}$$

A fluid undergoing a phase change consists of a mixture of vaporized particles and liquid particles. The quality represents the ratio of the mass of the vapor to the entire mass of liquid and vapor. Thus

$$X = \frac{\text{lb}_m \text{ of vapor}}{\text{lb}_m \text{ of vapor plus liquid}}$$

$$1 - X = \frac{\text{lb}_m \text{ of liquid}}{\text{lb}_m \text{ of vapor plus liquid}}$$

The properties of the mixture at any quality X may be found as the weighted average of the properties of the saturated liquid and saturated vapor in the mixture.

The determination of the entropy of a partially vaporized liquid will be taken as an example. The quality of the vapor is X. Then

$$X s_g = \text{entropy of vapor per pound of mixture}$$

$$(1 - X)s_f = \text{entropy of liquid per pound of mixture}$$

and $s = \text{entropy of mixture per pound of mixture}$

Obviously the specific entropy of the mixture is equal to the sum of the entropy of the vapor per pound of mixture plus the entropy of the liquid per pound of mixture. Thus

$$s = (1 - X)s_f + X s_g \tag{3.2a}$$

$$= s_f + X(s_g - s_f) \tag{3.2b}$$

But $s_{fg} = s_g - s_f$ (3.2c)

so that $s = s_f + X s_{fg}$ (3.2)

The above equation states that the property of the mixture is equal to the property at the saturated liquid condition plus the amount that the percentage of vaporization increases the property because of change in phase. Figure 3.4 will aid in visualizing the use of the quality to determine properties in the saturation region. Consider a partially vaporized fluid of quality X whose condition is shown at a point on the constant temperature vaporization curve T. It is apparent from this figure that the specific entropy at the point is given by Eq. (3.2). It is also apparent that the entropy could be obtained from the following relation

$$s = s_g - (1 - X)s_{fg} \tag{3.3}$$

Equations of the form of either Eq. (3.2) or Eq. (3.3) are correct for the determination of properties in the saturated region. If the quality is less than 0.5, Eq. (3.2) will allow greater accuracy for slide-rule calculations. If the quality is more than 0.5, Eq. (3.3) will allow greater accuracy for slide-rule calculations.

Example 3.1:

Determine the enthalpy of steam at 80 lb/in.² pressure with a quality of 90 per cent.

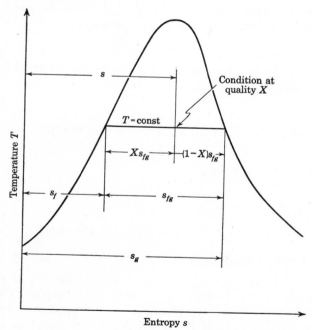

FIG. 3.4. *T–s* DIAGRAM SHOWING RELATION OF QUALITY TO PROPERTIES.

Solution:

Since the pressure is stated, Table 3 in the appendix should be used. The quality is over 50 per cent; so Eq. (3.3) will be more accurate. From Table 3 at 80 lb/in.^{2} the following values are obtained,

$$h_g = 1183.1, \qquad h_{fg} = 901.1$$

and from Eq. (3.3)

$$h = 1183.1 - 0.1(901.1) = 1093.0 \text{ B/lb}_m$$

A substance that has entirely vaporized but is not far removed from the saturated vapor condition is termed a superheated vapor. Since in this region no phase change is occurring, the pressure and temperature completely determine the condition of the vapor. Tables of properties of superheated vapors are usually given in terms of the pressure and temperature as shown in Table 4 of the Appendix for superheated water vapor. The term "quality" has no significance in the superheat region. The term "degrees superheat" is often used in the description of a point in the superheat region. The number of degrees superheat is the difference between the temperature of the point in question and the saturation temperature at the same pressure.

Example 3.2:

Determine the specific volume of water vapor at 100 lb/in.^{2} absolute pressure and 470F.

Solution:

From Table 4 of the Appendix for water at 100 lb/in.^{2} and 400F

$$v = 4.937$$

and at 100 lb/in.^{2} and 500F

$$v = 5.589$$

By linear interpolation for 470F

$$v = 4.937 + .7(5.589 - 4.937) = 5.393 \text{ ft}^3/\text{lb}_m$$

3.7 Compressed liquid tables

A substance that is entirely liquid and is not at the saturated liquid condition is termed a "compressed" liquid. Since no phase change is occurring in this region, the pressure and temperature completely determine the condition of the liquid. Tables of properties of compressed liquids are usually presented in the same form as super-heated vapor tables, that is, in terms of pressures and temperatures. Table 5 of the Appendix lists the properties of compressed water through a limited range of pressures and temperatures.

A comparison of Tables 2, 3, and 5 shows that the properties of compressed water are primarily a function of temperature and are relatively insensitive to pressure. It is, therefore, permissible for approximate engineering calculations to use the same properties for a compressed liquid as for a saturated liquid at the same temperature as the compressed liquid, for pressures up to 1000 lb/in.[2]

3.8 Gases

Many substances exist as gases at atmospheric conditions of pressure and temperature. The most familiar and plentiful gas is air, which is primarily a mixture of two gases—oxygen and nitrogen. Other familiar gases are helium, carbon dioxide, ammonia, and hydrogen.

While any saturated or superheated vapor may be considered a gas in that it will fill a container and presents no free surface, the term "gas" in thermodynamics usually refers to a highly superheated vapor, although no fine distinction between "vapor" and "gas" exists. It has been stated previously that it is possible to write a functional relation between the quantities pressure, temperature, and specific volume for any pure substance that will describe its condition or state. Such equations of state are complex for vapors near saturation but become less complex in the region of high superheat. At low pressures and high superheat the condition of gases can be described by a simple mathematical relation, called the equation of state of an ideal, or perfect, gas.

3.9 The ideal, or perfect, gas

The equation of state for an ideal gas was developed from the early experiments of Boyle and Charles, who used air for their investigations. Boyle's investigation showed that if a given quantity of air was held at a constant temperature the product of the pressure of the air and its volume remained constant. That is, for one pound of gas

$$Pv = \text{constant (temperature constant)} \qquad (3.4a)$$

Charles' experiments showed that the volume of a quantity of air was directly proportional to its absolute temperature if the pressure was held constant; and that the pressure was directly proportional to the absolute temperature if the volume was held constant. That is, for one pound

$$\frac{v}{T} = \text{constant (pressure constant)} \tag{3.4b}$$

$$\frac{P}{T} = \text{constant (volume constant)} \tag{3.4c}$$

A relation among the pressure, volume, and temperature may be obtained from Eqs. (3.4a) and (3.4b). Consider 1 lb_m of gas at conditions P_1, v_1, T_1 undergoing a constant temperature process to a second condition P_2, v_x, and T_1. From Eq. (3.4a)

$$P_1 v_1 = P_2 v_x$$

Now let the gas undergo a constant pressure process to a third condition P_2, v_2, and T_2. From Eq. (3.4b) for this process

$$\frac{v_x}{T_1} = \frac{v_2}{T_2}$$

Eliminating v_x from the above expressions results in

$$\frac{P_1 v_1}{T_1} = \frac{P_2 v_2}{T_2} = \text{constant} \tag{3.4}$$

Since the pressure and temperature at the final condition were arbitrarily chosen, the above equation can be stated in the form of an equation of state

$$Pv = RT \tag{3.5}$$

where R is a constant for the gas called the gas constant. The units of R in the English system are ft-lb/lb_m R. For air at atmospheric conditions the value of the gas constant has been determined experimentally to be 53.3 ft-lb/lb_m R. Values of the gas constant for other gases are given in Table 7 of the Appendix.

The apparatus used by Boyle and Charles was not refined, and later investigators have shown Eq. (3.5) to be only approximately true, but that all gases will approach this relation at conditions of very low pressure. A gas which behaves according to Eq. (3.5) is called an ideal, or perfect, gas and will be referred to here as an ideal gas. While no real gas exactly obeys the equation of state of an ideal gas, many gases at atmospheric conditions may be described by it with sufficient accuracy for most purposes.

The gas constant in Eq. (3.5) is a characteristic of a given gas but will be different for different gases. A more general equation of state that is independent of the gas can be developed by making use of Avogadro's Principle, which states that equal volumes of all gases at the same conditions of pressure and temperature contain equal numbers of molecules. Under these conditions the masses of equal volumes of gases are proportional to the molecular weights of the gases.

Consider a quantity of a gas A whose mass is equal to its molecular weight, M, in pounds. For this gas and quantity, Eq. (3.5) becomes

$$P_A M_A v_A = M_A R_A T_A \qquad (3.6a)$$

Consider also a quantity of any other gas B whose mass is equal to its molecular weight in pounds under the same conditions of pressure and temperature as gas A. In this case

$$P_A M_B v_B = M_B R_B T_A \qquad (3.6b)$$

But from Avogadro's Principle

$$M_B v_B = M_A v_A = \bar{v} \qquad (3.6)$$

the molar volume. Dividing Eq. (3.6a) by Eq. (3.6b) and making use of Eq. (3.6) results in

$$M_A R_A = M_B R_B \qquad (3.7a)$$

Since gas B was arbitrarily chosen, the product MR for any gas obeying Eq. (3.5) must be equal to the product MR for any other gas obeying the same relation. This product has been called the "universal" or "molar" gas constant and has been determined experimentally for a number of gases. Its average value is

$$\overline{R} = MR = 1544 \text{ ft-lb/Mol R} \qquad (3.7)$$

The above relation offers a simple method of determining the gas constant R of a gas when its molecular weight is known.

Example 3.3:

Determine the gas constant for carbon dioxide, CO_2.

Solution:

The molecular weight of carbon is 12, and the oxygen is 32, giving a molecular weight of carbon dioxide of 44. From Eq. (3.7) the gas constant is found to be

$$R = \frac{1544}{44} = 35.1 \text{ ft-lb/lb}_m \text{ R}$$

3.10 Gas tables

It can be shown for an ideal gas that the internal energy and enthalpy are dependent only upon the temperature. It is possible, therefore, to tabulate these properties in terms of the temperature alone, independent of the pressure. Such a tabulation can take into account the variation of specific heat with temperature. Table 6 of the Appendix gives the properties of air based on the ideal gas equation of state. In this table the variation of specific heat, determined experimentally, has been taken into account.

It is sometimes permissible to consider the specific heat of a gas as constant over a given temperature range. In this case, if the specific heat is known, it is possible to calculate all the thermodynamic properties without the aid of a table of properties, as will be shown in a later chapter.

Table 6 lists internal energy and enthalpy in terms of temperature. The specific volume of air can be determined from the ideal gas equation of state if the pressure and temperature are known. The other quantities listed in Table 6 will be discussed in a later chapter. It should be pointed out that zero for the values of Table 6 is based on a temperature of -459.7F, or absolute zero, while zero for the preceding tables is based on a temperature of 32F. Therefore, values from Table 6 cannot be compared directly with values from the preceding tables. The choice of a zero for any given table is arbitrary since only differences of values presented within that table are involved. Care should be taken, however, in comparing values at the same temperature between different tables.

Example 3.4:

Determine the enthalpy and specific volume for air at 80 lb/in.² absolute pressure and 120F temperature.

Solution:

The absolute temperature corresponding to 120F is 580R. From Table 6 for this temperature the enthalpy is

$$h = 138.7 \text{ B/lb}_m$$

The pressure is 11,520 lb/ft². The gas constant for air is 53.3 ft-lb/lb$_m$ R. From Eq. (3.5) the specific volume is

$$v = \frac{RT}{P} = \frac{53.3(580)}{11,520} = 2.68 \text{ ft}^3/\text{lb}_m$$

3.11 Other equations of state

The equation of state of an ideal gas is applicable to many gases at or near atmospheric pressure. As a gas approaches the saturated vapor region, however, large errors may result from the use of the ideal gas equation. Many investigators have sought to develop equations of state that will accurately describe the condition of a substance from the saturated liquid region to the ideal gas region. Two of the most widely used equations of state will be mentioned briefly.

3.12 Van der Waals equation of state

Van der Waals equation of state is

$$\left(P + \frac{a}{\bar{v}^2} \right) (\bar{v} - b) = \bar{R}T \tag{3.8}$$

where a and b are constants for a given gas. This equation applies in the superheat region and above the critical point but should not be used in the saturated vapor region.

3.13 Beattie-Bridgman equation of state

The Beattie-Bridgman equation of state is

$$P = \frac{\bar{R}T(1 - \epsilon)}{\bar{v}^2} (\bar{v} + B) - \frac{A}{\bar{v}^2} \tag{3.9}$$

with

$$A = A_0 \left(1 - \frac{a}{\bar{v}} \right)$$

$$B = B_0 \left(1 - \frac{b}{\bar{v}} \right)$$

$$\epsilon = \frac{c}{\bar{v}T^2}$$

where A_0, a, B_0, b, and c are constants for a given substance.

This equation applies in the superheat region and into the saturated vapor region. It is one of the most accurate of all the proposed equations of state, and also one of the most complex. It has been used in calculating vapor tables, such as those given in the Appendix.

The use of more complicated equations of state than that for an ideal gas is beyond the scope of this book. For most work in engineering thermodynamics tables of properties are available so that tedious and difficult mathematical operations involving the complex equations of state are not necessary.

PROBLEMS

1. A tank having a volume of 10 ft³ is filled with steam at a pressure of 100 lb/in.² and a quality of 92 per cent. (a) What is the mass of the steam? (b) What is the enthalpy of the steam? (c) What is the entropy of the steam?

2. Solve Prob. 1 if the quality of the steam is 33 per cent, all other data remaining the same.

3. Steam at a pressure of 450 lb/in.² has an enthalpy of 1300 B/lb$_m$ · What are its temperature, entropy, and specific volume?

4. Steam at a pressure of 450 lb/in.² has an enthalpy of 1100 B/lb$_m$ · What are its temperature, entropy, and specific volume?

5. A tank having a volume of 1 ft³ contains 1 lb$_m$ of steam at 212F. (a) What is the quality? (b) What is the internal energy?

6. A tank having a volume of 10 ft³ is filled with steam at a pressure of 100 lb/in.² and a temperature of 430F. What is the mass of the steam?

7. One pound of water is placed in an evacuated container having a volume of 1 ft³. What are the pressure and entropy of the steam when the container is heated to 400F?

8. A pressure cooker contains 0.5 lb$_m$ of water initially at a temperature of 60F. It is heated to the operating pressure of 15 lb/in.² gage pressure. What is the temperature inside the cooker if barometric pressure is 24.5 in. of mercury? How much heat is absorbed by the water to bring it to the boiling point?

9. What are the enthalpy, specific volume, internal energy, and entropy for steam at (a) 100 lb/in.² and 475F; (b) 600F and 87 per cent quality?

10. Determine the quality of steam at 300 lb/in.² if the enthalpy is 1175 B/lb$_m$.

11. What is the specific volume of steam at 350F if the entropy is 1.492 B/lb$_m$ R?

12. Determine the enthalpy of steam at a pressure of 180 lb/in.² if the specific volume is 3.6 ft³/lb$_m$.

13. Determine the internal energy, specific volume, and entropy of water at (a) 2000 lb/in.² and 150F; (b) 1000 lb/in.² and 150F.

14. What are the percentages of liquid and vapor in 1 lb of wet steam whose specific volume is 2.2 ft³/lb$_m$ and whose pressure is 120 lb/in.²?

15. What is the condition of steam at 300F whose specific volume is 6.6 ft³/lb$_m$?

16. What is the condition of steam at 80 lb/in.² whose enthalpy is 1170 B/lb$_m$?

17. A molar quantity of an ideal gas is at a pressure of 60 lb/in.² and temperature of 300F. What is its volume?

18. A molar quantity of an ideal gas occupies a volume of 100 ft^f at its temperature of 100F. What is its pressure?

19. What is the gas constant for nitrogen gas?

20. Methane gas, CH_4 , at a pressure and temperature of 14.7 lb/in.² and 60F has what specific volume?

21. A certain ideal gas has a specific volume of 13.1 ft³/lb$_m$ at a pressure and temperature of 14.7 lb/in.² and 60F. What is its molecular weight?

22. A molar volume of an ideal gas is 387 ft³ under standard atmospheric conditions. What would a molar volume be at an altitude where the pressure and temperature are 1.7 lb/in.² and −67F?

23. One pound of carbon dioxide gas, CO_2 , occupies a volume of 1 ft³ at a temperature of 60F. What is its pressure?

24. What are the enthalpy and internal energy of air at a pressure and temperature of 14.7 lb/in.² and 100F?

25. What is the change in enthalpy when air is heated from 100F to 300F at constant volume? At constant pressure?

26. What is the change in internal energy when air is heated from 100F to 300F at constant volume? At constant pressure?

27. Air expands in a constant pressure process from a pressure and specific volume of 14.7 lb/in.² and 13 ft³/lb$_m$ to a specific volume of 39 ft³/lb$_m$. What are the changes in enthalpy and internal energy for the process?

Chapter IV

THE FIRST LAW OF THERMODYNAMICS

4.1 Statement of the First Law

The field of thermodynamics is governed by two so-called "laws": the First Law of Thermodynamics and the Second Law of Thermodynamics. These are not physical laws in the true sense of the word, in that they cannot be proved absolutely. They must be accepted on the basis of observation; that is, they have been formulated from countless observations of physical systems and, once formulated, have never been disproved by any recorded observation.

The First Law of Thermodynamics is simply a statement of the conservation of energy. This may be stated as follows: *In a system undergoing energy change the sum of the initial energy of the system and any energy added to the system must equal the sum of the final energy of the system and any energy that has left the system.*

Applications of this law to various types of thermodynamic process will be made, involving the types of energy discussed in the preceding chapter.

4.2 Types of Process

Thermodynamic processes may be classified as those involving flow of a medium and those in which the aspects of flow are unimportant. These are termed "flow processes" and "nonflow" processes. Flow processes may be further classified as "steady" flow processes and "nonsteady" flow processes.

A nonflow process may be defined as a process in which the thermodynamic medium or media do not cross the boundaries of the system. Examples of nonflow processes are the heating of water in a closed vessel, and the compression of a gas in a closed cylinder under the action of a piston

A flow process may be defined as a process in which the thermodynamic medium or media are crossing a boundary of the system.

A steady flow process may be defined as a flow process in which the fluid properties are independent of time at the boundaries of the

53

system. While this type of process cannot be actually realized, many real processes closely approach the conditions for steady flow. Examples are the flow of air and combustion gas through gas turbines and jet engines, the flow of steam through steam turbines, and the flow of air through a fan or airplane propeller.

A nonsteady flow may be defined as a flow process in which the fluid properties at a boundary of the system vary with time. The analysis of most nonsteady flow processes is complex and beyond the scope of this book, although a few simple cases may be handled with the methods to be presented here. Examples of nonsteady flow processes are the intake and exhaust strokes in an internal combustion engine, or piston-type compressor.

In this chapter two important relations based on the First Law of Thermodynamics will be presented. These will be called the "steady flow energy equation" and the "nonflow energy equation."

4.3 Steady flow energy equation

Consider a schematic, steady flow thermodynamic system as shown in Fig. 4.1. The thermodynamic medium is entering the system at station 1 with a velocity V_1, a pressure P_1, a specific volume v_1, an internal energy u_1, and an elevation y_1 above a reference datum plane. Both shaft work and heat are transferred into and from the system; the medium leaves the system at station 2 with velocity V_2, pressure P_2, specific volume v_2, internal energy u_2, elevation y_2.

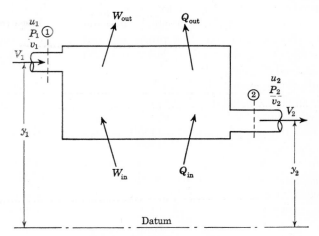

FIG. 4.1. STEADY FLOW SYSTEM.

Since only one medium is involved, all energy terms may be conveniently treated on a specific or per pound basis. Further, since the flow is steady, no energy is stored within the system; that is, the quantity of energy within the system is constant at all times. Application of the statement of the First Law then may be expressed as follows:

In a steady flow system, the energy entering the system is equal to the energy leaving the system.

The energy entering the system consists of internal energy u_1, flow work $P_1 v_1$, potential energy $g y_1 / g_c$, kinetic energy $V_1^2 / 2g_c$, work in W_{in}, and heat Q_{in}. The energy leaving the system consists of internal energy u_2, flow work $P_2 v_2$, potential energy $g y_2 / g_c$, kinetic energy $V_2^2 / 2g_c$, work W_{out}, and heat Q_{out}. Internal energy and heat are conventionally expressed in British thermal units per pound mass, while the other terms are conventionally expressed in foot-pounds per pound mass. In a mathematical statement of an energy balance consistent units are necessary. This may be accomplished by dividing all terms except internal energy and heat by the energy conversion factor J. Thus all energy terms will have the units of British thermal units per pound mass. The mathematical statement for the steady flow energy balance is then

$$u_1 + \frac{P_1 v_1}{J} + \frac{g y_1}{g_c J} + \frac{V_1^2}{2g_c J} + \frac{W_{in}}{J} + Q_{in} \qquad (4.1)$$

$$= u_2 + \frac{P_2 v_2}{J} + \frac{g y_2}{g_c J} + \frac{V_2^2}{2g_c J} + \frac{W_{out}}{J} + Q_{out}$$

The total energy rates involved in the process may be found by multiplying both sides of this equation by the mass rate of flow, $\dot{w}$. While Eq. (4.1) is somewhat cumbersome in its complete form and will be subsequently abbreviated, it is recommended that the student use the equation as stated until he becomes familiar with the principles of the energy balance involved. The student is reminded that W, as it appears in Eq. (4.1) and subsequent forms of the energy equation, represents *shaft* work.

Example 4.1:

An air compressor operates under the following steady flow conditions:

Mass rate of flow	0.5 lb_m/sec
Inlet pressure	14 lb/in.²
Inlet specific volume	13 ft³/lb_m
Inlet velocity	100 ft/sec
Power input	75.5 hp
Heat rejected to cooling water	8.65 B/sec
Discharge pressure	150 lb/in.²
Discharge specific volume	2.1 ft³/lb_m
Discharge velocity	200 ft/sec

The air intake is 3 ft above the floor, and the discharge line is 10 ft. above the floor.

What is the increase in specific internal energy for the process?

Solution:

The work input per pound in British thermal units is

$$\frac{W}{J} = \frac{75.5(550)}{0.5(778)} = 106.8 \text{ B}/lb_m$$

The heat output per pound is

$$Q = \frac{8.65}{0.5} = 17.3 \text{ B}/lb_m$$

The flow work input per pound in British thermal units is

$$\frac{P_1 v_1}{J} = \frac{144(14)13}{778} = 33.7 \text{ B}/lb_m$$

The flow work output per pound in British thermal units is

$$\frac{P_2 v_2}{J} = \frac{144(150)2.1}{778} = 58.3 \text{ B}/lb_m$$

The initial potential energy per pound in British thermal units is

$$\frac{g y_1}{g_c J} = \frac{3}{778} = 0.0038 \text{ B}/lb_m$$

The final potential energy per pound in British thermal units is

$$\frac{g y_2}{g_c J} = \frac{10}{778} = 0.0129 \text{ B}/lb_m$$

The initial kinetic energy per pound in British thermal units is

$$\frac{V_1^2}{2g_c J} = \frac{(100)^2}{2(32.2)778} = 0.2 \text{ B/lb}_m$$

The final kinetic energy per pound in British thermal units is

$$\frac{V_2^2}{2g_c J} = \frac{(200)^2}{2(32.2)778} = 0.8 \text{ B/lb}_m$$

Substitution of all these values in Eq. (4.1) and solving for the change in internal energy per pound gives

$$u_2 - u_1 = -17.3 + 106.8 + (0.0038 - 0.0129)$$
$$+ (33.7 - 58.3) + (0.2 - 0.8)$$
$$= 64.3 \text{ B/lb}_m \text{ internal energy increase}$$

It will be noted in this example that the potential and kinetic energy terms are quite small as compared with the other terms. This is especially true in the case of the potential energy terms.

Potential energy terms are not always small, however, as indicated by the following example.

Example 4.2:

Determine the work per pound necessary to pump water from a deep well under the following conditions:

Depth of well	500 ft
Pump inlet pressure	14 lb/in.²
Discharge pressure	15 lb/in.²
Specific volume of water	0.016 ft³/lb$_m$

Assume no heat flow and constant internal and kinetic energy.

Solution:

Consider the reference datum plane for potential energy to be at the bottom of the well.

The flow work into the system per pound is

$$P_1 v_1 = 144 \, (14) \, (0.016) = 32.2 \text{ ft-lb/lb}_m$$

The flow work leaving the system per pound is

$$P_2 v_2 = 144 \, (15) \, (0.016) = 34.6 \text{ ft-lb/lb}_m$$

The initial potential energy per pound is

$$\frac{g y_1}{g_c} = 0$$

The final potential energy per pound is

$$\frac{g y_2}{g_c} = 500 \text{ ft-lb/lb}_m$$

All other energy terms except the work input are zero. Solving Eq. (4.1) for the work input gives

$$W_{in} = (34.6 - 32.2) + 500$$

$$= 502.4 \text{ ft-lb/lb}_m$$

Problems of this type, involving appreciable changes in potential energy, occur primarily in the field of hydraulics. In the thermodynamic processes of heat engines and the flow of gases and vapors, potential energy changes are negligibly small compared with other energy terms and will be omitted from the steady flow energy equation.

It is frequently possible also to neglect the kinetic energy terms from the energy equation for many thermodynamic processes. There are important exceptions, however, and it is desirable to retain the kinetic energy terms in the general form of the equation.

The steady flow energy equation may be further abbreviated by collecting the work and heat terms. The purpose of heat engines is the conversion of heat supplied into output work. This has led to the sign convention that heat input is considered positive and work output is considered positive. The net work output for a thermodynamic process is then

$$W = W_{out} - W_{in} \qquad \text{(net work)} \quad (4.2)$$

and the net heat input for a thermodynamic process is then

$$Q = Q_{in} - Q_{out} \qquad \text{(net heat)} \quad (4.3)$$

It will be found that most thermodynamic processes involve the flow of work or heat in one direction only.

4.4 Enthalpy

The general form of the steady flow energy equation contains both internal energy and flow work terms. The internal energy is a property of the thermodynamic medium, and the flow work is expressed as the product of two properties, the pressure and the specific volume. It has been found convenient to combine these two terms from the energy equation. The combination is called "enthalpy", and the specific enthalpy has been defined by Eq. (3.1) which is repeated here for convenience.

$$h = u + \frac{Pv}{J} \qquad (3.1)$$

The conventional units for the specific enthalpy are B/lb_m .

This quantity, while convenient for steady flow processes, is often a source of confusion in regard to nonflow processes. As used in the steady flow energy equation, both the internal energy u and the product Pv represent energy terms, and the sum of these terms is also an energy term. However, the product Pv may also be evaluated for a medium at rest, since any homogeneous medium has both a pressure and a specific volume. For a medium at rest, there is no flow work, and the product Pv obviously is not an energy term, even though it has the units of energy, $ft\text{-}lb/lb_m$.

While enthalpy may be used in certain nonflow processes by manipulation, the student is cautioned against the use of the quantity in any but steady flow processes. It should be thought of as simply a combination of thermodynamic properties as given by Eq. (3.1) rather than as a combination of energy terms, and only in steady flow processes does it represent energy.

The steady flow energy equation may now be abbreviated from the lengthy form of Eq. (4.1). This may be accomplished by omitting the potential energy terms, making use of Eqs. (4.2), (4.3), and (3.1), and rearranging to give

$$Q = h_2 - h_1 + \frac{V_2^2 - V_1^2}{2g_c J} + \frac{W}{J} \qquad \begin{array}{l}\text{(steady flow,} \\ \text{constant potential} \\ \text{energy)}\end{array} \qquad (4.4)$$

This equation is the definite integral of the following differential equation, as may be verified by integration:

$$dQ = dh + \frac{V\,dV}{g_c J} + \frac{dW}{J} \qquad (4.5)$$

This equation is most useful for reversible processes where equations of work and heat can be expressed in terms of the thermodynamic coordinates. Equation (4.4) is most useful for actual (irreversible) processes where the work and heat are evaluated by some other means than integration, such as by experimental methods. In any event, Eq. (4.4) may be obtained by integrating Eq. (4.5).

4.5 Steady flow shaft work

Equation (4.5) may be further simplified for reversible steady flow processes in which the kinetic energy terms are negligibly small or for which the kinetic energy remains constant for the process. Under these conditions it is possible to express the steady flow shaft work in terms of the coordinates pressure and specific volume. The heat transferred in a reversible process is represented as the area under the curve of the process on a temperature-entropy diagram.

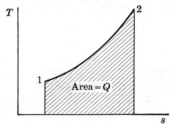

Fig. 4.2.

If the arbitrary locus of state points shown in Fig. 4.2 is a reversible nonflow process, Eq. (4.5) may be used to obtain an expression for the heat transferred. Keep in mind that kinetic energy and flow work will be equal to zero in a nonflow process.

$$dQ = dh + \frac{V\,dV}{g_c J} + \frac{dW}{J} \qquad (4.5)$$

$$= d\left(u + \frac{Pv}{J}\right) + \frac{V\,dV}{g_c J} + \frac{dW}{J}$$

$$= du + \frac{dW}{J}$$

and using Eq. (2.6)

$$dQ = du + \frac{P\,dv}{J}$$

$$Q = \int_{u_1}^{u_2} du + \int_{v_1}^{v_2} \frac{P \, dv}{J} = \text{area in Fig. 4.2}$$

The same arbitrary locus of state points shown in Fig. 4.2 could just as well be a reversible steady flow process with constant kinetic energy instead of the nonflow process mentioned above. Assuming it is such a process and using the same general method to obtain Q,

$$dQ = dh + \frac{V \, dV}{g_c J} + \frac{dW}{J}$$

$$= d\left(u + \frac{Pv}{J}\right) + 0 + \frac{dW}{J}$$

$$= du + \frac{P \, dv}{J} + \frac{v \, dP}{J} + \frac{dW}{J} \tag{4.6}$$

therefore

$$Q = \int_{u_1}^{u_2} du + \int_{v_1}^{v_2} \frac{P \, dv}{J} + \int_{p_1}^{p_2} \frac{v \, dP}{J} + \frac{W}{J}$$

$$= \text{area in Fig. 4.2}$$

Equating the two expressions for the area and solving for W yields the relationship for reversible steady flow shaft work with constant potential and kinetic energy.

$$\int_{u_1}^{u_2} du + \int_{v_1}^{v_2} \frac{P \, dv}{J} + \int_{p_1}^{p_2} \frac{v \, dP}{J} + \frac{W}{J} = \int_{u_1}^{u_2} du + \int_{v_1}^{v_2} \frac{P \, dv}{J}$$

$$W = -\int_{p_1}^{p_2} v \, dP \qquad \begin{array}{l}\text{(reversible steady flow,}\\ \text{constant potential, and} \quad (4.7)\\ \text{kinetic energy)}\end{array}$$

Substituting Eq. (4.7) into Eq. (4.5) gives a simple expression for the steady flow energy equation in differential form,

$$dQ = dh - \frac{v \, dP}{J} \qquad \begin{array}{l}\text{(reversible steady flow,}\\ \text{constant potential, and} \quad (4.8)\\ \text{kinetic energy)}\end{array}$$

Example 4.3:

Water is flowing through a heat exchanger under reversible, constant pressure, steady flow conditions. Determine the work done, heat added, and change in enthalpy in heating 10 lb of water from 70F to 140F if the specific heat at constant pressure for water is 1 B/lb$_m$ F. Assume no change in kinetic or potential energy for the process.

Solution:

The heat added per pound, from Eq. (2.17), is

$$Q = 1(140 - 70) = 70 \text{ B/lb}_m$$

The work done is zero since there is no change in pressure, as shown by Eq. (4.6)

The change in enthalpy from Eq. (4.8) is then

$$dQ = dh$$

$$Q = h_2 - h_1 = 70 \text{ B/lb}_m$$

For 10 lb of water the heat flow and enthalpy increase would be

$$\tilde{Q} = 700 \text{ B}, \qquad \tilde{h} = 700 \text{ B}$$

4.6 The effect of friction

It should be emphasized here that Eqs. (4.1), (4.4), (4.5) are not restricted to reversible (frictionless) processes since they apply only to the balance of energy or the First Law of Thermodynamics. Equations (4.6) and (4.8), however, are restricted to reversible processes since they involve mathematical operations valid only for reversible processes.

The concept of friction and the treatment of friction are two of the most difficult phases of thermodynamics to the beginning student. Friction may be broadly defined as resistance to motion. While the mechanism of friction will not be explained here, the general effect of friction will be discussed.

Rubbing friction, such as that developed by sliding a piece of furniture across a room, is a matter of everyday experience. Work is performed in sliding the furniture and is entirely dissipated by friction in heat to the atmosphere if the process takes place so slowly that the temperature (internal energy) of the furniture does not increase. If the process is accomplished rapidly, the temperature of the furniture and its internal energy will increase momentarily. This internal energy will, of course, be dissipated in heat flow to the atmosphere with the passage of time. One effect of friction, then, from the standpoint of thermodynamics would appear to be the dissipation of work into internal energy or heat.

The velocity of a bullet fired from a gun barrel in a horizontal direction decreases as a result of friction developed between the bullet and the atmosphere. In this case, friction has caused kinetic energy to be dissipated into heat or internal energy.

Another type of friction is the friction developed within a fluid that is in motion relative to some surface with which the fluid is in contact. This internal friction is measured by a fluid property called viscosity and is the result of shearing forces set up within the fluid that resist the relative motion.

Turbulence and eddies within a fluid are dissipative effects that are the result of fluid friction. Turbulence is a random motion of fluid particles and causes resistance to the directed motion of the fluid just as does viscous (shearing) friction.

In general, it may be stated that the effect of friction in a process is to convert mechanical forms of energy to thermal forms of energy. A more specific statement regarding friction will not be possible until the Second Law of Thermodynamics has been discussed in the next chapter. The energy balances of this chapter do apply to processes with friction (irreversible process) as well as reversible processes, and the effects of friction in any process must be studied, for the present, by comparing the actual process with a similar frictionless process.

Example 4.4:

A steady flow air compressor requires 64,000 ft-lb/lb$_m$ to compress air from a pressure and temperature of 14 lb/in.^{2} and 70F to a pressure of 56 lb/in.^{2} under adiabatic conditions. If the process had been frictionless, the calculated work input would have been 48,500 ft-lb/lb$_m$ to reach the same pressure under adiabatic conditions. Write and compare the energy equations for the actual and frictionless processes. Assume negligible kinetic energy.

Solution:

Since both processes are adiabatic, $dQ = 0$ and the energy equation for both processes, from Eq. (4.4), becomes

$$h_2 - h_1 = -\frac{W}{J}$$

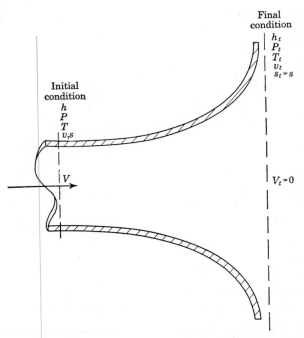

Fig. 4.3. Schematic diagram for stagnation conditions.

For the actual process,

$$h_2 - h_1 = \frac{64,000}{778} = 82.3 \text{ B/lb}_m$$

and for the frictionless process

$$h_2 - h_1 = \frac{48,500}{778} = 62.4 \text{ B/lb}_m$$

It is seen in this example that the additional work supplied to overcome friction has resulted in an increase in the enthalpy of the air leaving the compressor. This has increased both the internal energy and the flow work leaving the process.

4.7 Stagnation conditions

In thermodynamic processes in which the kinetic energy cannot be neglected it is frequently desirable to group internal energy, flow work, and kinetic energy together in a single term so that the only other types of energy to be considered are shaft work and heat. Since there are many ways in which kinetic energy can be converted into internal energy and flow work, a definite process for the conversion must be stated if the combination of internal energy, flow work, and kinetic energy is to describe a definite set of fluid properties when represented by a single energy term. This combination of energy terms into a single term is called the "stagnation enthalpy" and involves the assumption of a definite process for the combination—a reversible, adiabatic process with no shaft work.

Consider a steady flow system as shown in Fig. 4.3 in which a thermodynamic medium is flowing in a perfectly insulated duct with no shaft work. The fluid flows from an initial condition at the left to a final condition at station t. Imagine that the flow area at station t is infinitely large and that the flow between the two stations is frictionless. These are the conditions for a reversible adiabatic process. The energy equation for this process, from Eq. (4.4), is

$$ h + \frac{V^2}{2g_cJ} = h_t + \frac{V_t^2}{2g_cJ} \qquad (4.9a) $$

However, since the area at station t is infinitely large, the velocity at station t approaches zero and the above equation becomes

$$ h + \frac{V^2}{2g_cJ} = h_t \qquad \text{(reversible adiabatic)} \quad (4.9) $$

Thus the enthalpy at station t represents the sum of the internal energy, flow work, and kinetic energy entering the system. This enthalpy is called the stagnation enthalpy, and since a reversible adiabatic process has been specified for the conversion of kinetic energy, the fluid properties at the stagnation condition are fixed by Eq. (4.9). That is, for a given enthalpy and velocity there is only one value for each of the following stagnation properties: enthalpy, h_t; pressure, P_t; specific volume, v_t; temperature, T_t; internal energy, u_t; entropy, s_t. The student should realize that if stagnation properties are given in a problem, other stagnation properties for the same points can be obtained from gas tables (or steam tables) by the same methods used to obtain static properties. For example:

The stagnation temperature for a quantity of air is 1600°R. Using Table 6, what is the stagnation enthalpy?

Solution:

Opposite 1600°R in Table 6, read 395.7 B/lb$_m$.
Therefore $h_t = 395.7$ B/lb$_m$.

A further relation for stagnation properties exists in regard to the entropy. Since a reversible process has been assumed, Eq. (2.21) applies for the evaluation of heat flow in terms of entropy change. The process is assumed to be adiabatic; that is, the heat flow is zero. Therefore, from Eq. (2.21) it is seen that the entropy change must also be zero, and

$$s = s_t \tag{4.10}$$

Example 4.5:

A gas is flowing at high velocity in a channel. Its stagnation enthalpy is determined from a table of properties to be 308 B/lb_m and its static enthalpy is calculated to be 298 B/lb_m. What is the velocity of the gas?

Solution:

From Eq. (4.9)

$$V = \sqrt{2g_cJ(h_t - h)} = \sqrt{2(32.2)778(10)} = 707 \text{ ft/sec}$$

4.8 Isentropic processes

Processes for which there is no change in entropy are called "isentropic," and, as explained in the preceding paragraph, any reversible adiabatic process is isentropic. It does not follow that an isentropic process must be reversible adiabatic since it is theoretically possible to have a nonreversible process with friction and heat flow that has no change in entropy and is therefore isentropic although neither reversible nor adiabatic. However, the only isentropic processes of significance in engineering thermodynamics are reversible adiabatic, and, the two terms are frequently used interchangeably.

4.9 Abbreviated steady flow equation

The necessary requisite for stagnation conditions is that the fluid be brought to rest reversibly and adiabatically. Such a process can be imagined to occur at any location in the flow, and a fluid in motion, therefore, has stagnation properties at every location in the flow as well as state, or "static," properties. The steady flow energy equations may now be written in terms of the stagnation conditions. Equation (4.4) becomes

$$Q = h_{t_2} - h_{t_1} + \frac{W}{J} \qquad \begin{array}{l}\text{(steady flow,} \\ \text{constant potential} \qquad (4.11) \\ \text{energy)}\end{array}$$

and Eq. (4.5) becomes

$$dQ = dh_t + \frac{dW}{J}$$
(steady flow, constant potential energy)   (4.12)

Similarly, Eq. (4.7) can be written

$$dW = -v_t\,dP_t$$
(reversible steady flow, constant potential energy)   (4.13)

$$W = -\int_{P_{t1}}^{P_{t2}} v_t\,dP_t$$
(reversible steady flow, constant potential energy)   (4.14)

and Eq. (4.8) becomes

$$dQ = dh_t - \frac{v_t\,dP_t}{J}$$
(reversible steady flow, constant potential energy)   (4.15)

The validity of Eq. (4.15) may be demonstrated by reference to a temperature-entropy diagram, Fig. 4.4. Let points 1 and 2 be connected by any reversible steady flow process. Points 1_t and 2_t represent the stagnation conditions for these end points. The heat transferred may be obtained from

$$dQ = T_t\,ds$$

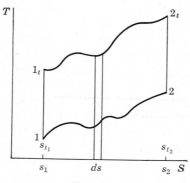

Fig. 4.4.

Notice that $dQ \neq T\,ds$ ($dQ = T\,ds$ ignores the effect of heat transfer on the kinetic energy of the medium). From the figure it can be seen that $s_2 - s_1 = s_{t_2} - s_{t_1}$ or $ds = ds_t$. Therefore

$$T_t\,ds = T_t\,ds_t$$

and

$$dQ = T_t\,ds_t = T_t\left(c_p\frac{dT_t}{T_t} - \frac{R}{J}\frac{dP_t}{P_t}\right)$$

If we simplify the term on the right side of the above equation there results;

$$dQ = c_p\,dT_t - \frac{v_t\,dP_t}{J} \quad \text{or} \quad dQ = dh_t - \frac{v_t\,dP_t}{J} \qquad (4.15)$$

In the above illustration relationships for an ideal gas were used. This was done for the sake of simplicity. The same result could be obtained regardless of the working substance as long as the process is reversible steady flow with constant potential energy.

It will be noted that the restriction of having constant kinetic energy has been dropped from the above equations and they may be applied to processes in which large changes in kinetic energy exist.

Aside from the convenience of being able to abbreviate the energy equation by the use of stagnation enthalpy, the concept of stagnation conditions has a much more important practical application. It is possible in experimental work to closely approach the measurement of both the static and the stagnation pressure and the stagnation temperature of a fluid in motion, but no practical technique has been found for measuring the static temperature of a fluid in motion.

Any temperature probe inserted into a moving stream of fluid will bring to rest essentially all the fluid in direct contact with the probe and will therefore read a temperature that approaches the stagnation temperature. By proper design of the probe the temperature reading can be made to agree closely with the true stagnation temperature. The static temperature could be measured if the probe were moving along with the stream and at the same velocity so that no kinetic energy conversion would take place. Such a method is impractical.

In many cases involving fluid flow the kinetic energy is so small that there is only a negligible difference between the static and stagnation temperatures. In such cases it is permissible to consider the temperature reading to be the static temperature in the fluid. Many other cases arise, however, where the kinetic energy is not negligible and static temperatures are much smaller than stagnation temperatures. It is here that the concept of stagnation conditions with regard to the steady flow energy equation is most valuable, since the evaluation of heat and work in terms of stagnation conditions does not require a knowledge of the kinetic energies involved.

Stagnation values are frequently termed "total" values in engineering literature—for example, total pressure, total temperature, total enthalpy. The term "stagnation" will be used here, however, since it is more descriptive of the concept involved.

Example 4.6:

A gas turbine develops 10,000 horsepower, and the flow of gas is 100 lb_m/sec through the turbine. If the process is adiabatic, determine the change in stagnation enthalpy for the process.

Solution:

The work per pound of gas is

$$W = \frac{10,000}{100} \, (550) = 55,000 \text{ ft-lb/lb}_m$$

From Eq. (4.12) the decrease in stagnation enthalpy is

$$h_{t1} - h_{t2} = \frac{W}{J} = \frac{55,000}{778}$$

$$= 70.7 \text{ B/lb}_m$$

4.10 Steady flow equation for more than one medium

In many steady flow processes more than one medium is involved. For example, in an internal combustion engine, fuel and air enter the engine, and products of combustion leave the engine. For such processes it is best to refer directly to the statement of the First Law for the energy balance. Since more than one medium is involved, the entire energy quantities associated with each medium must be considered in the energy balance rather than the specific quantities. This can be best illustrated by an example.

Example 4.7:

Air and fuel vapor enter the combustion chamber of a gas turbine engine and leave as products of combustion. The amounts involved are 100 lb_m of air per second and 2 lb_m of fuel per second. The stagnation enthalpies are determined from temperature measurements to be 127 B/lb_m for the air, 125 B/lb_m for the fuel, and 401 B/lb_m for the products of combustion. Determine the heat liberated per second by the process.

Solution:

The initial energy entering the system per second is

$$\dot{h}_t = \dot{w}h_t = 100(127) = 12{,}700 \text{ B/sec for air}$$

$$\dot{h}_t = \dot{w}h_t = 2(125) = 250 \text{ B/sec for fuel vapor}$$

The final energy leaving the system is in the combustion products whose mass rate is $100 + 2 = 102 \text{ lb}_m/\text{sec}$ and is

$$\dot{h}_t = \dot{w}h_t = 102(401) = 40{,}902 \text{ B/sec for products}$$

From the statement of the First Law, the heat supplied must equal the difference between the initial and final energies of the system.

$$\dot{Q} = 40{,}902 - (12{,}700 + 250) = 27{,}952 \text{ B/sec}$$

4.11 Non-flow energy equation

Many thermodynamic processes may be classified as nonflow processes. The application of the First Law of Thermodynamics to the nonflow process yields somewhat different results from those of the steady flow process. The requirement for a nonflow process is that the system be defined in such a way that the thermodynamic medium does not cross its boundaries. While motion occurs in a nonflow process, the analysis of the process can be thought of as covering the time interval from immediately before the inception of motion to immediately after the motion is complete. In this way it is unnecessary to include kinetic energy terms in the energy balance. As in the case of most steady flow processes, changes in potential energy are negligible for nonflow processes and will be so considered. Obviously there is no flow work for a nonflow process, and the types of energy to be considered are simply shaft work, heat, and internal energy.

Consider a nonflow system as shown by Fig. 4.5. The system contains a fixed mass of a thermodynamic medium. During the process in which work is performed one or more boundaries of the system must change. As shown in Fig. 4.5 the right-hand boundary has changed during the process. In general, work and heat may be both supplied to and removed from the system. Normally, however, work and heat will flow in only one direction for a nonflow process.

The balance of energy, then, for a nonflow process progressing from an initial state (state 1) to a final state (state 2) will be as follows: The initial internal energy plus the heat flow input plus the work input must equal the final internal energy plus the heat flow out plus the work output. That is,

$$u_1 + Q_{in} + \frac{W_{in}}{J} = u_2 + Q_{out} + \frac{W_{out}}{J} \qquad \begin{array}{l} \text{(nonflow} \\ \text{constant potential} \\ \text{energy)} \end{array} \qquad (4.16)$$

Making use of Eqs (4.2) and (4.3) for net work and net heat flow, this equation may be written

$$Q = u_2 - u_1 + \frac{W}{J} \qquad \begin{array}{l} \text{(nonflow,} \\ \text{constant potential energy)} \end{array} \qquad (4.17)$$

Equation (4.17) is the definite integral of the following differential equation,

$$dQ = du + \frac{dW}{J} \qquad \begin{array}{l} \text{(nonflow,} \\ \text{constant potential energy)} \end{array} \qquad (4.18)$$

which is a somewhat more flexible form than Eq. (4.17)

For reversible nonflow processes in the absence of potential energy change the total work is equal to the shaft work, since the flow work

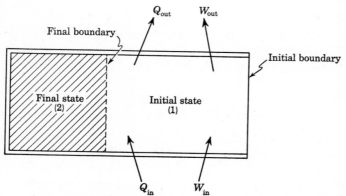

FIG. 4.5. SCHEMATIC DIAGRAM OF NONFLOW SYSTEM.

is zero. In this case the differential of shaft work is $P\,dv$, and Eq. (4.18) becomes

$$dQ = du + \frac{P\,dv}{J} \qquad \text{(reversible, nonflow,} \atop \text{constant potential energy)} \qquad (4.19)$$

Example 4.8:

Air expands adiabatically in a nonflow system consisting of an insulated cylinder and piston. The initial pressure and temperature are 100 lb/in.² and 492F, and the final pressure and temperature are 20 lb/in.² and 60F. From the temperature measurements the decrease in internal energy is found to be 75 B/lb$_m$. If the cylinder contains 0.01 lb$_m$ of air, what is the work performed by the air on the piston?

Solution:

Since the process is adiabatic, $dQ = 0$ and from Eq. (4.18)

$$du = -\frac{dW}{J}$$

and
$$u_2 - u_1 = -\frac{W}{J}$$

The work done per pound is then

$$W = J(u_1 - u_2) = 778(75) = 58{,}300 \text{ ft-lb/lb}_m$$

and the work for the process is then

$$\tilde{W} = wW = 0.01(58{,}300) = 583 \text{ ft-lb}$$

Example 4.9:

One pound of water initially at 80F and 14.7 lb/in.² pressure is heated reversibly at constant pressure in an open vessel until only 0.5 lb$_m$ remains. How much heat was added to the water?

Solution:

The nonflow energy equation for this process may be obtained by integrating Eq. (4.19) with the pressure constant,

$$Q = u_2 - u_1 + \frac{P(v_2 - v_1)}{J}$$

$$= u_2 - u_1 + \frac{P_2 v_2 - P_1 v_1}{J}$$

Inspection of the above expression shows that it may be regrouped to form $Q = h_2 - h_1$. Thus the heat input can be determined in this case by the change in enthalpy even though this is a nonflow process. The fact that the heat transferred reversibly in a constant pressure *nonflow* process happens to be equal to the change in enthalpy should not confuse the student. Enthalpy as a property has no real significance in a nonflow process. The above example should be regarded as a handy coincidence. In any event, the student who begins such a problem with the appropriate basic energy equation will have no difficulty. The initial enthalpy from Table 2 of the Appendix for 80F is

$$h_1 = h_f = 48.02 \text{ B/lb}_m$$

For the final condition half the water has turned to steam at a pressure of 14.7 lb/in.² The quality of the entire quantity (water and steam) is 0.5. From Table 3 of the Appendix for a saturation pressure of 14.7 lb/in.²

$$h_f = 180.07, \qquad h_{fg} = 970.3$$

and from Eq. (3.2) the final enthalpy for the original pound for the condition at which the steam was formed is

$$h_2 = h_f + Xh_{fg} = 180.7 + 0.5(970.3) = 665.8 \text{ B/lb}_m$$

The heat added has then been

$$Q = 665.8 - 48.02 = 617.8 \text{ B}$$

PROBLEMS

1. Four hundred cubic feet of air per minute at a pressure of 14.7 lb/in.², temperature of 60F, and a velocity of 100 ft/sec enters an air compressor. The specific volume is 13.1 ft³/lb$_m$. The air leaves the compressor at a pressure of 75 lb/in.², temperature of 400F, and a velocity of 100 ft/sec. If the process is adiabatic, what is the power required? (Use Table 6.)

2. Find entering and leaving stagnation enthalpies in Prob. 1.

3. Solve Prob. 1 if the process is not adiabatic but 200 B/min of heat is removed during compression and the exit temperature is 386F, all other values remaining the same.

4. A steady flow air compressor handles 0.3 lb$_m$/sec. The inlet stagnation conditions are 14 lb/in.² and 100F. The outlet stagnation

conditions are 56 lb/in.² and 400F. What is the power required if the process is adiabatic?

5. The discharge of a pump is 10 ft above the inlet. Water enters at a pressure of 20 lb/in.² and leaves at a pressure of 200 lb/in.² The specific volume of water is 0.016 ft³/lb$_m$. If there is no heat transfer and no change in kinetic or internal energy, what is the specific work?

6. Solve Prob. 5 if the pump discharge is 10 ft below the inlet, all other data remaining the same.

7. Steam enters a nozzle at a stagnation temperature and stagnation pressure of 450F and 100 lb/in.² It leaves the nozzle at a pressure and quality of 14.7 lb/in.² and 98 per cent. What is the velocity of the steam leaving the nozzle if the flow is steady and adiabatic?

8. Steam leaves a nozzle with a velocity of 2,000 ft/sec and a pressure and temperature of 20 lb/in.² and 300F. What is the inlet stagnation enthalpy if the process is adiabatic?

9. Air flows through a turbine at a rate of 10 lb$_m$/sec. The initial stagnation temperature is 1000F and the final stagnation temperature is 700F. What are the specific work and power output? (Use Table 6.)

10. A gas flows steadily through an insulated turbine. The expansion takes place according to the relation $Pv^{1.3} = C$. Neglecting kinetic and potential energy effects, what is the specific work in expanding from a pressure of 100 lb/in.² to a pressure of 20 lb/in.² if the value of the constant is 162,500, where P is in lb/ft² and v is in ft³/lb$_m$? What is the change in enthalpy?

11. If the initial and final velocities in Prob. 10 were 200 ft/sec and 300 ft/sec, what would be the effect on the specific work?

12. A gas in the amount of 100 lb$_m$/sec expands through a gas turbine. The initial enthalpy is 493 B/lb$_m$, and the initial velocity is 200 ft/sec. The final enthalpy is 401 B/lb$_m$, and the final velocity is 300 ft/sec. Assuming the process is adiabatic, what is the horsepower developed by the turbine?

13. Air is heated under steady flow conditions in a heat exchanger. The air enters at a stagnation temperature of 80F and leaves at a stagnation temperature of 180F. What is the heat absorbed per pound by the air?

14. The heat source in Prob. 13 is water, entering the exchanger at 210F and leaving at 190F. How many pounds of water are required to heat each pound of air?

15. Air is heated in a steady flow heat exchanger. Heat in the amount of 720,000 B/hr is transferred to the air, and the flow rate is 2 lb_m/sec. The initial temperature and velocity are 100F and 150 ft/sec. What is the final stagnation temperature? (Use Table 6.)

16. Water is heated in a steady flow boiler and superheater from stagnation conditions of 200 $lb/in.^2$ and 100F to steam at stagnation conditions of 160 $lb/in.^2$ and 400F. What is the heat added per pound?

17. Steam is condensed under steady flow conditions from a stagnation pressure and stagnation temperature of 1 $lb/in.^2$ and 200F to a stagnation pressure of 1 $lb/in.^2$ and 90F. What is the heat removed per pound?

18. A steam engine cylinder has a volume of 1 ft^3 when the piston is at top center. Superheated steam at a pressure and temperature of 100 $lb/in.^2$ and 700F enters the cylinder and expands adiabatically in a nonflow process to a pressure and temperature of 20 $lb/in.^2$ and 400F. What is the work per stroke?

19. Work in the amount of 180,000 ft-lb/lb_m is performed by the power stroke of a steam engine in an adiabatic nonflow process. Steam leaves the cylinder at 230F and 15 $lb/in.^2$ The entropy of the steam is constant for the process. What are the pressure and temperature of the steam prior to the expansion process?

20. A cylinder and piston contain 0.1 lb_m of air. Two thousand foot-pounds of work is supplied to the air by compression, and its temperature increases from 60F to 130F. What is the heat flow to or from the system?

21. Air is compressed adiabatically in a nonflow process from a pressure and temperature of 15 $lb/in.^2$ and 40F to a pressure and temperature of 100 $lb/in.^2$ and 420F. What is the specific work?

22. Air expands adiabatically in a cylinder and piston device from a pressure and temperature of 110 $lb/in.^2$ and 1540F. Work of 80,000 ft-lb/lb_m is performed. What is the final temperature?

23. Solve Prob. 22 if the process is not adiabatic, but 8 B/lb_m of heat is removed during expansion, all other data remaining the same.

24. A gas expands in an insulated cylinder and piston device under nonflow conditions according to the relation $Pv^{1.3} = C$. What is the specific work in expanding from a pressure of 100 lb/in.^{2} to a pressure of 20 lb/in.^{2} if the value of the constant is 162,500, where P is in lb/ft^2 and v is in ft^3/lb$_m$? Compare the result with that of Prob. 10, and explain the difference.

25. The internal energy per pound for a certain gas is given by

$$u = 0.17T + C$$

where C is a constant. The gas is heated in a rigid container from a temperature of 100F and 600F. What are the specific work and the heat added per pound? What is the change in entropy?

26. Heat in the amount of 14 B is supplied to a gas in a cylinder and piston device. The gas expands reversibly under constant pressure conditions. The pressure is 15 lb/in.^{2}, and the initial and final volumes are 0.15 ft^3 and 1.60 ft^3. What is the work done? What is the change in internal energy?

27. Heat in the amount of 14 B is supplied to 0.01 lb$_m$ of a gas in a closed rigid container. The initial pressure and volume are 15 lb/in.^{2} and 0.15 ft^3. The specific heat at constant volume is 0.2 B/lb$_m$ F. What are the increase in temperature and change in internal energy?

Chapter V

THE SECOND LAW OF THERMODYNAMICS

5.1 Statement of the Second Law

The First Law of Thermodynamics discussed in the preceding chapter states that all the energy involved in a thermodynamic system must be accounted for. No restrictions are placed on the way in which energy transfer may occur. Within the framework of the First Law it is possible for a heat engine to convert all the heat energy supplied to it into useful mechanical work. Such a phenomenon has never been observed, and the inability of converting all the heat supplied to an engine into useful work has led to the formulation of the Second Law of Thermodynamics, sometimes called the law of degradation of energy. This law, like the First Law, has no absolute proof but is based on the results of countless observations.

The Second Law is, in effect, a restriction on the First Law. Many statements of the Second Law have been made, some of them complex. A simple statement that will best suit the purposes of this book is as follows: *Heat will not flow continuously from a body at one temperature to a body at a higher temperature without the addition of some other form of external energy.*

Experience indicates that for a single process heat always flows in the direction of decreasing temperature and never in the direction of increasing temperature. An example is the heating of water on a stove where heat flows from a high-temperature burner to water which is at a lower temperature. Another example is ice freezing in a pond where heat is flowing from the water in the pond to the surrounding atmosphere, which is at a lower temperature. Countless examples such as these can be given. On the other hand, no one has observed a situation in which heat flows from a low-temperature body to a body at higher temperature without the expenditure of external work. Such is the basis of the Second Law. By means of the above statement of the Second Law it will be shown that no self-acting engine can convert all the heat energy supplied to useful external shaft work.

5.2 External reversibility

Reversible processes as defined in Chap. I require that the thermodynamic medium involved in the process be returned to its original condition if the process is made to proceed in the reverse direction, with all energy terms being equal and opposite in sign. Such processes are often called "internally reversible" processes. If a process is to be reversible with regard to both the thermodynamic system and its surroundings, the Second Law imposes an additional requirement for reversibility. For a heat transfer process between a system and its surroundings to be able to proceed in either direction, the system and its surroundings must be in thermal equilibrium. This obviously is an impossible requirement since no heat would flow if equilibrium were established. Such a process could be approached, however, if the temperature difference between the system and its surroundings was infinitesimally small. That is, reversibility between the system and its surroundings for heat transfer processes can be approached only if the system and its surroundings are essentially at identical temperatures; otherwise the direction of the process could not be reversed without violating the Second Law.

Processes that are reversible with regard to both the thermodynamic system and its surroundings are called "externally reversible" processes. An externally reversible process may then be defined as an internally reversible process in which the system and its surroundings are at the same temperature if heat transfer takes place. In general, the temperature of the surroundings must be considered as constant.

By the above definition, it may be seen that only two types of thermodynamic process can be externally reversible. These are constant temperature heat transfer processes and adiabatic processes (in which no heat transfer occurs.) The reversal of either of these types of process does not violate the Second Law.

5.3 Engine cycles and thermal efficiency

The Second Law of Thermodynamics leads to the study of heat engines and the concept of thermodynamic cycles. A thermodynamic cycle is a series of processes performed on a thermodynamic medium in which heat transfer takes place, work is done, and the final process returns the medium to its original condition. In heat engines the cycle is arranged in such a way that heat energy is supplied to produce useful shaft work output.

Because the purpose of heat engines is to convert as much of the heat supplied as possible into useful shaft work, the thermal efficiency of a heat engine cycle is defined as the ratio of the useful shaft work to the heat supplied. This may be written as a simple equation

$$\eta = \frac{\tilde{W}_{net}}{J\tilde{Q}_s} \qquad \text{(heat engine thermal efficiency)} \qquad (5.1)$$

In order to avoid confusion the following symbols are defined:

$\tilde{Q}_{in}$,   heat added in a process;
$\tilde{Q}_{out}$,   heat rejected in a process;
$\tilde{Q}_s$,   net heat supplied in a cycle;
$\tilde{Q}_r$,   net heat rejected in a cycle.

For any nonflow engine cycle, the sum of energy balances for all the processes shows that the net work output is equal to the heat supplied to the system (heat input) minus the heat rejected by the system (heat output), since the initial and final internal energy of the system must be equal by the definition of a cycle. Consider a cycle consisting of four processes: the equation applicable to each is

1st process:

$$(\tilde{Q}_{in} - \tilde{Q}_{out})_{1-2} = \tilde{u}_2 - \tilde{u}_1 + \left(\frac{\tilde{W}_{out} - \tilde{W}_{in}}{J}\right)_{1-2} \qquad (5.2a)$$

2nd process:

$$(\tilde{Q}_{in} - \tilde{Q}_{out})_{2-3} = \tilde{u}_3 - \tilde{u}_2 + \left(\frac{\tilde{W}_{out} - \tilde{W}_{in}}{J}\right)_{2-3} \qquad (5.2b)$$

3rd process:

$$(\tilde{Q}_{in} - \tilde{Q}_{out})_{3-4} = \tilde{u}_4 - \tilde{u}_3 + \left(\frac{\tilde{W}_{out} - \tilde{W}_{in}}{J}\right)_{3-4} \qquad (5.2c)$$

4th process:

$$(\tilde{Q}_{in} - \tilde{Q}_{out})_{4-1} = \tilde{u}_1 - \tilde{u}_4 + \left(\frac{\tilde{W}_{out} - \tilde{W}_{in}}{J}\right)_{4-1} \qquad (5.2d)$$

If the above equations are added, it will be seen that all internal energy terms disappear. The sum of the heat terms on the left is equal to the difference between the heat supplied to the cycle and the heat rejected by the cycle, and the sum of the work terms on the right is equal to the net work for the cycle. That is,

$$\tilde{W}_{net} = J(\tilde{Q}_s - \tilde{Q}_r) \qquad \text{(nonflow engine cycle)} \qquad (5.2)$$

Combining Eqs. (5.1) and (5.2), it is possible to write

$$\eta = \frac{\tilde{Q}_s - \tilde{Q}_r}{\tilde{Q}_s} \qquad (5.3)$$

The processes of a cycle when the medium for the cycle is represented on a pressure-volume diagram or a temperature-entropy diagram will always form a closed curve since the medium is returned to its initial condition. The area enclosed by the curve in the pressure-volume diagram represents the net work of the cycle. Figure 5.1

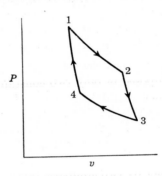

FIG. 5.1. P-v DIAGRAM FOR AN ENGINE CYCLE.

shows a P–v diagram for the medium of an arbitrary cycle composed of four processes occurring in the direction shown. Work is supplied in processes 3–4 and 4–1, putting into the medium an amount of work energy equal to the area under the curves 3–4 and 4–1. Work is delivered in processes 1–2 and 2–3, removing from the medium an amount of work energy equal to the area under the curves 1–2 and 2–3. The net external work developed by the cycle is the difference between the work output from the medium and the work input to the medium. Subtracting the area corresponding to the input work from the area corresponding to the output work leaves the area within the closed curve, which then corresponds to the net work of the cycle.

5.4 Reversible engines—the Carnot cycle

For a heat engine to be externally reversible, its thermodynamic cycle must be composed of externally reversible processes. As indicated in Art. 5.2, the only possible externally reversible processes are constant temperature processes in which the system and its surroundings are at the same temperature and adiabatic processes. Therefore, the processes of an externally reversible cycle must consist of only reversible constant temperature and reversible adiabatic processes. The minimum number of each type of process for the cycle to develop net work output is two, as will be shown.

Let processes 1–2 and 3–4 in Fig. 5.1 be constant temperature externally reversible processes and processes 2–3 and 4–1 be adiabatic externally reversible processes. A cycle composed of only two adiabatic processes would yield no net work since one of the processes would be the exact reverse of the other—such a cycle could be represented in Fig. 5.1 by the process 2–3 and its reverse, process 3–2. Similarly, a cycle composed of only two constant temperature processes would yield no net work.

It can be shown that constant temperature lines never cross each other on a *P–v* diagram, nor do different adiabatic lines. Therefore, it would be impossible to have an externally reversible cycle composed of three processes since the medium could not be returned to its original condition either by two adiabatic processes and one constant temperature process or by two constant temperature processes and one adiabatic process.

A cycle composed of four processes, two externally reversible constant temperature processes and two externally reversible adiabatic processes, can yield a net work output and return the working medium to its original condition, as shown in Fig. 5.1. Such a cycle is thus seen to be the simplest externally reversible cycle and is called the Carnot cycle, after Sadi Carnot, who first proposed a cycle of this type in 1824.

It would, of course, be possible to conceive of an externally reversible cycle composed of more than four processes, as shown, for example, in Fig. 5.2, where the cycle consists of four adiabatic processes and four constant temperature processes. Obviously such a cycle consisting of more than four processes could not operate between only two fixed temperatures. Therefore, an externally reversible cycle operating between two fixed temperatures is a Carnot cycle, and any other externally reversible cycle can be treated as a thin series of Carnot cycles, as shown by the thin lines in Fig. 5.2.

While the Carnot cycle was first proposed in 1824, no one has yet been able to make a practical engine that operates on this cycle. The difficulty, in addition to friction, lies in the inability to produce an infinitely large heat source that can be used as the surroundings of the system for the constant temperature heat addition process and that can be quickly removed and replaced by a lower temperature heat receiver, or sink, that is also infinitely large and that can be used for the surroundings of the system for the constant temperature heat rejection. The atmosphere is essentially such an infinitely large heat receiver, or sink, and a constant temperature heat rejection to the atmosphere is possible if a process is made to take place so slowly that it is in equilibrium with the atmosphere at all times.

It should be noted that the above discussion of a reversible engine cycle requires externally reversible processes but does not specify the working medium to be used in the cycle.

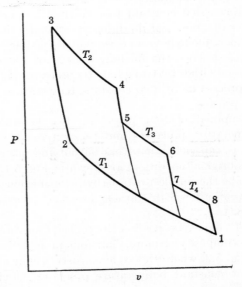

FIG. 5.2. EXTERNALLY REVERSIBLE CYCLE OF MORE THAN FOUR PROCESSES.

5.5 *Carnot's Principle*

All heat engines operate between two temperature extremes, the maximum temperature at which heat is added, and the minimum temperature at which heat is rejected. A reversible engine in which all the heat supplied is at a constant temperature and in which all the heat rejected is at a lower constant temperature operates on the Carnot cycle, as indicated in the preceding article. In view of the Second Law, it is now possible to show that no engine can be more efficient than a Carnot engine when operating between the same temperature limits.

Consider a system of two engines as shown in Fig. 5.3, both of which operate between an infinite heat source at temperature T_s and an infinite receiver at temperature T_r. Engine A is a Carnot engine, and engine B is another engine, which is not reversible. Since engine A is reversible, it may be operated in the reverse direction as a "heat pump" where all energy terms are equal and opposite in sign to those resulting from its operation as an engine. The thermal

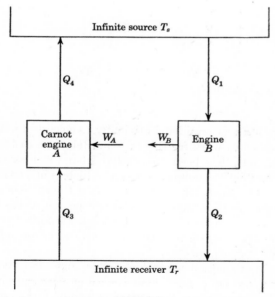

FIG. 5.3. DIAGRAM FOR ILLUSTRATION OF CARNOT'S PRINCIPLE.

efficiencies of both engines when operated as engines are, from Eqs. (5.1) and (5.3),

$$\eta_A = \frac{\tilde{W}_A}{J\tilde{Q}_4} = \frac{\tilde{Q}_4 - \tilde{Q}_3}{\tilde{Q}_4} \tag{5.4a}$$

$$\eta_B = \frac{\tilde{W}_B}{J\tilde{Q}_1} = \frac{\tilde{Q}_1 - \tilde{Q}_2}{\tilde{Q}_1} \tag{5.4b}$$

Let the engines be so proportioned that the net work output of engine B is just sufficient to drive engine A when operated as a heat pump. That is,

$$\tilde{W}_A = \tilde{W}_B \tag{5.4c}$$

or, from Eqs. (5.4a) and (5.4b),

$$\eta_A \tilde{Q}_4 = \eta_B \tilde{Q}_1 \tag{5.4d}$$

Now assume that the efficiency of engine B is greater than that of engine A and that engine B is driving engine A as a heat pump so that $\tilde{Q}_1$ is heat removed from the source and $\tilde{Q}_4$ is heat returned to the source. If the efficiency of B is greater than that of A, Eq. (5.4d) shows that

$$\tilde{Q}_4 > \tilde{Q}_1 \tag{5.4e}$$

and since

$$\tilde{Q}_4 - \tilde{Q}_3 = \tilde{Q}_1 - \tilde{Q}_2 \tag{5.4f}$$

the following inequality also exists:

$$\tilde{Q}_3 > \tilde{Q}_2 \tag{5.4}$$

Since the system was considered originally to consist of both engines, there is no external work for the system. Relations (5.4e) and (5.4) indicate that heat has been transferred from the low-temperature receiver to the high-temperature source, which is in violation of the Second Law. Obviously, the assumption that the efficiency of engine B could be greater than that of the Carnot engine A was erroneous. Thus a principle can be established, called Carnot's Principle: *No heat engine can be more efficient than a Carnot engine operating between the same temperature limits.*

It also follows that all reversible engines operating between the same temperature limits must have the same efficiency. If engine B is assumed to be an externally reversible engine and is driven as a heat pump by engine A, and if the efficiency of engine B is less than engine A, using the same argument as above, the Second Law would again be violated. Therefore, if both engines are reversible, they must have the same efficiency and would, of course, both be Carnot engines since they are operating between constant temperature limits.

It is thus seen that the efficiency of a Carnot cycle is independent of any characteristics of the working fluid employed but depends only on the source and receiver temperature, a fact that can be used to formulate a true thermodynamic temperature scale.

5.6 Thermodynamic temperature scale

The brief discussion of temperature in Chap. 1 indicated the dependence of a temperature scale upon the thermodynamic medium used as the basis for the scale. With the aid of the Carnot cycle, it is possible to define a temperature scale that is independent of any medium—a true thermodynamic temperature scale.

Suppose, now, that no temperature scale has been defined. The efficiency of a Carnot cycle on a specific basis is

$$\eta = 1 - \frac{Q_r}{Q_s} \qquad (5.5a)$$

Since the efficiency of the Carnot cycle is independent of the working medium and depends only on the source and receiver temperatures, Eq. (5.5a) indicates that the ratio of the heat rejected to the heat supplied must depend only on the source and receiver temperatures even though no scale has been assigned for the determination of these temperatures.

The ratio of these two heat quantities can then be used to define a temperature scale. Such a temperature scale can be shown to be defined by†

$$\frac{Q_r}{Q_s} = \frac{\theta_r}{\theta_s} \qquad (5.5b)$$

where θ is the thermodynamic temperature.

Equation (5.5b) serves as the basis of the thermodynamic temperature scale originally known as the Kelvin temperature scale and can

† See, for example, M. W. Zemansky, *Heat and Thermodynamics*, McGraw-Hill Book Company, Inc., New York, 2nd ed., 1943, pp. 142–143.

be used to define absolute zero. As shown by Eq. (5.5b), as the receiver temperature is lowered, the heat rejected decreases; and the temperature at which no heat would be rejected by a Carnot engine is absolute zero.

Since the temperature scale defined by Eq. (5.5b) is independent of the thermodynamic medium, it must apply to all media and any medium can be chosen to measure the temperature. It will be shown in Chap. VI that the temperature defined for the medium of an ideal gas, $T = Pv/R$, is identical with the temperature defined by Eq. (5.5b). That is,

$$\theta = T \tag{5.5c}$$

and from Eq. (5.5b)

$$\frac{Q_r}{Q_s} = \frac{T_r}{T_s} \tag{5.5}$$

for a Carnot cycle using any thermodynamic medium. The thermodynamic temperature can then be measured with a gas thermometer as discussed in Chap. I. The absolute scale in centigrade units is called the Kelvin scale and in Fahrenheit units is called the Rankine scale. Equation (5.5) may also be obtained by equating the areas on a temperature-entropy diagram for a Carnot cycle (Fig. 5.4) to the corresponding quantities of heat.

$$\text{Area of heat supplied} = T_s \, \Delta_s = Q_s$$
$$\text{Area of heat rejected} = T_r \, \Delta_s = Q_r$$

Therefore $\Delta_s = \dfrac{Q_s}{T_s} = \dfrac{Q_r}{T_r}$ and $\dfrac{Q_r}{Q_s} = \dfrac{T_r}{T_s}$ \hfill (5.5)

5.7 Efficiency of a Carnot cycle

Based on the definition of the thermodynamic temperature scale, the efficiency of a Carnot cycle may now be expressed in terms of the source and receiver temperatures. Substitution of Eq. (5.5) into (5.5a) gives

$$\eta = 1 - \frac{T_r}{T_s} \qquad \text{(Carnot cycle, for any medium)} \tag{5.6}$$

Since no engine can be more efficient than a Carnot engine operating between the same temperature limits, Eq. (5.6) indicates that no engine can have a thermal efficiency of 100 per cent unless its lower temperature limit is absolute zero or unless its upper temperature is infinitely high. Infinitely high temperatures are, of course, impossible. Since all thermodynamic systems are ultimately surrounded by the atmosphere, the atmosphere serves as a universal receiver; and atmospheric temperature which is far above absolute zero is the temperature which the heat rejected by a system must ultimately approach. It is thus apparent that, even if an externally reversible engine could be made, its efficiency would not be 100 per cent. In other words, no self-acting heat engine can convert all the heat energy supplied to it into useful work.

Example 5.1:

Assume that a Carnot engine could be made and that 200 B/lb$_m$ of heat is supplied to the engine at 2000R. Atmospheric temperature (the receiver temperature) is 540R. What is the thermal efficiency of the cycle, and what quantity of heat is rejected by the engine?

Solution:

From Eq. (5.6), the efficiency is

$$\eta = 1 - \frac{540}{2000} = 73 \text{ per cent}$$

From Eq. (5.5), the heat rejected is

$$Q_r = 200 \left(\frac{540}{2000} \right) = 54 \text{ B/lb}_m$$

5.8 Entropy

Entropy has been defined in Chap. II as an extensive quantity used for evaluating heat flow for a reversible process. The concept of entropy as a property of a thermodynamic medium is based on the Carnot cycle and the definition of the thermodynamic temperature scale.

The definition of the thermodynamic temperature scale, Eq. (5.5), may be rearranged to give

$$\frac{Q_s}{T_s} = -\frac{Q_r}{T_r} \tag{5.7a}$$

The negative sign has been introduced here since the direction of Q_r is opposite that of Q_s. Since the values of the source and receiver temperatures for the Carnot cycle of Eq. (5.7a) are arbitrary, the values of the ratios Q_s/T_s and Q_r/T_r could be constant for an infinite number of Carnot cycles having different source and receiver temperatures. Now define a thermal quantity such that the value of the ratios Q_s/T_s and Q_r/T_r represents the change in this quantity. Let this quantity be called entropy. Based on this definition, Eq. (5.7a) becomes

$$\frac{Q_s}{T_s} = -\frac{Q_r}{T_r} = \Delta s \quad \begin{array}{l}\text{(Carnot cycle} \\ \text{for any medium)}\end{array} \quad (5.7)$$

where Δs indicates an increase in entropy.

The quantity entropy defined by Eq. (5.7) must be an intensive quantity since the heat quantities are given on a specific basis. If more or less than a unit mass is involved in the Carnot cycle, the total heat flow and hence the total entropy will be proportional to the mass. By means of Eq. (5.7) it is possible to represent the total heat supplied and the total heat rejected as the product of an intensive quantity, temperature, and an extensive quantity, total entropy change. If temperature and entropy are used as coordinates, the heat supplied and heat rejected will appear as rectangular areas. Since the difference between the heat supplied and the heat rejected for any cycle represents the net work, the difference between the above two areas represents the net work for the cycle in heat units. This is shown in Fig. 5.4. It will be noted that the two reversible adiabatic processes in the Carnot cycle are represented as vertical lines in Fig. 5.4 with no change in entropy. Thus by the definition of Eq. (5.7) reversible adiabatic processes ($Q_s = Q_r = 0$) are isentropic processes.

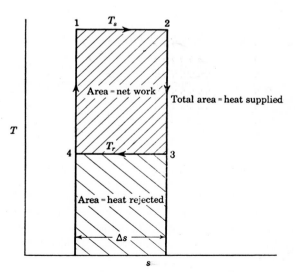

FIG. 5.4. TEMPERATURE-ENTROPY DIAGRAM FOR A CARNOT CYCLE.

If the quantity called entropy defined by Eq. (5.7) can be treated as a thermodynamic property of a medium, it must depend only on the state or condition of the medium and be independent of any process by which the condition of the medium is changed. That is, it must be a point function. That entropy is a point function will be proved in the following manner:

Assume that a cycle composed of two reversible (internally reversible) processes can be represented on a temperature-entropy diagram as shown in Fig. 5.5. This cycle, 1–2–1, may be approximated as a summation of a number of smaller Carnot cycles, as shown. For the Carnot cycles, Eq. (5.7) applies. The total change in entropy for process 1–2 can be determined as the sum of the changes in entropy for all the Carnot cycles using the ratio Q_s/T_s from Eq. (5.7). That is,

$$\frac{Q_{sA}}{T_{sA}} + \frac{Q_{sB}}{T_{sB}} + \frac{Q_{sC}}{T_{sC}} + \ldots = s_2 - s_1 \qquad (5.8a)$$

From Eq. (5.7) this expression can also be written

$$-\frac{Q_{rA}}{T_{rA}} - \frac{Q_{rB}}{T_{rB}} - \frac{Q_{rC}}{T_{rC}} - \ldots = s_2 - s_1 \qquad (5.8b)$$

The total change in entropy for the process 2–1 can be determined as the sum of changes in entropy for all the Carnot cycles using the ratio Q_r/T_r from Eq. (5.7). Since the entropy is decreasing along

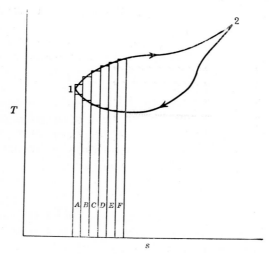

Fig. 5.5. Reversible cycle.

process 2–1, the change in entropy is negative and has the same sign as the heat rejected. Thus

$$\frac{Q_{rA}}{T_{rA}} + \frac{Q_{rB}}{T_{rB}} + \frac{Q_{rC}}{T_{rC}} + \ldots = s_1 - s_2 \qquad (5.8c)$$

Since the process 2–1 is reversible, it can proceed in the opposite direction from that shown, changing the sign of all the heat terms in Eq. (5.8c) and also the sign of the entropy change. The resulting equation would then be identical to Eq. (5.8b), and the entropy change for the reversed process 2–1 is the same as for the process 1–2. Since the reversed process 2–1 is different from the process 1–2 but acts between the same thermodynamic states, it is thus established that entropy is a point function and can be considered as a property of a medium.

In the above discussion, as the number of small Carnot cycles used to approximate the given cycle is increased, the quantities of heat in each Carnot cycle become smaller and smaller. If the quantities of heat are so small as to be considered infinitesimal, the entropy change is also an infinitesimal and Eq. (5.7) becomes for any reversible process

$$ds = \frac{dQ_s}{T_s} = -\frac{dQ_r}{T_r} \qquad (5.8d)$$

or simply

$$ds = \frac{dQ}{T} \qquad \text{(reversible)} \quad (5.8)$$

where dQ is transferred at temperature T. Equation (5.8) may be rearranged to solve for the heat flow for a reversible process in terms of temperature and entropy as given in Chap. II.

It should be noted that, while entropy is a point function, a change in entropy can be evaluated only for a reversible process. However, since the entropy change is independent of the process, a medium undergoing a reversible process (or processes) from one state to another will have the same change in entropy as though the process had been irreversible between the same states.

Example 5.2:

One pound of air in a closed, insulated container is agitated by a paddle wheel driven by an electric motor. Its initial temperature is 60F, and its temperature is increased 60F by the agitation of the paddle. What is the change in entropy for the process? Assume $c_v = 0.171$ B/lb$_m$ F, $c_p = 0.24$ B/lb$_m$ F for air.

Solution:

Since all the work put into the system is dissipated by the friction of the paddle wheel in the air, this is obviously an irreversible process. Further, since the container is insulated, there is no external heat flow; that is, $dQ = 0$ for the process. The process does take place at constant volume, however. The change in entropy can be evaluated, then, by any reversible process acting between the states fixed by the initial temperature and volume and by the final temperature and volume. The simplest process in this case would be a reversible constant volume heat addition for which

$$dQ = c_v \, dT$$

Substitution of this relation into Eq. (5.8) gives

$$ds = c_v \frac{dT}{T}$$

and since c_v is given as 0.171 B/lb$_m$ F, the integration may be performed between the temperature limits of 520 and 580R.

$$s_2 - s_1 = \int_{T_1}^{T_2} c_v \frac{dT}{T} = 0.171 \ln \frac{580}{520}$$

$$= 0.0186 \text{ B/lb}_m \text{ R}$$

The above example shows that the area under a temperature-entropy curve does not represent the heat transfer to or from the system for an irreversible process. In this case there is no heat transfer, but an area not equal to zero exists since both temperature and entropy have changed.

5.9 Available and unavailable energy

The purpose of heat engines is the conversion of heat energy into useful work. The Second Law of Thermodynamics imposes a limit on the amount of useful work that can be obtained from heat. In the study of thermodynamic systems it is frequently desirable to analyze systems on the basis of the maximum amount of useful work that could be obtained from any heat addition process if that process were a part of an engine cycle. This has led to the concept of the so-called "available" and "unavailable" energy of a process.

The available energy, Q_a, for a process to which heat is supplied is the amount of net work that would be obtainable from the most efficient engine cycle of which the process could be made a part. The unavailable energy, Q_u for the process is the amount of energy that would be rejected as heat from the most efficient engine cycle of which the process could be made a part.

The Carnot cycle has been shown to be the most efficient engine cycle. Therefore, the most efficient use of the energy for any process would be in a cycle approaching the Carnot cycle as closely as possible. The most efficient cycle for any heating process would then be composed of the given process plus three other externally reversible processes from a Carnot cycle, two reversible adiabatic processes and a constant temperature heat rejection. Since the atmosphere is effectively the lowest temperature receiver into which an engine can reject heat, the Carnot constant temperature process would be at atmospheric temperature, T_0.

Consider now any reversible heating process as shown by process 1–2 in Fig. 5.6. The most efficient use of the energy for this process

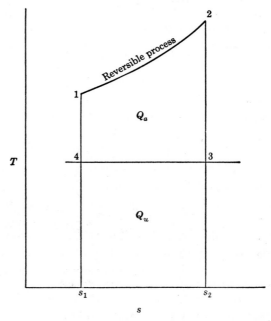

FIG. 5.6. AVAILABLE AND UNAVAILABLE ENERGY FOR A REVERSIBLE PROCESS.

would be in a cycle composed of a reversible adiabatic process 2–3 from state 2 to the receiver temperature, a constant temperature process 3–4, and a reversible adiabatic process returning to state 1 and closing the cycle. Since the given process is reversible, the heat input to the cycle may be found as the area under the curve 1–2 and is

$$Q_{in} = \int_{s_1}^{s_2} T \, ds \qquad (5.9a)$$

The heat rejected is the area under the receiver temperature,

$$Q_u = T_0(s_2 - s_1) \qquad (5.9b)$$

This is the unavailable energy for the process and is that part of the heat supplied by the given process that becomes unavailable for useful work.

The available energy is the net work of the cycle and is then the difference between the heat supplied and the heat rejected and is

$$Q_a = Q_{in} - Q_u \qquad (5.9)$$

5.10 Entropy and irreversibility

The above discussion applies to any reversible heating process. Suppose now that a process is not reversible; that is, friction is present. Since friction converts mechanical energy into thermal energy, the work output for a process with friction is less than if the process was frictionless. The net work output of the cycle involving a friction process will then be less than if the process had been frictionless. The available energy (net work) of the cycle is still the difference between the heat supplied by the process and the heat rejected.

Consider an irreversible process similar to and having the same heat input as the reversible process of the preceding discussion. Since the heat input for both processes is the same, the following relation can be written

$$(Q_a + Q_u)_{rev} = (Q_a + Q_u)_{irrev} \qquad (5.10a)$$

The available energy for the irreversible process will be less than that for the reversible process, and from the above relation it is then apparent that the unavailable energy for the irreversible process must be greater than that for the reversible process. Now, since the heat rejection processes of both cycles are reversible, Eq. (5.9b) is valid for the unavailable energy for the irreversible process, and the final entropy for the irreversible process must be greater than the final entropy for the reversible process. A temperature-entropy diagram for these processes is shown in Fig. 5.7.

Since the unavailable energy for the irreversible process is greater than that for the reversible process by an amount $T_0(s_3 - s_2)$, from Eq. (5.9b), the available energy for the irreversible process would be an area equal to Q_a for the reversible process minus $T_0(s_3 - s_2)$. This would be

$$Q_a = \int_{s_1}^{s_2} T \, ds - T_0(s_3 - s_1) \tag{5.10}$$

and the heat supplied is an area equal to the heat supplied for the reversible process since the processes were arbitrarily chosen to have the same heat input. Since the area under the irreversible process curve is larger than this area, it is again demonstrated that entropy can be used to evaluate heat flow only for a reversible process.

The area under a temperature-entropy curve for an irreversible process may be interpreted as equivalent to the external heat transfer

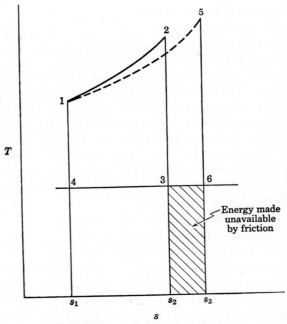

Fig. 5.7. T-s DIAGRAM FOR REVERSIBLE AND IRREVERSIBLE PROCESSES.

plus the mechanical energy converted to thermal energy by friction. In general, however, the exact curve for an irreversible process cannot be determined since the medium for an irreversible process is not in equilibrium and the properties are not constant throughout. In this text, irreversible processes will be shown as dashed lines to emphasize that the area under or behind the curve has no significance.

Example 5.3:

Heat in the amount of 100 B/lb$_m$, is supplied to air in a nonflow process in which the average pressure remains constant and work is done. The initial temperature is 70F, and the final average temperature is 550F. The temperature of the surroundings (atmosphere) is 50F. Assume that the constant pressure specific heat for air may be considered to be $c_p = 0.24$ B/lb$_m$ F in this temperature range.

   a. Determine the entropy change for the process.
   b. Determine the entropy change and available energy if the process had been reversible with the same heat addition.
   c. Determine the available energy for the process.

Solution:

   a. The entropy change for the process may be determined by replacing the actual process by a reversible constant pressure process acting between the same limits for which $dQ = c_p\, dT$. Substitution of this relation in Eq. (5.8) and integrating between the temperature limits of 530R and 1010R gives

$$s_2 - s_1 = \int_{T_1}^{T_2} c_p \frac{dT}{T} = 0.24 \ln \frac{1010}{530}$$

$$= 0.1555 \text{ B/lb}_m \text{ R}$$

   b. If the process had been reversible with 100 B/lb$_m$ heat addition, the final temperature can be found from $dQ = c_p\, dT$, which for a constant specific heat

$$Q = c_p(T_2 - T_1)$$

$$100 = 0.24(T_2 - 530)$$

$$T_2 = 947\text{R}$$

Substitution in Eq. (5.8) and integrating gives

$$s_2 - s_1 = \int_{T_1}^{T_2} c_p \frac{dT}{T} = 0.24 \ln \frac{947}{530}$$

$$= 0.1403 \text{ B/lb}_m \text{ R}$$

The unavailable energy for the reversible process is

$$Q_u = T_0(s_2 - s_1) = 510(0.1403) = 71.5 \text{ B/lb}_m$$

The available energy is then

$$Q_a = Q_{in} - Q_u = 100 - 71.5 = 28.5 \text{ B/lb}_m$$

c. The unavailable energy for the given process is

$$Q_u = T_0(s_2 - s_1) = 510(0.1555) = 79.2 \text{ B/lb}_m$$

and the available energy is

$$Q_a = Q_{in} - Q_u = 100 - 79.2 = 20.8 \text{ B/lb}_m$$

Thus, the effect of friction is to increase the entropy of the system, and an important principle regarding friction can be stated:

The final entropy of a process involving friction will always be greater than that for a similar reversible process (providing Q is the same).

Since reversible processes are frequently used as a thermodynamic ideal to be approached, the above rule is extremely important in the analysis of actual thermodynamic processes and it is in this connection that the concept of entropy is most useful.

Summary

Important points resulting from the Second Law of Thermodynamics will be summarized here for emphasis.

1. The only processes which could be conceived to be externally reversible are heat transfer processes in which the system and its surroundings are at the same temperature throughout, and reversible adiabatic processes.

2. The simplest externally reversible cycle is the Carnot cycle composed of two constant temperature processes and two adiabatic processes.

3. No heat engine can be more efficient than a Carnot engine operating between the same temperature limits.

4. No heat engine operating in a cycle can convert all the heat supplied into useful work.

5. Entropy is a point function, independent of any process, and may be considered as a property of a medium, just as internal energy is a property of a medium.

6. The final entropy of a process involving friction will always be greater than that for a similar reversible process (providing Q is the same).

PROBLEMS

1. A Diesel engine consumes 400 lb_m of fuel per hour. Heat in the amount of 17,500 B is liberated for every pound of fuel consumed The engine develops 837 horsepower. What is the thermal efficiency? How much heat is rejected?

2. A gas turbine has a thermal efficiency of 18 per cent. Heat in the amount of 18,000 B is liberated for every pound of fuel consumed. The horsepower developed is 8000. What is the rate of fuel consumption?

3. A steam power plant has a thermal efficiency of 23 per cent. The plant produces 30,000 kilowatts of electrical energy. What is the heat supplied?

4. The temperatures shown in Fig. 5.2 are $T_1 = 500R$, $T_2 = 2000R$, $T_3 = 1500R$, and $T_4 = 1000R$. For each heat addition process, the heat added is proportional to the temperature at which it is added. What is the thermal efficiency of the cycle?

5. For a receiver temperature of 500R plot a curve of Carnot efficiency versus source temperature for source temperatures from 1000R to 5000R.

6. A Carnot engine develops 100 horsepower and operates between temperatures of 1040F and 40F. What is the heat supplied? What is the heat rejected? What is the thermal efficiency?

7. A Carnot engine operates between temperatures of 100F and 2000F. The entropy change for heat addition is 0.2 B/lb_m R. What is the specific work?

8. One pound of air is heated at constant volume. The initial temperature is 60F, and 300 B is added to the air. If the specific heat at constant volume is $c_v = 0.171$ B/lb_m R and is constant for the process, what is the change in entropy?

9. One pound of air is heated at constant pressure. The initial temperature is 60F, and 300 B is added to the air. If the specific heat at constant pressure is $c_p = 0.24$ B/lb_m R and is constant for the process, what is the change in entropy?

10. Based on a receiver temperature of 60F, determine the available energy for Probs. 8 and 9. Sketch a T–s diagram for the processes

11. Solve Prob. 9 if the initial temperature is 300F, all other data remaining unchanged.

12. One pound of air is heated at constant temperature at 60F, and 300B is added to the air. What is the change in entropy for the process? What is the available energy based on a receiver temperature of 60F?

13. Solve Prob. 12 if the air temperature is 1000F, all other data remaining unchanged.

14. Water is heated at 30 lb/in.² pressure from 60F to 1000F. What is the heat supplied per pound? What is the change in entropy? How much of the heat supplied is unavailable energy? Sketch a T–s diagram for the process.

15. Steam is heated in a steady flow process from stagnation conditions of 200 lb/in.² and 382F to stagnation conditions of 600F and 180 lb/in.² (a) What is the heat added? (b) What is the change in entropy? (c) What is the available energy based on a receiver temperature of 60F?

16. Solve Prob. 15 if the final pressure is 200 lb/in.², all other data remaining unchanged.

17. An engine operates on a Carnot cycle except for the adiabatic expansion process, in which friction occurs, increasing the entropy by 4 per cent of the entropy increase for the isothermal heat addition process. If the source and receiver temperatures are 1000R and 500R, what is the thermal efficiency? Compare with the value from Prob. 5. Sketch a T–s diagram for the cycle.

18. The same as Prob. 17 except that the source temperature is 2000R.

19. An engine operates on a Carnot cycle except for the adiabatic compression and adiabatic expansion processes, in which friction occurs, increasing the entropy for each process by 4 per cent of the entropy increase for the heat addition process. If the source and receiver temperatures are 1000R and 500R, what is the thermal efficiency? Sketch a T–s diagram for the cycle.

20. The same as Prob. 19 except that the source temperature is 2000R.

Chapter VI

THE IDEAL GAS

6.1 Introduction

The equation of state of an ideal gas based on the observations of Boyle and Charles has been derived in Chap. III. This equation will be repeated here for convenience.

$$Pv = RT \qquad (6.1)$$

Air is an example of a gas that closely follows Eq. (6.1) at atmospheric conditions. Another example is the products of combustion of an internal combustion engine. Many other gases used in thermodynamic processes can be described by this equation. Since a great many actual gases closely approach this relation, thermodynamic equations based on the ideal gas equation of state will be studied in some detail.

6.2 Internal energy—Joule's Law

One of the earliest discoveries of the properties of an ideal gas was made by Joule, in which he determined that the internal energy of such a gas depended only on its temperature. It is obvious that increasing the temperature of a gas increases its internal energy, but it is not obvious that a change in volume or pressure will not also change the internal energy. Joule's early experiments were performed on an apparatus similar to that shown in Fig. 6.1, which shows a thermodynamic system consisting of two tanks connected by a valve. The system was submerged in a tank of water in which a thermometer was placed. One of the tanks was evacuated while a gas (air) at some pressure was sealed in the other tank. The temperature of the water was noted, and the valve was slowly opened, allowing the air to fill the evacuated tank. After the valve was opened and time allowed for equilibrium to be attained, Joule noted that there was no change in the temperature of the water. That is, there was no heat transfer to or from the system. No work was performed on or by the system. Therefore, from the First Law there must have been no change in the internal energy of the system even though both the pressure and specific volume of the air in the system changed. Joule, therefore, concluded that the internal energy of the gas was a function of only the temperature. That is,

$$u = f(T) \tag{6.2}$$

where f is an unknown function.

Later, more refined experiments did show a slight change in the temperature of the water, the magnitude of the change depending on the gas. These later experiments indicated that the internal energy of a gas was dependent to an extent on the specific volume (or pressure). But for many gases this change in internal energy was negligibly small, and the more closely a gas approached Eq. (6.1) in behavior the more negligible the change in internal energy became. It was therefore concluded that for ideal gases Joule's Law and Eq. (6.2) hold.

The internal energy for any medium is a property of the medium and is therefore a point function dependent only on the condition of the medium and independent of any process used to cause the medium to be at its given state. For evaluating a change in internal energy of an ideal gas, since the internal energy is dependent only on the temperature of the gas, any process involving a temperature change can be used to evaluate the function in Eq. (6.2). The most convenient process for this purpose is a reversible nonflow constant volume proc-

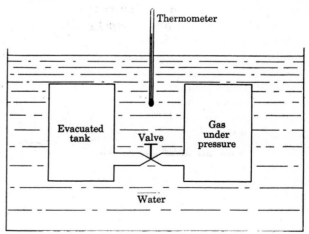

FIG. 6.1. APPARATUS FOR JOULE'S EXPERIMENT.

ess. For such a process the nonflow energy equation is

$$dQ = du \qquad (6.3a)$$

and from the definition of specific heat at constant volume

$$dQ = c_v \, dT \qquad (6.3b)$$

Eliminating dQ from these equations gives

$$\underline{du = c_v \, dT} \qquad \text{(ideal gas, any process)} \qquad (6.3)$$

For a gas for which Joule's Law holds, comparison of Eqs. (6.2) and (6.3) shows that the specific heat at constant volume must be either a constant or a function of temperature only. If the specific heat is constant, integration of Eq. (6.3) between limits of u_1, T_1 and u_2, T_2 gives

$$u_2 - u_1 = c_v(T_2 - T_1) \qquad \text{(constant specific heat)} \qquad (6.4a)$$

and if the specific heat is a function of temperature,

$$u_2 - u_1 = \int_{T_1}^{T_2} c_v \, dT \qquad (6.4)$$

where the relation between the specific heat and temperature must be supplied in order to perform the integration on the right.

It should be emphasized that since the internal energy for an ideal gas is a point function, dependent only on temperature, the change in internal energy for *any* process may be evaluated from Eq. (6.3). While a constant volume process was assumed in the derivation of Eq. (6.3), the relation applies equally well to any other process. This fact is extremely useful in analyzing thermodynamic processes involving ideal gases.

Example 6.1:

Determine the change in specific internal energy for an adiabatic compression process for an ideal gas in which the initial and final temperatures are 40F and 340F. The specific heat at constant volume for the gas is given by

$$c_v = 0.162 + 0.00046T$$

Solution:

The Rankine temperatures for the process are 500R and 800R.

Integration of Eq. (6.3) gives

$$u_2 - u_1 = \int_{500}^{800} (0.162 + 0.00046T)\, dT$$

$$= 138.3 \text{ B/lb}_m$$

6.3 Relation between specific heats

Based on Joule's Law and the equation of state of an ideal gas, a relation between the specific heat at constant pressure and the specific heat at constant volume may be found.

For a reversible nonflow constant pressure heating process for an ideal gas the energy equation is

$$dQ = du + \frac{P\, dv}{J} \tag{6.5a}$$

Since the process is at constant pressure, from the definition of specific heat,

$$dQ = c_p\, dT \tag{6.5b}$$

and from Joule's Law

$$du = c_v\, dT \tag{6.5c}$$

Differentiating the equation of state for a constant pressure process gives

$$P\, dv = R\, dT \tag{6.5d}$$

Substitution of Eqs. (6.5b) to (6.5d) in Eq. (6.5a) gives

$$c_p\, dT = c_v\, dT + \frac{R}{J}\, dT \tag{6.5e}$$

from which the following relation is obvious:

$$c_p = c_v + \frac{R}{J} \qquad \text{(ideal gas)} \tag{6.5}$$

Since the specific heat at constant volume has been shown to be either a constant or a function of temperature and since the quantity R/J is constant for an ideal gas, the specific heat at constant pressure must be either a constant or a function of temperature alone. Further, if either specific heat is known, the other may be found from Eq. (6.5).

Example 6.2:

The specific heat at constant pressure for air at or near atmospheric temperature is

$$c_p = 0.24 \text{ B/lb}_m \text{ F}$$

The gas constant for air is 53.3 ft-lb/lb$_m$ F. What is the corresponding specific heat at constant volume?

Solution:

From Eq. (6.5) the specific heat at constant volume is

$$c_v = 0.24 - \frac{53.3}{778}$$

$$= 0.171 \text{ B/lb}_m \text{ F}$$

In the thermodynamic relations for an ideal gas, the ratio of the specific heat at constant pressure to the specific heat at constant volume occurs so frequently that a symbol for the ratio is justified. This ratio, usually termed simply the "specific heat ratio" is given the symbol γ. By definition then

$$\gamma = \frac{c_p}{c_v} \tag{6.6}$$

Solving Eq. (6.5) for the specific heat at constant pressure in terms of γ gives

$$c_p = \frac{R}{J} \frac{\gamma}{\gamma - 1} \tag{6.7}$$

Solving Eq. (6.5) for the specific heat at constant volume in terms of γ gives

$$c_v = \frac{R}{J} \frac{1}{\gamma - 1} \tag{6.8}$$

6.4 Enthalpy

It is now possible to develop an equation for the enthalpy of an ideal gas showing that enthalpy, like internal energy, is a function of temperature alone. Substitution from the equation of state for an ideal gas into the equation defining enthalpy gives

$$h = u + \frac{RT}{J} \tag{6.9}$$

Since the internal energy has been shown to be a function of temperature alone, Eq. (6.9) indicates that the enthalpy is also a function of temperature alone.

Since enthalpy is the sum of two point functions, it must itself be a point function. Therefore, if a relation between enthalpy and temperature can be found, it can be used to evaluate the enthalpy change for any process when the initial and final temperatures are known.

Differentiation of Eq. (6.9) gives

$$dh = du + \frac{R}{J} dT \qquad (6.10a)$$

Substitution of Joule's Law, Eq. (6.3), in the above equation gives

$$dh = c_v \, dT + \frac{R}{J} \, dT$$

$$= \left(c_v + \frac{R}{J} \right) dT \qquad (6.10b)$$

However, the quantity in the parentheses is recognized to be the specific heat at constant pressure, from Eq. (6.5). Thus

$$dh = c_p \, dT \qquad \text{(ideal gas, any process)} \qquad (6.10)$$

Equation (6.10) is seen to be similar to Eq. (6.3) for internal energy. If the specific heat is constant, integration of Eq. (6.10) between limits of h_1, T_1 and h_2, T_2 gives

$$h_2 - h_1 = c_p(T_2 - T_1) \qquad \text{(constant specific heat)} \qquad (6.11a)$$

and if the specific heat is a function of temperature,

$$h_2 - h_1 = \int_{T_1}^{T_2} c_p \, dT \qquad (6.11)$$

where the relation between specific heat and temperature must be supplied in order to perform the integration on the right.

The above equations apply equally well to stagnation enthalpy by replacing the temperature by the stagnation temperature.

Example 6.3:

An ideal gas expands through a gas turbine from an initial stagnation temperature of 1400F to a final stagnation temperature of 1200F.

The specific heat for the gas is given by

$$c_p = 0.317 - \frac{1.2(10^2)}{T} + \frac{4(10^4)}{T^2}$$

Determine the change in stagnation enthalpy

Solution:

Integration of Eq. (6.10) between the temperature limits of 1860R and 1660R gives

$$h_{t2} - h_{t1} = \int_{1860}^{1660} \left[0.317 - \frac{1.2(10^2)}{T} + \frac{4(10^4)}{T^2} \right] dT$$

$$= -52.4 \text{ B/lb}_m$$

6.5 Entropy

Entropy, like internal energy and enthalpy, has been shown to be a point function. Unlike internal energy and enthalpy for an ideal gas, however, entropy is not dependent on temperature alone, as will be shown.

The nonflow energy equation for a reversible process of an ideal gas may be written

$$dQ = c_v \, dT + \frac{P \, dv}{J} \tag{6.12a}$$

However,
$$ds = \frac{dQ}{T} \tag{6.12b}$$

for a reversible process, and substitution of (6.12a) into (6.12b) gives

$$ds = c_v \frac{dT}{T} + \frac{P \, dv}{JT} \tag{6.12c}$$

From the equation of state for an ideal gas

$$\frac{P}{T} = \frac{R}{v} \tag{6.12d}$$

and Eq. (6.12c) may be written

$$ds = c_v \frac{dT}{T} + \frac{R}{J} \frac{dv}{v} \quad \begin{array}{l}\text{(ideal gas,}\\\text{any process)}\end{array} \tag{6.12}$$

Since entropy is a point function, Eq. (6.12) may be used to calculate the entropy change for any process. An alternate equation may be developed, however, that is sometimes more convenient than Eq. (6.12).

Differentiation of the equation of state for an ideal gas gives

$$P \, dv + v \, dP = R \, dT \qquad (6.13a)$$

from which

$$P \, dv = R \, dT - v \, dP \qquad (6.13b)$$

Substitution of Eq. (6.13b) into Eq. (6.12c) gives

$$ds = c_v \frac{dT}{T} + \frac{R \, dT}{JT} - \frac{v \, dP}{JT} \qquad (6.13c)$$

Making use of Eq. (6.5) and the relation

$$\frac{v}{T} = \frac{R}{P} \qquad (6.13d)$$

results in

$$ds = c_p \frac{dT}{T} - \frac{R}{J} \frac{dP}{P} \qquad \begin{matrix} \text{(ideal gas,} \\ \text{any process)} \end{matrix} \qquad (6.13)$$

Either Eq. (6.12) or (6.13) may be used to evaluate the entropy change for any process of an ideal gas. Obviously, for constant volume processes Eq. (6.12) is more convenient, while, for constant pressure processes, Eq. (6.13) is more convenient.

Example 6.4:

The specific heat at constant pressure for a certain ideal gas is 0.3 B/lb$_m$ F. Determine the change in entropy for a process in which the temperature changes from 100F to 300F and the pressure changes from 15 lb/in.^{2} to 30 lb/in.^{2} The gas constant is 40 ft-lb/lb$_m$ R.

Solution:

Integrating Eq. (6.13) between the given limits gives

$$s_2 - s_1 = \int_{560}^{760} 0.3 \, \frac{dT}{T} - \frac{40}{778} \int_{15}^{30} \frac{dP}{P}$$

$$= 0.0918 - 0.0356 = 0.0562 \, \text{B/lb}_m \, \text{R}$$

6.6 Isentropic gas relation

The equation of state for an ideal gas can be used to describe the relation between the thermodynamic coordinates for constant pressure processes, constant volume processes, and constant temperature processes. Many actual thermodynamic processes occur so rapidly that they approach the adiabatic condition of no external heat transfer. It has been previously shown that a reversible adiabatic process is isentropic. Isentropic processes are therefore important since they are ideal processes that are approached by many actual processes. The equation of state for an ideal gas does not indicate the relation between the thermodynamic coordinates for an isentropic process. However, several such relations may be easily derived.

For an isentropic process, $ds = 0$, and Eqs. (6.12) and (6.13) may be written

$$c_v \frac{dT}{T} = -\frac{R}{J}\frac{dv}{v} \qquad \text{(ideal gas, isentropic)} \qquad (6.14)$$

$$c_p \frac{dT}{T} = \frac{R}{J}\frac{dP}{P} \qquad \text{(ideal gas, isentropic)} \qquad (6.15)$$

If the relation between specific heat and temperature is known, these equations may be integrated. If the specific heat may be considered constant for a process, a simple relation between the thermodynamic coordinates exists.

For constant specific heat, integration of Eq. (6.14) results in

$$c_v \ln \frac{T_2}{T_1} = -\frac{R}{J} \ln \frac{v_2}{v_1} \qquad (6.16a)$$

Rearranging this expression, making use of Eq. (6.8), and taking antilogs gives

$$\frac{T_2}{T_1} = \left(\frac{v_1}{v_2}\right)^{\gamma-1} \qquad (6.16b)$$

Similar integration of Eq. (6.15), making use of Eq. (6.7), gives

$$\frac{T_2}{T_1} = \left(\frac{P_2}{P_1}\right)^{(\gamma-1)/\gamma} \qquad (6.16c)$$

Equations (6.16b) and (6.16c) may be combined to give

$$\frac{T_2}{T_1} = \left(\frac{P_2}{P_1}\right)^{(\gamma-1)/\gamma} = \left(\frac{v_1}{v_2}\right)^{\gamma-1} \qquad \text{(ideal gas, isentropic, constant specific heat)} \qquad (6.16)$$

Elimination of the temperature ratio between Eqs. (6.16b) and (6.16c) results in

$$\frac{P_2}{P_1} = \left(\frac{v_1}{v_2}\right)^{\gamma} \qquad (6.17a)$$

Since the initial and final conditions for the process are arbitrary, Eq. (6.17a) is equivalent to

$$Pv^\gamma = C \qquad \text{(ideal gas, isentropic, constant specific heat)} \qquad (6.17)$$

where C is a constant.

Example 6.5:

The initial and final temperatures for an isentropic compression of air are 40F and 340F. The initial pressure is 15 lb/in.² What is the final pressure? Assume constant specific heats and $c_p = 0.24$.

Solution:

From Example 6.2, for $c_p = 0.24$, $c_v = 0.171$, and $\gamma = c_p/c_v = 1.4$. From Eq. (6.16)

$$\frac{P_2}{P_1} = \left(\frac{T_2}{T_1}\right)^{\gamma/(\gamma-1)} = \left(\frac{800}{500}\right)^{3.5}$$

$$= 5.19$$

from which

$$P_2 = 15(5.19) = 77.8 \text{ lb/in.}^2$$

6.7 Stagnation conditions

Consider a conduit, Fig. 6.2, in which an ideal gas is flowing. Imagine that two thermometers are inserted into this flow. Thermometer A is mounted on a device which moves at a velocity equal to the velocity of the gas flow. Thermometer B is stationary.

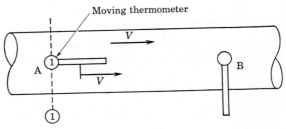

Fig. 6.2.

The relationship between the temperatures recorded on these thermometers can be derived from the steady-flow energy equation. If the distance from section 1 to thermometer B is small, it can be said that negligible heat is transferred between these two points, and that the effects of friction are also negligible. The gas flows from 1 to B in a reversible adiabatic process, during which the specific heat may be considered to be constant. The velocity of the gas in contact with A as it crosses section 1 will be V, the velocity of the gas in the conduit. The velocity of the gas in contact with B will be zero. Thermometer A will record T, the temperature of the moving gas. Thermometer B will record T_t, the stagnation temperature.

$$Q = h_B - h_1 + \frac{V_B^2}{2g_cJ} - \frac{V_1^2}{2g_cJ} + \frac{W}{J}$$

$$0 = c_p(T_t - T) + 0 - \frac{V^2}{2g_cJ} + 0$$

$$T_t = T + \frac{V^2}{2g_cJc_p} \qquad \text{(ideal gas, constant specific heat} \qquad (6.18)$$

Since an isentropic process has been specified for the flow of gas from section 1 to thermometer B, Eq. (6.16) may be applied to give

$$\frac{T_t}{T} = \left(\frac{P_t}{P}\right)^{(\gamma-1)/\gamma} = \left(\frac{v}{v_t}\right)^{\gamma-1} \qquad \text{(ideal gas, constant specific heat)} \qquad (6.19)$$

Equation (6.19) may also be combined with Eq. (6.1) to prove

$$P_t v_t = R T_t \qquad \qquad \text{(ideal gas)} \quad (6.20)$$

Equations (6.18), (6.19), and (6.20) can be used to obtain unknown stagnation or static properties of a moving gas with constant specific heat, given the velocity V and any two of the following properties: P, v, T, P_t, v_t, and T_t. It should be noted, however, that when v, T and T_t are the only known properties, no solution can be obtained.

It should be pointed out that stagnation properties exist for any moving fluid undergoing any kind of process. The thermometers A and B may be imagined to exist at any point in such a fluid, and Eqs. (6.18), (6.19), and (6.20) would apply at that point regardless of the type of process between that point and some other point in the fluid. The only restriction on the above equations is that the moving fluid must be an ideal gas with constant specific heat.

As discussed in Chap. IV, a direct measurement of the actual temperature of a fluid in motion is not possible by the insertion of a temperature-sensitive element into the flow. It is possible to measure the stagnation temperature. It is also possible to measure the stagnation pressure as well as the actual (static) pressure. The stagnation or total pressure may be measured by a Pitot tube, as shown in Fig. 6.3, in which the fluid is brought to rest relative to the probe. The static pressure may be measured by a flush-opening tube as shown in Fig. 6.3. For low velocity flows these two instruments are frequently combined into what is called a Pitot-static tube, as shown in Fig. 6.3, and connected to a differential manometer.

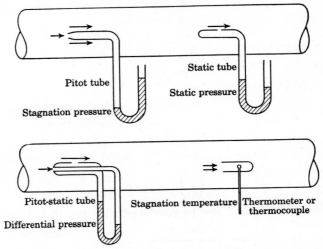

FIG. 6.3. PRESSURE AND TEMPERATURE PROBES.

From measurements of the stagnation and static pressure in a flowing gas and from Eq. (6.19) the actual (static) temperature in the flow can be determined if the stagnation temperature is measured.

Example 6.6:

From a Pitot tube the stagnation pressure in a flow of air is found to be 16 lb/in.² The static pressure is 14 lb/in.², and the total temperature is 83F. What is the actual temperature in the flow and the flow velocity?

Solution:

The specific heat for air at this temperature is $c_p = 0.24$ B/lb$_m$ F. The corresponding specific heat ratio is $\gamma = 1.4$. From Eq. (6.19)

$$\frac{T_t}{T} = \left(\frac{16}{14}\right)^{0.286} = 1.0387$$

$$T = \frac{543}{1.0387} = 523\text{R or } 63\text{F}$$

From Eqs. (6.11a) and (4.9)

$$h_t - h = c_p(T_t - T) = \frac{V^2}{2g_c J}$$

$$= 0.24(20) = 4.8 \text{ B/lb}_m$$

$$V = \sqrt{2g_c J(4.8)} = 490 \text{ ft/sec}$$

6.8 Polytropic gas relation

It is sometimes convenient to consider a general class of reversible processes for which the pressure-volume relation is given by

$$Pv^n = C$$
     (ideal gas, reversible polytropic)   (6.21)

where C and n are constant for the process. Such processes are called "polytropic" processes. From Eq. (6.21) and the equation of state for an ideal gas an equation similar to Eq. (6.16) may be developed and is

$$\frac{T_2}{T_1} = \left(\frac{P_2}{P_1}\right)^{(n-1)/n} = \left(\frac{v_1}{v_2}\right)^{n-1}$$
     (ideal gas, reversible polytropic)   (6.22)

Constant pressure processes, constant volume processes, constant temperature processes, and constant entropy processes may all be represented by Eq. (6.21) by proper choice of the exponent n. For example, by referring to the equation of state of an ideal gas and Eqs. (6.17) and (6.21),

constant pressure process $n = 0$

constant temperature process $n = 1$

isentropic process $n = \gamma$

constant volume process $n = \infty$

In general, the polytropic relation, Eq. (6.21), is most useful for processes in which the exponent n is not equal to any of the values listed above. In some cases of actual processes the actual process may be approximated by a polytropic process, and the exponent n may be determined from the initial and final condition for the process.

Example 6.7:

A gas expands in a nonflow system from an initial pressure and temperature of 100 lb/in.^{2} and 400F to a final pressure and temperature of 20 lb/in.² and 140F. Assuming the process may be considered polytropic, determine the exponent n and the specific work for the process. The gas constant is 50.

Solution:

The pressure ratio for the process is 5, and the temperature ratio is 1.433. Let the quantity $(n - 1)/n = C$. Then from Eq. (6.22)

$$1.433 = (5)^C$$

from which

$$C = 0.223$$

and

$$n = \frac{1}{1 - C} = 1.29$$

From the equation of state for an ideal gas

$$v_1 = \frac{50(860)}{144(100)} = 2.98 \text{ ft}^3/\text{lb}_m$$

$$v_2 = \frac{50(600)}{144(20)} = 10.42 \text{ ft}^3/\text{lb}_m$$

and from Eq. (6.21)

$$Pv^n = 144(100)2.98^{1.29} = 58,800$$

The work is then

$$W = \int_{v_1}^{v_2} P \, dv = 58,800 \int_{2.98}^{10.42} \frac{dv}{v^{1.29}}$$

$$= 58,800 \left[-\frac{v^{-.29}}{0.29} \right]_{2.98}^{10.42} = 44,900 \text{ ft-lb}/\text{lb}_m$$

6.9 Gas tables

The use of tables of properties of gases was discussed in Chap. III. It is now possible to explain the development of the tables and to show the use of tabulated quantities not discussed in Chap. III.

It has been shown that the enthalpy and internal energy of an ideal gas are functions of temperature alone. The relation for enthalpy is given by Eq. (6.10). Since only differences in enthalpy are involved in thermodynamic processes, the zero value of enthalpy for a table may be arbitrarily chosen and Eq. (6.10) may be integrated to give

$$h = \int_{T_0}^{T} c_p \, dT \tag{6.23}$$

where T_0 is arbitrarily chosen and the specific heat temperature function is supplied from experimental data. The enthalpy values in Table 6 of the Appendix were determined from Eq. (6.23) with $T_0 = 0R$.The values of internal energy were determined from the enthalpy values and Eq. (6.9).

Entropy is not a function of temperature alone, and no values for entropy are given in Table 6. Entropy may be easily determined from Eq. (6.13) and a temperature function listed as ϕ in Table 6. The function ϕ is defined by the following relation:

$$\phi = \int_{T_0}^{T} c_p \frac{dT}{T} \tag{6.24}$$

Integration of Eq. (6.13) between limits gives

$$s_2 - s_1 = \int_{T_1}^{T_2} c_p \frac{dT}{T} - \frac{R}{J} \ln \frac{P_2}{P_1} \tag{6.25a}$$

which is equivalent to

$$s_2 - s_1 = \int_{T_0}^{T_2} c_p \frac{dT}{T} - \int_{T_0}^{T_1} c_p \frac{dT}{T} - \frac{R}{J} \ln \frac{P_2}{P_1} \tag{6.25b}$$

From the definition of ϕ this expression is seen to be

$$s_2 - s_1 = \phi_2 - \phi_1 - \frac{R}{J} \ln \frac{P_2}{P_1} \tag{6.25}$$

It will be noted that for a constant pressure process the entropy change is equal to the difference between the values of ϕ for the limiting temperatures.

Example 6.8:

Determine the entropy change for air for a process acting between a pressure and temperature of 15 lb/in.² and 40F and a pressure and temperature of 20 lb/in.² and 540F.

Solution:

From Table 6, for the two temperatures

$$\phi_1 = 0.58233, \qquad \phi_2 = 0.75042$$

From Eq. (6.25), the entropy change is

$$s_2 - s_1 = 0.75042 - 0.58233 - \frac{53.3}{778} \ln \frac{20}{15}$$

$$= 0.14849 \ B/lb_m \ R$$

Two other useful functions are those termed "relative pressure," P_r, and "relative volume," v_r. These are pressure and volume relations for isentropic processes. For a constant specific heat, the pressure-volume-temperature relation for an isentropic process is given by Eq. (6.16). If the specific heat is variable with temperature, no such simple relation exists. Pressure ratios and volume ratios may be determined from the tables, however.

For an isentropic process, integration of Eq. (6.15) gives

$$\frac{R}{J} \ln \frac{P_2}{P_1} = \int_{T_1}^{T_2} c_p \frac{dT}{T} \qquad (6.26a)$$

The relative pressure is defined by the relation

$$\ln P_r = \frac{J}{R} \int_{T_0}^{T} c_p \frac{dT}{T} \qquad (6.26b)$$

Now, Eq. (6.26a) is equivalent to

$$\frac{R}{J} \ln \frac{P_2}{P_1} = \int_{T_0}^{T_2} c_p \frac{dT}{T} - \int_{T_0}^{T_1} c_p \frac{dT}{T} \qquad (6.26c)$$

which, from Eq. (6.26b), may be written

$$\frac{R}{J} \ln \frac{P_2}{P_1} = \frac{R}{J} \ln P_{r2} - \frac{R}{J} \ln P_{r1} \qquad (6.26d)$$

or

$$\ln \frac{P_2}{P_1} = \ln \frac{P_{r2}}{P_{r1}} \qquad (6.26e)$$

Taking antilogs of Eq. (6.26e) shows that

$$\frac{P_2}{P_1} = \frac{P_{r2}}{P_{r1}} \qquad \text{(isentropic)} \qquad (6.26)$$

Thus, for an isentropic process, the ratio of the limiting pressures is the same as the ratio of the relative pressures.

The relative volume is defined by the relation

$$\ln v_r = -\frac{J}{R} \int_{T_0}^{T} c_v \frac{dT}{T} \qquad (6.26a)$$

and a development similar to the above based on Eq. (6.14) gives

$$\frac{v_2}{v_1} = \frac{v_{r2}}{v_{r1}} \qquad \text{(isentropic)} \qquad (6.27)$$

It should be emphasized that the relative pressure and relative volume of Table 6 are useful only for isentropic processes.

Example 6.9:

Air is expanded isentropically from a temperature of 1440F to a temperature of 1000F. Determine the pressure ratio and volume ratio, (a) assuming constant specific heat and $\gamma = 1.4$ and (b) using Table 6.

Solution:

a. From Eq. (6.16) the pressure ratio is

$$\frac{P_2}{P_1} = \left(\frac{1460}{1900}\right)^{3.5} = 0.4$$

and the volume ratio is

$$\frac{v_2}{v_1} = \left(\frac{1900}{1460}\right)^{2.5} = 1.93$$

b. From Table 6, for $T_1 = 1900$ and $T_2 = 1460$

$$P_{r1} = 141.51, \qquad P_{r2} = 50.34$$
$$v_{r1} = 4.974, \qquad v_{r2} = 10.743$$

Making use of Eq. (6.26), the pressure ratio is

$$\frac{P_2}{P_1} = \frac{50.34}{141.51} = 0.356$$

and the volume ratio is, from Eq. (6.27),

$$\frac{v_2}{v_1} = \frac{10.743}{4.947} = 2.16$$

It will be noted from this example that considerable error may result from the use of constant specific heats equal to the atmospheric temperature values when the temperatures are appreciably different from atmospheric.

6.10 Specific heats for air

Since air is the basic medium for a large number of thermodynamic processes, the knowledge of variation of specific heat with temperature for air is often useful in approximate calculations where more accuracy is desired than that obtained from using $c_p = 0.24$ B/lb$_m$ F.

Figure 6.4 shows the variation of specific heat and specific heat ratio with temperature for air at low pressures, where the ideal gas equation of state is applicable.

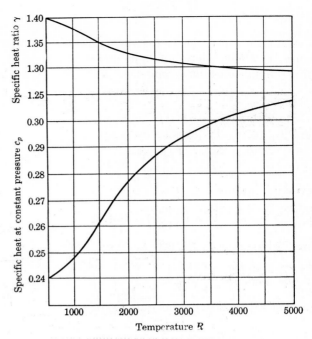

Fig. 6.4. Specific heat for air.

6.11 Carnot efficiency

The efficiency of a Carnot cycle using an ideal gas as the working medium will now be derived. For simplicity the specific heat for the cycle will be assumed to be constant, although the same result may be obtained if the specific heat is variable with temperature.

It will be recalled that the Carnot cycle is composed of two reversible adiabatic processes and two reversible constant temperature processes. Thus heat is added or removed only during the constant temperature processes. The four cycle processes will be numbered:

1 to 2   constant temperature heat addition at T_s

2 to 3   reversible adiabatic expansion

3 to 4   constant temperature heat rejection at T_r

4 to 1   reversible adiabatic compression

The process equation for the constant temperature heat addition is

$$Pv = RT_s \tag{6.28a}$$

and the energy equation for this process is

$$dQ = du + \frac{P\,dv}{J} \tag{6.28b}$$

Since the temperature is constant, $du = 0$ and, from Eq. (6.28a), Eq. (6.28b) may be integrated to give

$$Q_s = \frac{R}{J}\,T_s \ln \frac{v_2}{v_1} \tag{6.28c}$$

Similarly, for the heat rejection process,

$$Q_r = \frac{R}{J}\,T_r \ln \frac{v_3}{v_4} \tag{6.28d}$$

From the definition of thermal efficiency, Eq. (5.3), the Carnot efficiency in terms of Eqs. (6.28c) and (6.28d) is

$$\eta = 1 - \frac{T_r \ln (v_3/v_4)}{T_s \ln (v_2/v_1)} \tag{6.28e}$$

Since the expansion from 2 to 3 is isentropic, Eq. (6.16) applies and

$$\frac{T_r}{T_s} = \left(\frac{v_2}{v_3}\right)^{\gamma-1} \tag{6.28f}$$

Similarly for the compression from 4 to 1

$$\frac{T_r}{T_s} = \left(\frac{v_1}{v_4}\right)^{\gamma-1} \tag{6.28g}$$

Combining Eqs. (6.28f) and (6.28g) gives

$$\frac{v_2}{v_3} = \frac{v_1}{v_4} \tag{6.28h}$$

which may be rearranged as follows:

$$\frac{v_2}{v_1} = \frac{v_3}{v_4} \tag{6.28i}$$

Substituting Eq. (6.28i) in Eq. (6.26e) gives the final result

$$\eta = 1 - \frac{T_r}{T_s} \tag{6.28}$$

This is the result stated in Chap. V in the discussion of the true thermodynamic temperature scale and indicates that the absolute temperature in the equation of state for an ideal gas is the same as the absolute temperature defined by the Carnot cycle.

PROBLEMS

1. The specific heats at constant pressure and constant volume for air near atmospheric temperature are $c_p = 0.24$ and $c_v = 0.171$ B/lb$_m$ F. What is the change in specific internal energy when air is heated at constant pressure from 60F to 360F, assuming constant specific heat? Compare this answer with that obtained from Table 6 of the Appendix.

2. What is the change in enthalpy in Prob. 1? Compare this answer with that obtained from Table 6 of the Appendix.

3. What is the work done in Prob. 1 if the process is nonflow? Compare this answer with that obtained using Table 6 of the Appendix.

4. Solve Prob. 1 if the final temperature is 1360F, all other data remaining unchanged.

5. Solve Prob. 3 if the final temperature is 1360F, all other data remaining unchanged.

6. The specific heat at constant volume for a gas having a molecular weight of 2 is 2.42 B/lb$_m$ F. What is the specific heat at constant pressure?

7. The specific heat at constant volume for CH_4 gas is 0.159 B/lb$_m$ F. What is the specific heat at constant pressure?

8. The ratio of specific heats for a gas is $\gamma = 1.3$, and the specific heat at constant pressure is 0.20 B/lb$_m$ F. What is the molecular weight of the gas?

9. The gas constant for a certain gas is 48 ft-lb/lb$_m$ R, and the specific heat ratio is 1.4. What are the specific heats at constant volume and constant pressure?

10. An ideal gas having a constant $R = 35.1$ ft-lb/lb$_m$ R undergoes a process from 14 lb/in.² and 60F to 60 lb/in.² and 300F. The specific heat at constant volume for this temperature range is 0.154 B/lb$_m$ F.

What are the respective changes in entropy and enthalpy for the process?

11. One mole of an ideal gas undergoes a reversible constant pressure process from a temperature of 40F to a temperature of 600F. What is the work done?

12. An ideal gas having a specific heat ratio of 1.35 and a gas constant of 48.2 ft-lb/lb$_m$ R undergoes an expansion process from a pressure and temperature of 100 lb/in.^{2} and 500F to a pressure and temperature of 50 lb/in.^{2} and 300F. What is the change in entropy?

13. An ideal gas (air) undergoes a reversible constant temperature heat addition from a pressure and temperature of 100 lb/in.^{2} and 300F to a pressure of 20 lb/in.^{2} What is the heat added per pound of air? What is the change in entropy?

14. An ideal gas (air) undergoes a constant volume heat addition in which 160 B/lb$_m$ of heat is added. The initial temperature is 80F, and the initial pressure is 20 lb/in.^{2} Assuming the specific heat at constant volume is 0.172 B/lb$_m$ F, what are the final temperature and change in entropy?

15. The gas of Prob. 8 undergoes a reversible adiabatic compression from a pressure and temperature of 15 lb/in.^{2} and 60F to a pressure of 65 lb/in.^{2} What is the final temperature?

16. An ideal gas has a constant specific heat ratio of 1.4. It undergoes a reversible adiabatic expansion from a pressure and temperature of 80 lb/in.^{2} and 600F to a temperature of 400F. What is the final pressure?

17. An ideal gas undergoes an isentropic expansion from a pressure and temperature of 100 lb/in.^{2} and 400F to a pressure and temperature of 20 lb/in.^{2} and 80F. What is the specific heat ratio?

18. An ideal gas (air) is flowing at a velocity of 800 ft/sec. The stagnation temperature is 100F. Assuming a constant specific heat of $c_p = 0.24$ B/lb$_m$ F, what is the static temperature? What is the ratio of the stagnation pressure to the static pressure?

19. The stagnation pressure and temperature of a flowing stream of air are 20 lb/in.^{2} and 80F. The static pressure is 19 lb/in.^{2} What is the static temperature if $c_p = 0.24$ B/lb$_m$ F?

20. Solve Prob. 19 for the flow velocity.

21. Air is heated at constant pressure from a temperature of 60F to a temperature of 1540F. What is the change in entropy, using Table 6 of the Appendix? What is the change in entropy for a constant specific heat of $c_p = 0.24$ B/lb$_m$ F?

22. Compare the enthalpy change in Prob. 21, using Table 6 and the constant specific heat value.

23. Air is heated at constant volume from a temperature of 60F to a temperature of 2000R. What is the change in entropy. using Table 6 of the Appendix? What is the change in entropy for a constant specific heat of $c_v = 0.175$ B/lb$_m$ F?

24. Compare the internal energy change in Prob. 23, using Table 6 and the constant specific heat value.

25. Air is compressed isentropically from a pressure and temperature of 14.7 lb/in.² and 60F to a temperature of 300F. What is the final pressure, (a) based on Table 6 of the Appendix; (b) based on a constant specific heat ratio of $\gamma = 1.4$?

26. What is the mean specific heat at constant pressure for the process of Prob. 25, using Table 6 and the temperature difference?

27. Air is expanded isentropically from a pressure and temperature of 100 lb/in.² and 1600R to a pressure of 48 lb/in.² What is the final temperature, (a) based on Table 6 of the Appendix; (b) based on a constant specific heat ratio of $\gamma = 1.4$?

28. What constant specific heat ratio would give the same final temperature in Prob. 27 as that obtained from the use of Table 6?

Chapter VII

THERMODYNAMIC PROCESSES

7.1 Basic relations

The purpose of this chapter is to correlate the material previously presented in order to solve problems involving thermodynamic processes, both actual and reversible. The fundamental relations developed in the preceding chapters can best be divided into two groups—those which apply to any thermodynamic medium and those which apply specifically to the ideal gas. In general, the differential form of the basic relations is most flexible and will be used in the following table, which summarizes the work of the preceding chapters.

Eighteen basic relations are shown in Table 7.1, and with these relations, or combinations of these relations, it is possible to set up the great majority of problems in elementary thermodynamics. The procedure for the use of the table in the solution of thermodynamic processes is as follows:

1. Write the applicable energy equation for the process.

2. Substitute as many of the relations following the energy equations as are applicable to the process into the energy equation, and integrate.

3. If tables of properties are available, the tabular values should be used in the integrated equation to solve for the unknown energy terms.

4. If the thermodynamic medium is an ideal gas, approximate solutions can be obtained by making use of the relations applicable to the ideal gas and constant specific heat values determined from Table 7 of the Appendix. More accurate solutions can be obtained from mean specific heat data, if available.

The remainder of this chapter will be concerned with the discussion and application of Table 7.1 to the most important thermodynamic processes—constant temperature, constant pressure, constant volume, and constant entropy.

TABLE 7.1

IMPORTANT THERMODYNAMIC RELATIONS

(Potential energy changes are assumed to be negligible in the following relations.)

For Any Medium	For an Ideal Gas
Energy Equations	*Equation of State*
1. $dQ = du + \dfrac{dW}{J}$ (nonflow)	10. $Pv = RT$
	11. $MR = \bar{R} = 1544$ ft-lb/Mol R
2. $dQ = dh_t + \dfrac{dW}{J}$ (steady flow)	*Internal Energy and Enthalpy*
	12. $du = c_v\, dT$
Reversible Shaft Work	13. $dh = c_p\, dT$
3. $dW = P\, dv$ (nonflow)	*Specific Heat*
4. $dW = -v_t\, dP_t$ (steady flow)	14. $c_p = c_v + \dfrac{R}{J}$
Reversible Heat Flow	15. $\gamma = \dfrac{c_p}{c_v}$
5. $dQ = c_p\, dT$ (constant pressure)	*Entropy*
6. $dQ = c_v\, dT$ (constant volume)	16. $ds = c_p \dfrac{dT}{T} - \dfrac{R}{J}\dfrac{dP}{P}$
7. $dQ = T\, ds$ (constant kinetic energy)	17. $ds = c_v \dfrac{dT}{T} + \dfrac{R}{J}\dfrac{dv}{v}$
Enthalpy	*Isentropic Process*
8. $h = u + \dfrac{Pv}{J}$	18. $\dfrac{T_2}{T_1} = \left(\dfrac{P_2}{P_1}\right)^{(\gamma-1)/\gamma} = \left(\dfrac{v_1}{v_2}\right)^{\gamma-1}$
9. $h_t = h + \dfrac{V^2}{2g_c J}$ $(Q = 0, W = 0)$	(constant specific heat)

7.2 P–v and T–s diagrams

It has been shown that the area on a pressure-volume diagram represents the shaft work of the medium for reversible processes and the area under a temperature-entropy curve represents the heat flow for the medium for reversible processes. It has been proven that reversible steady flow work with constant potential energy can be obtained by the following equation:

$$W = -\int_{P_{t1}}^{P_{t2}} v_t\, dP_t$$

Notice that this work will be equal to the area "behind the curve" on a pressure-volume diagram (Fig. 7.1). A knowledge of the orienta-

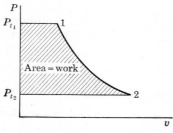

Fig. 7.1.

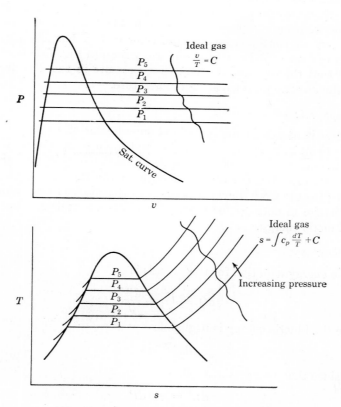

Fig. 7.2. Constant pressure processes.

tion of various reversible process curves in the P–v and T–s planes is an important aid in visualizing and solving thermodynamic problems. It is recommended that P–v and T–s sketches be made in the solution of process problems. Such sketches will be included in the discussion of processes which follows.

7.3 Constant pressure processes

Many important thermodynamic processes take place at or near constant pressure. Such processes include the combustion process in a gas turbine or rocket motor, the addition of heat in the boiler of a steam power plant, the removal of heat in the condenser of a refrigerator, and many others.

Schematic pressure-volume and temperature-entropy diagrams extending from the compressed liquid to the ideal gas region are shown for reversible constant pressure processes in Fig. 7.2. The ideal gas region is shown to the right of the wavy lines in Fig. 7.2. It will be noted that the direction of increasing pressure in the T–s diagram is in the direction of increasing temperature.

Example 7.1:

Water is heated in the boiler and superheater of a steam turbine power plant at a pressure of 160 lb/in.² from a temperature of 100F to a temperature of 550F. If the process is reversible and operates under steady flow conditions, determine (a) the heat added per pound; (b) the work done per pound; (c) the change in enthalpy; (d) the change in entropy for the process. Assume negligible potential and kinetic energy.

Solution:

The energy equation for the process is

$$dQ = dh_t + \frac{dW}{J}$$

Since the kinetic energy is negligible

$$dh_t = dh$$

and since the process is reversible

$$dW = -v\, dP$$

Thus, for a constant pressure process, the work is zero, and the energy equation becomes

$$dQ = dh$$

from which

$$Q = h_2 - h_1$$

The initial enthalpy of the compressed liquid is essentially equal to the enthalpy of saturated liquid at 100F. The initial enthalpy from Table 2, of the Appendix is then

$$h_1 = 67.97 \text{ B/lb}_m$$

and the entropy at this condition is

$$s_1 = 0.1295 \text{ B/lb}_m \text{ R}$$

The final enthalpy and entropy of the superheated steam, by interpolation in Table 4 of the Appendix, are found to be

$$h_2 = 1299.1, \qquad s_2 = 1.6776$$

Therefore,

$$h_2 - h_1 = Q = 1231.1 \text{ B/lb}_m$$

$$s_2 - s_1 = 1.5481 \text{ B/lb}_m \text{ R}$$

Example 7.2:

Water is heated in the boiler and superheater of a steam turbine power plant from an initial pressure and temperature of 160 lb/in.^{2} and 100F to a final pressure and temperature of 140 lb/in.^{2} and 550F. The process is similar to that of Example 7.1 but is not reversible. Determine (a) the work done per pound; (b) heat added per pound; (c) change in enthalpy; (d) change in entropy for the process.

Solution:

As before, the steady flow energy equation is

$$dQ = dh_t + \frac{dW}{J}$$

Since there is no shaft work in a boiler and superheater process,

$$dW = 0$$

Thus, as before, the energy equation becomes, since the kinetic energy is negligible,

$$dQ = dh, \quad \text{and} \quad Q = h_2 - h_1$$

The initial enthalpy and entropy, from Table 2, are

$$h_1 = 67.97, \qquad s_1 = 0.1295$$

The final enthalpy and entropy of the superheated steam by interpolation in Table 4 are

$$h_2 = 1300.8, \qquad s_2 = 1.6937$$

Therefore

$$h_2 - h_1 = Q = 1232.8 \text{ B/lb}_m$$

$$s_2 - s_1 = 1.5642 \text{ B/lb}_m \text{ R}$$

Example 7.3:

Heat is removed at constant pressure from an ideal gas in a reversible nonflow process. The initial pressure and temperature are 30 lb/in.² and 300F. The final temperature is 60F. What are the heat flow per pound, work supplied per pound, change in internal energy, and change in entropy for the process if the specific heat at constant pressure is constant and equal to 0.25 B/lb$_m$ F and the gas constant is 53.3 ft-lb/lb$_m$ R?

Solution:

The energy equation for the process is

$$dQ = du + \frac{dW}{J}$$

The heat may be evaluated from

$$dQ = c_p \, dT$$

and

$$Q = 0.25(520 - 760) = -60 \text{ B/lb}_m$$

The change in internal energy may be determined from

$$du = c_v \, dT = \left(c_p - \frac{R}{J}\right) dT$$

$$u_2 - u_1 = (0.25 - 0.0685)(520 - 760)$$

$$= -43.6 \text{ B/lb}_m$$

The work is then, from the energy equation,

$$W = J[Q - (u_2 - u_1)]$$

$$= 778(-60 + 43.6)$$

$$= 12,770 \text{ ft-lb/lb}_m$$

and the change in entropy is

$$ds = c_p \frac{dT}{T}$$

$$s_2 - s_1 = 0.25 \int_{760}^{520} \frac{dT}{T} = -0.095 \text{ B/lb}_m \text{ R}$$

It should be noted that the area under and to the left of a given point on a line of constant pressure on a temperature-entropy diagram represents the enthalpy of that point.

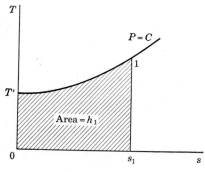

Fig. 7.3.

The proof of the above statement is easily worked out for an ideal gas with constant specific heat. It can be similarly proved for any medium, but the proof becomes involved for vapors and gases with varying specific heats.

Integrating Eq. (16) in Table 7.1, for a constant pressure process of an ideal gas, results in the following:

$$\int_0^s ds = \int_{T'}^T c_p \frac{dT}{T} \quad \text{or,}$$

$$s = c_p \ln \frac{T}{T'}, \quad \text{and} \quad T = T'e^{s/c_p}$$

This is the equation of the constant pressure line shown in Fig. 7.3. Temperature T' is the temperature at which the entropy is arbitrarily set equal to zero.

Solving for the area under this line to the left of point 1:

$$A = \int_0^{s_1} T \, ds = \int_0^{s_1} T' e^{s/c_p} \, ds$$

$$= c_p T'(e^{s_1/c_p} - 1) = c_p(T_1 - T') = h_1 - h'$$

It can be seen that the area A will be equal to the enthalpy of the point in question, provided the entropy and the enthalpy are arbitrarily set equal to zero at the base temperature, T'. As this is entirely permissible (Arts. 2.2 and 2.12), the area under and to the left of a given point on a line of constant pressure on any T–s diagram can be interpreted as the enthalpy of that point. If the constant pressure line represents stagnation pressure, the resulting area will be the stagnation enthalpy. A parallel proof also shows that the area under a constant volume line is equal to the internal energy.

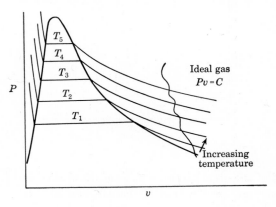

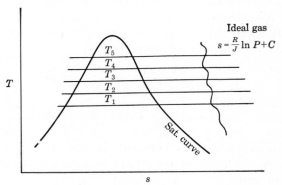

FIG. 7.4. CONSTANT TEMPERATURE PROCESSES.

7.4 Constant temperature processes

While constant temperature processes are more difficult to approach than are constant pressure processes except where phase change occurs, many thermodynamic processes approach constant temperature conditions. Such processes include evaporating and condensing, and the cooling processes of gas compressors.

Schematic pressure-volume and temperature-entropy diagrams for reversible constant temperature processes are shown in Fig. 7.4. The ideal gas region is shown to the right of the wavy lines in Fig. 7.4. It will be noted that the direction of increasing temperatures in the P–v diagram is in the direction of increasing pressure and that the equation for constant temperature lines in the ideal gas region is that of an equilateral hyperbola.

Example 7.4:

Water is heated in the boiler of a steam power plant from saturated liquid to saturated vapor at a temperature of 300F under steady-flow conditions. Determine (a) the work done per pound; (b) heat added per pound; (c) change in enthalpy; (d) change in entropy for the process. Assume the kinetic energy is negligible.

Solution:

There is no shaft work for the process and the kinetic energy is negligible. The steady flow energy equation for the process is then

$$dQ = dh, \quad \text{or} \quad Q = h_2 - h_1$$

The initial and final enthalpy and entropy, from Table 2, are

$$h_1 = 269.59, \qquad h_2 = 1179.7$$

$$s_1 = 0.4369, \qquad s_2 = 1.6350$$

Therefore
$$h_2 - h_1 = Q = 910.1 \text{ B/lb}_m$$

$$s_2 - s_1 = 1.1981 \text{ B/lb}_m \text{ R}$$

Example 7.5:

Air is compressed by a small high-pressure compressor which discharges into a tank having a volume of 12.8 ft.^{3} The compression of air in the tank takes place at constant temperature of 80F. The initial pressure in the tank is 14 lb/in.^{2}, and the final pressure is 500 lb/in.^{2} If the process is reversible, what are the work required, heat transfer, change in internal energy, and change in entropy?

Solution:

The system in this case may be considered as the entire quantity of air in the tanks at the end of compression, and the process may be considered as nonflow compression of this quantity.

The energy equation for a reversible process of an ideal gas is

$$dQ = du + \frac{dW}{J}$$

$$dQ = c_v \, dT + \frac{P \, dv}{J}$$

However, for a constant temperature process, from the equation of state for an ideal gas

$$Pv = RT$$

and

$$P \, dv = -v \, dP = -RT \frac{dP}{P}$$

The energy equation then becomes

$$dQ = \frac{dW}{J}, \qquad dQ = -\frac{RT}{J} \frac{dP}{P}$$

and

$$Q = \frac{W}{J} = -\frac{53.3(540)}{778} \ln \frac{500}{14}$$

$$= -132 \text{ B/lb}_m$$

$$W = 778(-132) = -102,900 \text{ ft-lb/lb}_m$$

The final specific volume is

$$v_2 = \frac{RT}{P_2} = \frac{53.3(540)}{144(500)}$$

$$= 0.4 \text{ ft}^3/\text{lb}_m$$

and the mass that is compressed is then

$$w = \frac{\tilde{v}}{v} = \frac{12.8}{0.4}$$

$$= 32 \text{ lb}_m$$

The heat transfer is then

$$\tilde{Q} = wQ = -132(32)$$
$$= -4220 \text{ B}$$

and the work is

$$\tilde{W} = wW = -102,900(32)$$
$$= -3,290,000 \text{ ft-lb}$$

Since the temperature is constant, there is no change in internal energy. The change in entropy is, for a constant temperature process,

$$s_2 - s_1 = \frac{Q}{T} = \frac{-132}{540}$$
$$= -0.244 \text{ B/lb}_m \text{ R}$$

and

$$\tilde{s}_2 - \tilde{s}_1 = 32(-0.244)$$
$$= -7.81 \text{ B/R}$$

7.5 *Constant volume processes*

Constant volume processes constitute an important field in thermodynamics. The combustion process in high-speed internal combustion piston engines approaches constant volume conditions. Pumping processes of liquids are essentially constant volume processes.

Schematic pressure-volume and temperature-entropy diagrams are shown in Fig. 7.5 for reversible constant volume processes. The ideal gas region is shown to the right of the wavy lines in Fig. 7.5. It will be noted that the direction of increasing volume in the T–s diagram is in the direction of decreasing temperature.

Example 7.6:

Saturated steam at a pressure of 14.7 lb/in.^{2} is heated in a closed rigid tank to a pressure of 20 lb/in.^{2} What are the work done, heat input, change in internal energy, and change in entropy for 1 lb$_m$ of steam?

Solution:

There is no external work done in heating steam in a closed tank. The nonflow energy equation is then

$$dQ = du \quad \text{or} \quad Q = u_2 - u_1$$

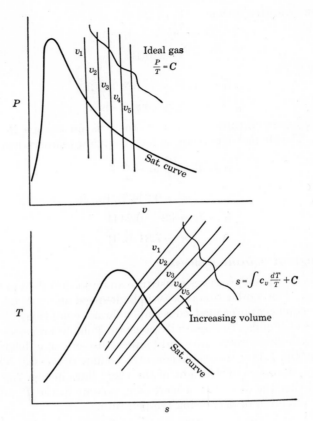

FIG. 7.5. CONSTANT VOLUME PROCESSES.

From Table 3 of the Appendix, the properties of the saturated steam are

$$v_1 = 26.8, \qquad h_1 = 1150.4, \qquad s_1 = 1.7566$$

The initial internal energy is then

$$u_1 = 1150 - \frac{144(14.7)26.8}{778}$$

$$= 1077.5 \; \text{B/lb}_m$$

The final volume is equal to the initial volume, and from Table 4, for a pressure of 20 lb/in.², the final temperature is seen to be between

400 and 450F. For a volume of 26.8 ft³/lb$_m$ the final conditions are found, by interpolation, to be

$$v_2 = 26.8, \qquad h_2 = 1260.6, \qquad s_2 = 1.8632$$

from which

$$u_2 = 1260.9 - \frac{144(20)26.8}{778}$$

$$= 1161.4 \text{ B/lb}_m$$

Therefore,

$$u_2 - u_1 = Q = 83.9 \text{ B/lb}_m$$

$$s_2 - s_1 = 0.1066 \text{ B/lb}_m \text{ R}$$

Example 7.7:

Air is heated in a closed rigid container from an initial pressure and temperature of 100 lb/in.² and 240F to a final temperature of 740F. Determine the work, heat, change in internal energy, and change in entropy, (a) assuming c_v is constant and equal to 0.171 B/lb$_m$ F; (b) determining an average specific heat from Fig. 6.4 (c), using Table 6 of the Appendix.

Solution:

There is no work for the process, and the energy equation is

$$dQ = du = c_v\, dT$$

a. If the specific heat is constant,

$$Q = u_2 - u_1 = 0.171(500) = 85.5 \text{ B/lb}_m$$

and

$$s_2 - s_1 = \int_{T_1}^{T_2} c_v \frac{dT}{T} = 0.171 \ln \frac{1200}{700} = 0.0921 \text{ B/lb}_m \text{ R}$$

b. From Fig. 6.4 for a temperature range of 700 to 1200R the specific heat is judged to be

$$c_{pm} = 0.247$$

from which

$$c_v = 0.247 - \frac{53.3}{778} = 0.1785$$

and

$$Q = u_2 - u_1 = 0.1785(500) = 89.25 \text{ B/lb}_m$$

$$s_2 - s_1 = 0.1785 \ln \frac{1200}{700} = 0.0962 \text{ B/lb}_m \text{ R}$$

c. The specific volume is

$$v_1 = v_2 = \frac{RT}{P} = \frac{53.3(700)}{144(100)} = 2.591 \text{ ft}^3/\text{lb}_m$$

and the final pressure is

$$P_2 = P_1 \frac{T_2}{T_1} = 100 \left(\frac{1200}{700}\right) = 171.4 \text{ lb/in.}^2$$

From Table 6 of the Appendix $u_1 = 119.6$, $u_2 = 209.0$, $\phi_1 = 0.6632$ $\phi_2 = 0.7963$

The heat flow and internal energy change are then

$$Q = u_2 - u_1 = 89.4 \text{ B/lb}_m$$

The entropy change is

$$s_2 - s_1 = \phi_2 - \phi_1 - \frac{R}{J} \ln \frac{P_2}{P_1}$$

$$= 0.7963 - 0.6632 - 0.0685 \ln \frac{171.4}{100}$$

$$= 0.09620 \text{ B/lb}_m \text{ R}$$

As shown by the preceding example, neglecting the variation in specific heat with temperature results in an appreciable error compared with the use of the values of Table 6, while estimating a mean specific heat from Fig. 6.4 gives values in close agreement with those based on Table 6. For many purposes, the use of a constant specific heat is satisfactory, however.

7.6 Reversible adiabatic (isentropic) processes

Many actual thermodynamic processes are essentially adiabatic and approach isentropic conditions. Such processes include the compression or expansion of a gas or vapor in which work is supplied to or delivered by the thermodynamic medium. The expansion of a gas or vapor through a nozzle in which no work is done, but in which a large change in kinetic energy takes place, constitutes another class of processes that approach isentropic conditions.

An adiabatic process is one in which no external heat transfer occurs. Only if an adiabatic process is also frictionless (reversible) is it isentropic, since

$$ds = \frac{dQ}{T}$$

only for a reversible process. While it is possible to conceive of a nonreversible, nonadiabatic process occurring with no change in entropy, the only isentropic processes of interest in thermodynamics are those which are reversible and adiabatic. Therefore, the terms "isentropic" and "reversible adiabatic" will be used synonymously.

Schematic pressure-volume and temperature-entropy diagrams are shown in Fig. 7.6 for isentropic processes. The ideal gas region is shown to be right of the wavy lines in Fig. 7.6. It will be noted that the direction of increasing entropy in the P–v diagram is in the direction of increasing volume.

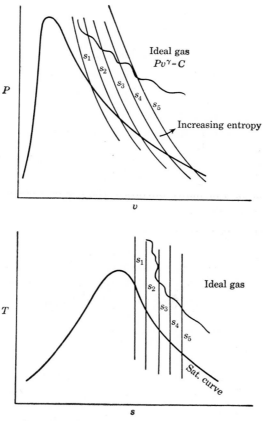

FIG. 7.6. CONSTANT ENTROPY PROCESSES.

Example 7.8:

Steam expands reversibly and adiabatically under steady flow conditions through a turbine from a stagnation pressure and temperature of 100 lb/in.² and 500F to a stagnation pressure of 15 lb/in.² What are the heat transfer, work done, change in enthalpy, and change in entropy for the process?

Solution:

Since the process is adiabatic, the heat transfer is zero, and since it is also reversible, there is no change in entropy. The steady flow energy equation for the process is

$$dh_t + \frac{dW}{J} = 0 \quad \text{or} \quad h_{t1} - h_{t2} = \frac{W}{J}$$

From Table 4 of the Appendix, the initial conditions are

$$h_{t1} = 1279.1, \qquad s_{t1} = 1.7085$$

Saturation conditions for 15 lb/in.² from Table 3 of the Appendix are

$$h_g = 1150.8, \qquad s_g = 1.7549$$

$$h_{fg} = 969.7, \qquad s_{fg} = 1.4415$$

Since the process is isentropic,

$$s_{t1} = s_{t2} = 1.7085$$

and from Eq. (3.3)

$$1 - X = \frac{s_g - s_{t2}}{s_{fg}} = \frac{1.7549 - 1.7085}{1.4415}$$

$$= 0.0322$$

The final stagnation enthalpy is then

$$h_{t2} = h_g - (1 - X)h_{fg}$$

$$= 1150.8 - (0.0322)969.7$$

$$= 1119.6$$

Therefore

$$h_{t1} - h_{t2} = \frac{W}{J} = 159.5 \text{ B/lb}_m$$

and

$$W = 157.3(778) = 122,300 \text{ ft-lb/lb}_m$$

Example 7.9:

Air is compressed isentropically in a piston compressor from an initial pressure and temperature of 14.7 lb/in.² and 60F to a pressure of 100 lb/in.² Determine the work and change in internal energy for 1 lb$_m$ of air, assuming a constant specific heat at constant volume of 0.171 B/lb$_m$ F and specific heat ratio of 1.4.

Solution:

The energy equation for the process is

$$du + \frac{dW}{J} = 0$$

but

$$du = c_v \, dT$$

so that

$$\frac{W}{J} = c_v(T_1 - T_2)$$

The final temperature from the isentropic gas relation is

$$\frac{T_2}{T_1} = \left(\frac{P_2}{P_1}\right)^{(\gamma-1)/\gamma} = \left(\frac{100}{14.7}\right)^{0.286} = 1.737$$

$$T_2 = 1.737(520) = 903\text{R}$$

Substitution into the energy equation gives

$$\frac{W}{J} = u_1 - u_2 = 0.171(520 - 903)$$

$$= -65.5 \text{ B/lb}_m$$

and

$$W = 778(-65.5) = -51,000 \text{ ft-lb/lb}_m$$

Example 7.10:

Air expands isentropically through the nozzle of a jet engine from a stagnation pressure and temperature of 25 lb/in.² and 840F to a static pressure of 14.7 lb/in.² Determine the nozzle exit velocity, using Table 6 of the Appendix.

Solution:

The energy equation for the process is

$$dh_t = 0$$

or $$h_{t1} = h_{t2} = h_2 + \frac{V_2^2}{2g_c J}$$

From Table 6 of the Appendix for the initial conditions at 1300R

$$h_{t1} = 316.94, \qquad P_{rt1} = 32.39$$

Since the process is isentropic, Eq. (6.24) applies and

$$\frac{P_{rt1}}{P_{r2}} = \frac{P_{t1}}{P_2} = \frac{25}{14.7} = 1.7$$

from which $$P_{r2} = \frac{32.39}{1.7} = 19.05$$

The corresponding enthalpy determined by interpolation from Table 6 is

$$h_2 = 272.4$$

and the exit velocity is

$$V_2 = \sqrt{2g_c J (316.94 - 272.4)}$$

$$= 1488 \text{ ft/sec}$$

7.7 Actual adiabatic processes

Many thermodynamic processes may be considered adiabatic even though they are not reversible (frictionless). As stated in Chap. V, the effect of friction is always to increase the entropy of the system. Figure 7.7 shows T–s diagrams for adiabatic compression and ex-

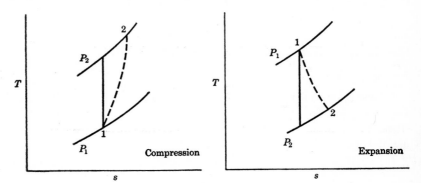

FIG. 7.7. ADIABATIC COMPRESSION AND EXPANSION.

pansion processes in the superheat or ideal gas region. The corresponding reversible adiabatic (isentropic) processes for compression and expansion between the same pressures are also shown in Fig. 7.7. While the exact process path for a nonreversible process is difficult to define, the energy equation for such processes may be solved with no other knowledge of the path than its initial and final conditions, as illustrated by the following examples.

Example 7.11:

Steam expands adiabatically under steady flow conditions through a turbine from a stagnation pressure and temperature of 100 lb/in.² and 500F to a stagnation pressure of 16 lb/in.² The final quality is determined to be 99.6 per cent. What are the work done and change in entropy for the process?

Solution:

Since the process is adiabatic, the heat transfer is zero and the energy equation is

$$dh_t + \frac{dW}{J} = 0 \quad \text{or} \quad h_{t1} - h_{t2} = \frac{W}{J}$$

From Table 4 of the Appendix, the initial conditions are

$$h_{t1} = 1279.1, \qquad s_{t1} = 1.7085$$

Saturation conditions for 16 lb/in.² from Table 3 of the Appendix are

$$h_g = 1152.0, \qquad s_g = 1.7549$$

$$h_{fg} = 969.7, \qquad s_{fg} = 1.4415$$

The final stagnation enthalpy for a quality of 0.996 is

$$h_{t2} = h_g - (1 - X)h_{fg}$$

$$= 1152 - (0.004)969.7$$

$$= 1148.1$$

and the final entropy is

$$s_{t2} = 1.7549 - (0.004)1.4415$$

$$= 1.7491$$

Therefore,

$$h_{t1} - h_{t2} = \frac{W}{J} = 131 \text{ B/lb}_m$$

$$W = 778(131) = 102,000 \text{ ft-lb/lb}_m$$

$$s_{t2} - s_{t1} = 0.0406 \text{ B/lb}_m \text{ R}$$

The conditions of this example are similar to those of Example 7.8, except that the process of Example 7.8 is reversible and hence isentropic. It will be noted that the output work of Example 7.8 is greater than that of Example 7.11.

Example 7.12:

Air is compressed adiabatically in a piston compressor from a pressure of temperature of 14.7 lb/in.² and 60F to a pressure and temperature of 100 lb/in.² and 470F. What are the work done and change in entropy for the process? Use $c_v = 0.171$ B/lb$_m$ F.

Solution:

The energy equation is

$$du + \frac{dW}{J} = 0 \quad \text{or} \quad \frac{W}{J} = c_v(T_1 - T_2)$$

from which

$$\frac{W}{J} = 0.171(-410) = -70.1 \text{ B/lb}_m$$

and　　　　$$W = 778(-70.1) = -54,500 \text{ ft-lb/lb}_m$$

The change in entropy is

$$s_2 - s_1 = c_p \ln \frac{T_2}{T_1} - \frac{R}{J} \ln \frac{P_2}{P_1}$$

$$= 0.24 \ln \frac{930}{520} - 0.0685 \ln \frac{100}{14.7}$$

$$= 0.0088 \text{ B/lb}_m \text{ R}$$

7.8 Air compressors

The air compressor is a machine that clearly illustrates an actual thermodynamic process. In addition it lends itself ideally to a simple

First Law analysis. The air compressor can be considered as a steady flow machine, but it should not be analyzed as a thermodynamic cycle. Even though there is a series of thermodynamic events during the functioning of this device, only a single process occurs. Compressed air is widely used in such diversified fields as operating portable tools, starting diesel engines, operating air brakes on trucks and trains, and in the operation of all gas turbine engines.

7.9 Positive displacement compressors

As discussed in the Glossary of Thermodynamic Terms in the Appendix, compressors may be either positive displacement or turbo types. The reciprocating air compressor is of the positive displace-

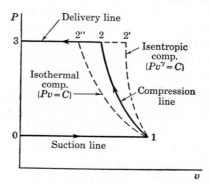

Fig. 7.8.

ment type and presently has the widest field of application. The simplest reciprocating compressor is one which accomplishes the entire compression process in a single cylinder. Such compressors are called single-stage compressors, and may be single- or double-acting, depending on whether the compression is effected in one end of the cylinder only or in both ends. First consider Fig. 7.8, which shows a theoretical P–v diagram for a compressor without clearance. Air is drawn into the cylinder as indicated by line 0–1. Compression takes place from 1 to 2. At point 2 the discharge valve opens and air is pushed out of the cylinder until the end of the stroke at point 3. The nature of the compression line depends on the design and operation of the compressor. One extreme case is that of isentropic compression, labeled 1–2′. Another extreme is isothermal compression labeled 1–2″. Since the area enclosed represents work done *on* the air, it is evident that isentropic compression requires the most work and isothermal the least. In actuality, compressors usually operate between these extremes. The relation between the pressure P and the specific volume v during a reversible adiabatic compression of air is $Pv^\gamma = C$, and during an isothermal compression it is $Pv = C$ (see Art. 6.8). Hence, it is logical to expect the relation between these properties during the actual compression process might be approximately $Pv^n = C$, where n is a constant having a value between unity and γ. Experiments show that this is actually true. This relationship defines a polytropic process with which you are already familiar. Although isothermal compression would require the minimum amount of work, such a process is difficult to approach, because the time used during compression is so short that little heat transfer can take place. This suggests that isothermal operation might be approached simply by (a) keeping the cylinder walls cool by a water-jacket, and (b) running the compressor at a very low speed. The second alternative, however, would not be practical because the capacity of the compressor, the quantity of air handled per unit time, would be too small. In practice, both water cooling and air cooling are used, each with practical advantages. As might be expected, water cooling is more efficient. Values of n from 1.25 to 1.3 represent the best results from water-jacketed compressors. Under *favorable circumstances* values of n around 1.35 are normal for air cooling.

The preceding discussion has been based upon compression in a cylinder with no clearance. In actual practice, when the piston is at the end of its inward travel, there remains a volume within the cylinder proper, plus a volume within the passages leading to the valves. The total is called the *clearance volume*. The clearance volume can be made small, but cannot be made zero since the face of the piston cannot be allowed to come into contact with the cylinder head. In addition, the passages leading to the valves will always contribute to the clearance volume. Since no actual compressor can have a clearance volume of zero, the diagram shown in Fig. 7.8 must be modified, although the principles already presented remain unchanged.

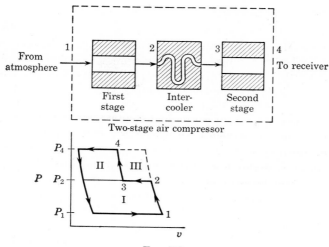

Fig. 7.9.

In order to understand next the *actual* operation of an air compressor, consider the schematic diagram, Fig. 7.9. This shows a typical layout for a two-stage compressor delivering compressed air. "Free air" (air at the local conditions of atmospheric pressure and temperature) is introduced into the first stage of the air compressor at point 1. In the first stage, the air pressure is increased from atmospheric pressure, P_1, to pressure P_2, as shown on the air compressor Pv diagram. Area I on the diagram is the indicated work done on the air in the first stage. One of the most common methods of accomplishing both first- and second-stage compressions is by the action of a piston within a cylinder. As shown by hatched areas on the schematic diagram, the air is normally cooled during compression by water flowing in a jacket around the cylinder. From the first stage the air at pressure P_2 passes through the intercooler. Here the temperature of the air is reduced by cooling water. A constant pressure process is assumed. At point 3 the air leaves the intercooler and enters the second stage, where it is compressed to pressure P_4. Area II on the Pv diagram is the indicated work done on the air in the second stage. Area III is the work saved by cooling the air in the intercooler.

7.10 Turbo-compressors

Many industrial operations, as well as all gas turbine engines, require tremendous quantities of compressed air. The inability of the conventional positive-displacement compressor to meet the volume demand has led to the development and use of dynamic or turbo-compressors. The turbo-compressors include both centrifugal and axial flow compressors. Both these compressors operate on the air to produce a change in momentum, with a resulting increase in pressure.

Most centrifugal compressors consist of a rotating vaned member called an *impeller*, and a stationary member known as a *diffuser*. Air is introduced near the shaft of the impeller and accelerated in a radial direction by the rotation of the impeller. As the air leaves the outer perimeter of the impeller it is collected in the diffuser where its kinetic energy is reduced with a resulting increase in pressure.

The axial flow compressor usually consists of a series of "stages." Each stage includes a row of rotating blades (rotor blades) and a row of stationary blades (stator blades). As the air passes through the succeeding stages, it is accelerated and decelerated in an axial direction, with an ultimate increase in pressure.

In both the centrifugal and axial flow compressors, the actual compression process is accompanied by a considerable amount of fluid friction. However, if there is no inter-cooling, the flow may be assumed to be adiabatic since the heat loss to the surroundings is negligible. The turbo-compressors are true steady-flow machines, and the compressor work may easily be computed by applying the steady-flow energy equation.

A compressor analysis using the steady flow energy equation is applicable to both the centrifugal and the axial flow compressor because it is concerned with entrance and exit properties and does not touch upon the internal mechanics of compression.

7.11 Enthalpy-entropy diagrams

The enthalpy-entropy diagram has been found to be extremely useful for the presentation of steady flow adiabatic processes, both actual and reversible. The change in enthalpy for a steady flow adiabatic process is equal to the external work for the process plus the change in kinetic energy for the process. By proper use of stagnation conditions the change in enthalpy may be made to show either the external work or the kinetic energy.

As shown in the preceding examples, for steady flow adiabatic processes, the energy equation becomes

$$\frac{dW}{J} = -dh_t \qquad (7.1a)$$

or
$$\frac{W}{J} = h_{t1} - h_{t2} \qquad \text{(adiabatic, steady-flow)} \quad (7.1)$$

Thus, for a turbine or compressor the work is shown as the difference of stagnation enthalpies for the process.

If, in addition to being adiabatic, the process occurs with no shaft work, such as the expansion of a gas or vapor through a nozzle or the compression of a gas or vapor in a diffuser, the above equation becomes

$$h_{t1} = h_{t2} \qquad \begin{array}{l}\text{(Adiabatic, steady flow,}\\ \text{no shaft work)}\end{array} \quad (7.2)$$

For a nozzle, the final kinetic energy is of interest, and by making use of the definition of stagnation enthalpy Eq. (7.2) may be written

$$h_{t1} = h_2 + \frac{V_2^2}{2g_c J} \qquad \begin{array}{l}\text{(adiabatic,}\\ \text{nozzle flow)}\end{array} \quad (7.3)$$

For a diffuser, Eq. (7.2) may be written

$$h_1 + \frac{V_1^2}{2g_c J} = h_{t2} \qquad \begin{array}{l}\text{(adiabatic,}\\ \text{diffuser flow)}\end{array} \quad (7.4)$$

Thus, for a nozzle or diffuser, the kinetic energy is shown as the difference between a stagnation and static enthalpy for the process.

Recalling that the stagnation condition at a given location in a flow has the same entropy as the static condition at the same location, the presentation of stagnation conditions in an h–s diagram may be shown as in Fig. 7.10. This figure shows the stagnation pressure to be greater than the static pressure, and the stagnation enthalpy to exceed the static enthalpy by an amount equal to the kinetic energy at the given location.

The use of the h–s diagram for actual processes is shown in Fig. 7.11 for compressor, turbine, nozzle, and diffuser processes that are adiabatic but not reversible.

It is important to note that energy is represented as a vertical displacement rather than as an area in these diagrams.

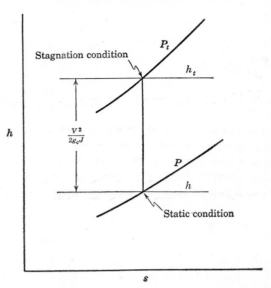

FIG. 7.10. h-s DIAGRAM OF STAGNATION AND STATIC CONDITIONS.

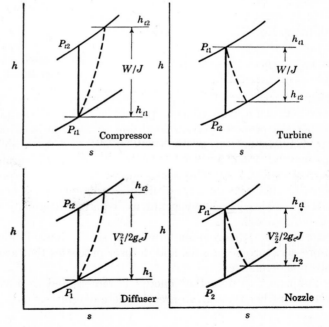

FIG. 7.11. h-s DIAGRAMS OF STEADY-FLOW ADIABATIC PROCESSES.

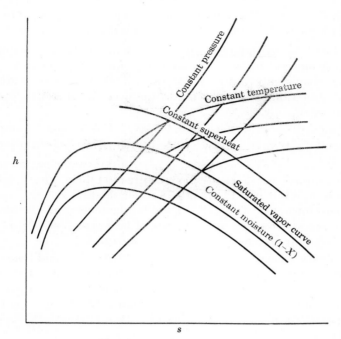

FIG. 7.12. MOLLIER CHART.

A convenient chart for the solution of adiabatic processes involving steam is the Mollier chart, which plots the properties of steam in an h–s diagram as shown in Fig. 7.12. Such a chart is given in Chart I of the Appendix (in the envelope inside the back cover). The saturated vapor line is shown in Fig. 7.12, as well as lines of constant quality, constant pressure, constant temperature, and constant superheat. Adiabatic processes will appear on a Mollier chart in the same form as those of Fig. 7.11.

PROBLEMS

1. Water is heated at constant pressure in the boiler of a steam power plant at a pressure of 600 lb/in.² from a temperature of 200F to dry, saturated steam. The process operates under steady flow conditions, and kinetic effects are negligible. Determine the heat added, work done, change in enthalpy, and change in entropy for 1 lb$_m$.

2. Solve Prob. 1 if the pressure loss in the boiler necessary to overcome friction is 40 lb/in.^{2}, all other data remaining unchanged.

3. Air is heated under steady flow conditions in the combustion chamber of a gas turbine at a stagnation pressure of 80 lb/in.^{2} from a stagnation temperature of 300F to a stagnation temperature of 1600F. Determine, for 1 lb$_m$ of air, the heat added, work done and change in entropy.

4. Solve Prob. 3 if the pressure loss in the burner necessary to overcome friction is 4 lb/in.^{2}, all other data remaining unchanged.

5. An ideal gas is compressed under constant temperature steady flow conditions from a stagnation pressure of 14 lb/in.^{2} to a stagnation pressure of 40 lb/in.^{2} The stagnation temperature is 100F, and the gas constant is 48 ft-lb/lb$_m$ R. If 100 lb$_m$/hr is compressed, what are the horsepower required and the rate of heat rejection? What is the change in entropy? Sketch $P-v$ and $T-s$ diagrams.

6. Steam is heated under irreversible steady flow conditions in the superheater of a steam power plant from dry saturated vapor at 300 lb/in.^{2} stagnation pressure to a stagnation pressure and stagnation temperature of 260 lb/in.^{2} and 800F. What is the change in entropy? What is the heat added per pound of steam? Sketch $P-v$ and $T-s$ diagrams.

7. If the process in Prob. 6 is frictionless, that is, if the exit stagnation pressure were 300 lb/in.^{2}, all other data remaining the same, what would be the heat added per pound and the change in entropy?

8. An ideal gas is heated in a nonflow constant volume process from a pressure and temperature of 14.7 lb/in.^{2} and 60F to a temperature of 2000F. If the specific heat is given by

$$c_v = 0.158 + 0.00046T$$

determine, for 1 lb$_m$ of gas, the heat added, work done, change in internal energy, and change in entropy. Sketch $P-v$ and $T-s$ diagrams.

9. The gas of Prob. 8 undergoes an isentropic compression from a pressure and temperature of 14.7 lb/in.^{2} and 60F to a final temperature of 440F. If the gas constant is 70, what is the final pressure?

10. Water is compressed under steady flow constant volume conditions from a stagnation pressure of 14 lb/in.^{2} to a stagnation pressure of 300 lb/in.^{2} What power is required for a water flow of 100 lb$_m$/min?

11. Air is compressed reversibly and adiabatically in a nonflow process from a pressure and temperature of 15 lb/in.^{2} and 60F to a pressure of 80 lb/in.^{2} Assuming air to be an ideal gas with constant specific heat ($c_p = 0.24$ B/lb$_m$ F), what are the specific work and change in internal energy for the process? Sketch P–v and T–s diagrams.

12. Air is expanded reversibly and adiabatically in a steady flow process from stagnation conditions of 100 lb/in.^{2} and 1300F to a stagnation pressure of 20 lb/in.^{2} Assuming air to be an ideal gas with constant specific heat ($c_p = 0.26$ B/lb$_m$ F), what is the specific work for the process?

13. Air is expanded adiabatically but not reversibly in an air turbine under steady flow conditions. The initial stagnation conditions are 100 lb/in.^{2} and 100F. The final stagnation conditions are 20 lb/in.^{2} and -80F. What are the specific work and increase in entropy? (Use $c_p = 0.24$ ft-lb/lb$_m$ F.)

14. How much more work could have been done in Prob. 12 if the flow had been isentropic to the same final pressure?

15. Steam expands reversibly and adiabatically through the nozzles of a steam turbine under steady flow conditions from a stagnation pressure and stagnation temperature of 300 lb/in.^{2} and 700F to a static pressure of 150 lb/in.^{2} What is the nozzle exit velocity? Use Mollier Chart.

16. Steam expands adiabatically but not reversibly through the nozzles of a steam turbine under steady flow conditions from a stagnation pressure and stagnation temperature of 300 lb/in.^{2} and 700F to a static pressure and temperature of 150 lb/in.^{2} and 560F. What are the nozzle exit velocity and change in entropy for the process? Use Mollier Chart.

17. Air is flowing in a duct under steady flow conditions. At one point in the flow the stagnation pressure and stagnation temperature are 19.5 lb/in.^{2} and 103F. The static pressure at this point is 17 lb/in.^{2} What is the velocity at this point? What is the static temperature at this point?

18. Steam is flowing in a pipe under steady flow conditions. At one point in the flow the stagnation conditions are 200 lb/in.^{2} and 450F, and the static pressure is 190 lb/in.^{2} What is the velocity at this

point? What is the static temperature at this point?

19. Air is compressed adiabatically but not reversibly in a nonflow process from a pressure and temperature of 15 lb/in.² and 60F to a pressure and temperature of 80 lb/in.² and 420F. Assuming air to be an ideal gas with constant specific heat ($c_p = 0.24$ B/lb$_m$ F), what are the specific work and change in entropy for the process? Sketch P–v and T–s diagrams, and compare results with those of Prob. 11.

20. Tell whether the following processes result in superheated steam, wet vapor, or compressed liquid. Sketch P–v and T–s diagrams.

(a) Saturated vapor is heated at constant pressure.

(b) Saturated vapor is compressed reversibly and adiabatically.

(c) Superheated vapor, near saturation, is expanded reversibly and adiabatically.

(d) Saturated liquid is heated at constant volume.

(e) Saturated vapor is cooled at constant pressure.

Chapter VIII

GAS ENGINE CYCLES

8.1 Cycles

A cycle has been previously defined as a series of thermodynamic processes, applied to a working fluid, in which heat is transferred and work is done and which returns the working fluid to its original condition. Several theoretical thermodynamic cycles, in addition to the Carnot cycle, are of significance in the study of heat engines, in that actual engines approach these theoretical cycles in operation.

Heat engine cycles may be broadly classed as gas cycles and vapor cycles. Three theoretical gas cycles are of importance; they are the Otto cycle, which is approached by the familiar gasoline internal combustion engine; the Diesel cycle, which is approached by compression ignition engines; and the Brayton cycle, which is approached by the gas turbine engine. The most important theoretical vapor cycle is the Rankine cycle, which is approached by steam power plants.

In general, all engine cycles consist of the following processes: compression, heat addition, expansion, and heat rejection. In most gas power cycles heat addition is obtained by combustion of fuel in air, the working medium. The heat rejection process occurs in the atmosphere after the products of combustion have been exhausted from the engine. Such engines do not operate in a true cycle since the working medium is not returned to its initial state and cannot be re-used in another cycle. The medium after it is exhausted is returned to its original pressure and temperature even though it is not returned to its original chemical composition. Such engines are said to operate on "open" cycles. Whether the heat rejection process occurs within the engine or in the atmosphere does not alter the analysis of performance of the cycle as long as no shaft work occurs during the process.

The following assumptions will be made for the analysis of the theoretical gas cycles:

1. All processes are reversible.
2. The working medium is a gas (air) having constant specific heat.

3. The addition of heat does not change the chemical composition or mass of the working medium.

Cycles analyzed under the above assumptions are termed "air standard" cycles.

8.2 Otto cycle

The theoretical Otto cycle, which is approached by automotive and aircraft piston engines, is composed of four nonflow processes: reversible adiabatic compression, constant volume heat addition, reversible adiabatic expansion, and constant volume heat rejection, returning the medium to its original condition. These processes are shown in $P-v$ and $T-s$ diagrams in Fig. 8.1.

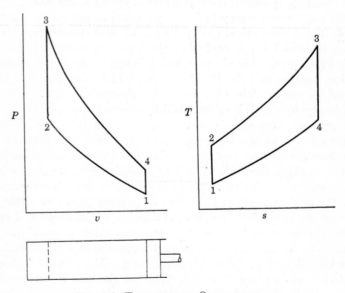

FIG. 8.1. THEORETICAL OTTO CYCLE.

Process 1–2 in Fig. 8.1 is a reversible adiabatic compression for which the energy equation is

$$\frac{W_{1-2}}{J} = u_1 - u_2 \tag{8.1a}$$

The work input may also be found by evaluating $\int P\, dv$, where $P = C/v^{\gamma}$. That is,

$$W_{1-2} = \frac{P_2 v_2 - P_1 v_1}{1 - \gamma} = \frac{R(T_2 - T_1)}{1 - \gamma} \tag{8.1b}$$

Process 2–3 is a constant volume heat addition for which the energy equation is

$$Q_{2-3} = u_3 - u_2 = c_v(T_3 - T_2) \tag{8.1c}$$

Process 3–4 is a reversible adiabatic expansion for which the energy equation is

$$\frac{W_{3-4}}{J} = u_3 - u_4 \tag{8.1d}$$

The work output may also be found by evaluating $\int P\, dv$ as in Eq. (8.1b). That is,

$$W_{3-4} = \frac{P_4 v_4 - P_3 v_3}{1 - \gamma} = \frac{R(T_4 - T_3)}{1 - \gamma} \tag{8.1e}$$

Process 4–1 is a constant volume heat rejection for which the energy equation is

$$Q_{4-1} = u_1 - u_4 = c_v(T_1 - T_4) \tag{8.1f}$$

Any of the above equations may be used in the determination of the thermal efficiency of the cycle. As shown in Chap. V, the thermal efficiency for any cycle may be expressed as

$$\eta = 1 - \frac{Q_{\text{out}}}{Q_{\text{in}}} \tag{8.1}$$

Inspection of Eqs. (8.1a)–(8.1f) shows that the entire heat input is given by Eq. (8.1c) and the entire heat output is given by Eq. (8.1f). Making use of these equations, the thermal efficiency becomes

$$\eta = 1 - \frac{T_4 - T_1}{T_3 - T_2} \tag{8.2a}$$

where the sign of Eq. (8.1f) has been changed to make the heat output positive.

It is possible to replace the temperatures in the above equation by a function of the volume ratio for the compression or expansion processes as follows: Both compression and expansion are isentropic, and the relations between temperature and volume are

$$\frac{T_2}{T_1} = \left(\frac{v_1}{v_2}\right)^{\gamma-1} \tag{8.2b}$$

$$\frac{T_3}{T_4} = \left(\frac{v_4}{v_3}\right)^{\gamma-1} \tag{8.2c}$$

However, $v_1 = v_4$ (8.2d)

$$v_2 = v_3 \tag{8.2e}$$

so that Eqs. (8.2b) and (8.2c) may be combined to give

$$\frac{T_4}{T_1} = \frac{T_3}{T_2} \tag{8.2f}$$

Subtracting 1 from both sides of Eq. (8.2f) and rearranging results in

$$\frac{T_1}{T_2} = \frac{T_4 - T_1}{T_3 - T_2} \tag{8.2g}$$

Substituting Eq. (8.2g) in Eq. (8.2a) and making use of Eq. (8.2b) gives

$$\eta = 1 - \frac{1}{(v_1/v_-)^{\gamma-1}} \tag{8.2}$$

Equation (8.2) shows that the theoretical efficiency of the Otto cycle is a function of the ratio of the initial and final volumes of the compression process. This volume ratio is called the "compression ratio," a term widely used in the field of piston engines. The choice of this term is rather unfortunate since it refers to a volume ratio rather than a pressure ratio.

Example 8.1:

A theoretical Otto cycle has a compression ratio of 7. Heat in the amount of 300 B/lb$_m$ is supplied to the cycle. The initial conditions are 60F and 14.7 lb/in.² What are the temperature at the end of heat addition, the output work per pound, and the thermal efficiency based on a constant volume specific heat of 0.1715 B/lb$_m$ F?

Solution:

The temperature at the end of compression is

$$\frac{T_2}{T_1} = \left(\frac{v_1}{v_2}\right)^{\gamma-1} = (7)^{0.4} = 2.17$$

$$T_2 = 2.17(520) = 1130\text{R}$$

The temperature at the end of combustion is

$$Q = c_v(T_3 - T_2), \qquad T_3 - T_2 = \frac{300}{0.1715} = 1750\text{R}$$

$$T_3 = 1130 + 1750 = 2880\text{R}$$

The thermal efficiency is

$$\eta = 1 - \frac{1}{2.17} = 0.539$$

The output work is

$$\frac{W_{\text{net}}}{J} = \eta Q_{\text{in}} = 0.539(300)$$

$$= 161.7 \text{ B/lb}_m$$

$$W_{\text{net}} = 778(161.7) = 125{,}800 \text{ ft-lb/lb}_m$$

The theoretical Otto cycle is approached in actual spark ignition engines as shown in Fig. 8.2 for a four-stroke cycle. Position 1 in Fig. 8.2 is called the head end position, or top dead center. The volume enclosed at this position is called the clearance volume. Position 2 is called the crank end position, or bottom dead center. The volume swept through by the piston—volume 2 minus volume 1—is called the displacement volume. During the intake stroke, 1–2, the intake valve is open and the exhaust valve closed. This process takes place with some loss of pressure, due to fluid friction. With the piston in position 2 the cylinder is full of a combustible mixture of air and fuel, and both valves are closed. The compression process, which is essentially adiabatic, is from position 2–3. The spark occurs near the end of this stroke, and combustion is initiated. The combustion process, 3–4, takes place rapidly and is complete before the piston has moved far from the end of the stroke, approach-

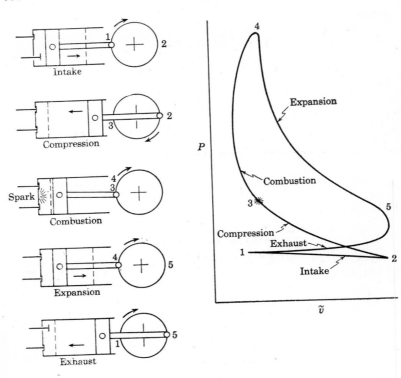

FIG. 8.2. FOUR-STROKE SPARK-IGNITION CYCLE.

ing constant volume conditions. The expansion process, 4–5, approaches adiabatic conditions. At position 5 the exhaust valve opens, causing a rapid drop in pressure. The combustion products are discharged during the stroke from 5 to 1, and the cycle is repeated.

The area on the P–$\tilde{v}$ diagram between the intake and exhaust strokes, called the pumping loop, represents negative work and must be subtracted from the upper area to obtain the net work for the cycle. For this reason and because the air standard analysis is based on reversible rather than real processes, the efficiency of actual spark ignition engines is considerably less than that given by Eq. (8.2) for a given compression ratio. In general, however, increasing the compression ratio will increase the thermal efficiency. The practical upper limit on compression ratio is imposed by the detonation, or "knock," limitations of the fuel used. Detonation is an uncontrolled, exceedingly rapid burning that will ultimately lead to engine failure if it is allowed to continue. The tendency of a fuel to detonate increases with increasing compression ratio in a spark ignition engine.

Example 8.2:

A six-cylinder spark ignition engine has a cylinder diameter (bore) of 3 in. and a crank diameter (stroke) of 5 in. The compression ratio is 7, and the engine is turning at 3000 revolutions per minute and operates on a four-stroke cycle. The engine is tested on a dynamometer and develops 50 horsepower while consuming 24.2 lb_m of fuel per hour. The fuel is calculated to liberate 18,000 B/lb_m under ideal combustion conditions.

  a. What is the thermal efficiency of the engine?
  b. What would be the temperature at the end of combustion and the power developed if the engine operated on the ideal Otto cycle with the same heat addition and inlet conditions of 14.7 $lb/in.^2$ and 60F?

Solutions:

  a. The thermal efficiency is

$$\eta = \frac{\dot{W}}{J\dot{Q}}$$

$$= \frac{50(550)3600}{778(24.2)18,000} = 0.282$$

  b. The volume displaced by the pistons per revolution is

$$\bar{v} = \frac{\pi}{4}\left(\frac{3}{12}\right)^2\left(\frac{5}{12}\right)6 = 0.123 \text{ ft}^3$$

For the theoretical cycle the volume of gas inducted per second is equal to the displacement volume times half the rotational speed, since two complete revolutions are required for a complete cycle.

$$\dot{v} = \bar{v}\left(\frac{1}{2}\right)\frac{3000}{60} = 3.075 \text{ ft}^3/\text{sec}$$

The specific volume of the inlet gas is

$$v_1 = \frac{RT_1}{P_1} = \frac{53.3(520)}{144(14.7)} = 13.09 \text{ ft}^3/lb_m$$

The mass rate of flow is

$$\dot{w} = \frac{\dot{v}}{v_1} = 0.235 \text{ lb}_m/\text{sec}$$

The heat addition per second is

$$\dot{Q} = \frac{24.2(18,000)}{3600} = 121 \text{ B/sec}$$

and the heat addition per pound is

$$Q = \frac{\dot{Q}}{\dot{w}} = \frac{121}{0.235} = 515 \text{ B/lb}_m$$

The temperature at the end of compression is found from

$$\frac{T_2}{T_1} = \left(\frac{v_1}{v_2}\right)^{\gamma-1} = (7)^{0.4} = 2.175$$

$$T_2 = 520(2.175) = 1130\text{R}$$

The heat addition at constant volume is given by

$$Q = c_v(T_3 - T_2)$$

from which

$$T_3 - T_2 = \frac{515}{0.1715} = 3010$$

$$T_3 = 3010 + 1130 = 4140\text{R}$$

The thermal efficiency for the theoretical cycle is

$$\eta = 1 - \frac{1}{(7)^{0.4}} = 0.539$$

The work rate output is then

$$\frac{\dot{W}}{J} = \eta\dot{Q} = 0.539(121) = 65.3 \text{ B/sec}$$

and the horsepower output is then

$$\dot{W} = \frac{65.3(778)}{550} = 92.5 \text{ hp}$$

8.3 Diesel cycle

The theoretical Diesel cycle which is approached by compression ignition engines is composed of four nonflow processes: reversible

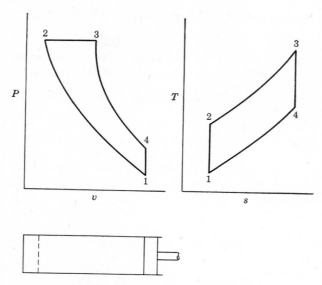

FIG. 8.3. THEORETICAL DIESEL CYCLE.

adiabatic compression, constant pressure heat addition, reversible adiabatic expansion, and constant volume heat rejection, returning the medium to its original condition. These processes are shown in P–v and T–s diagrams in Fig. 8.3.

Process 1–2 in Fig. 8.3 is a reversible adiabatic compression for which the energy equation is

$$\frac{W_{1-2}}{J} = u_1 - u_2 \tag{8.3a}$$

The work input may also be found by evaluating $\int P\ dv$ for an isentropic process. That is

$$W_{1-2} = \frac{P_2 v_2 - P_1 v_1}{1 - \gamma} = \frac{R(T_2 - T_1)}{1 - \gamma} \tag{8.3b}$$

Process 2–3 is a constant pressure heat addition for which the energy equation is

$$Q_{2-3} = u_3 - u_2 + \frac{W_{2-3}}{J} \tag{8.3c}$$

The heat input may be found from the specific heat relation

$$Q_{2-3} = c_p(T_3 - T_2) \tag{8.3d}$$

and the work may be found by evaluating $\int P \, dv$ at constant pressure,

$$W_{2-3} = P_2(v_3 - v_2) = R(T_3 - T_2) \tag{8.3e}$$

Process 3–4 is a reversible adiabatic expansion for which the energy equation is

$$\frac{W_{3-4}}{J} = u_3 - u_4 \tag{8.3f}$$

The work for this process may also be found by evaluating $\int P \, dv$ as in Eq. (8.3b). That is,

$$W_{3-4} = \frac{P_4 v_4 - P_3 v_3}{1 - \gamma} = \frac{R(T_4 - T_3)}{1 - \gamma} \tag{8.3g}$$

Process 4–1 is a constant volume heat rejection for which the energy equation is

$$Q_{4-1} = u_1 - u_4 = c_v(T_1 - T_4) \tag{8.3h}$$

Any of the above equations may be used in the determination of the thermal efficiency of the cycle. As in the case of the Otto cycle, the simplest method is that using the heat input and output. All the heat added is in process 2–3, and all the heat rejected is in process 4–1. The thermal efficiency may then be expressed by

$$\eta = 1 - \frac{c_v(T_4 - T_1)}{c_p(T_3 - T_2)} \tag{8.3}$$

The above equation may be expressed in terms of volume ratios as follows: Eq. (8.3) may be rearranged to give

$$\eta = 1 - \frac{1}{\gamma} \frac{T_1}{T_2} \left[\frac{(T_4/T_1) - 1}{(T_3/T_2) - 1} \right] \tag{8.4a}$$

For the reversible adiabatic compression the following relation applies:

$$\frac{T_1}{T_2} = \left(\frac{v_2}{v_1} \right)^{\gamma-1} \tag{8.4b}$$

For the constant pressure process

$$\frac{T_3}{T_2} = \frac{v_3}{v_2} \tag{8.4c}$$

For the reversible adiabatic expansion

$$\frac{T_4}{T_3} = \left(\frac{v_3}{v_4}\right)^{\gamma-1} \tag{8.4d}$$

Equations (8.4b) and (8.4d) may be combined to give

$$\frac{T_4}{T_1} = \frac{T_3}{T_2}\left(\frac{v_3}{v_4}\right)^{\gamma-1}\left(\frac{v_1}{v_2}\right)^{\gamma-1} \tag{8.4e}$$

But $v_4 = v_1$, so that Eq. (8.4e) becomes

$$\frac{T_4}{T_1} = \frac{T_3}{T_2}\left(\frac{v_3}{v_2}\right)^{\gamma-1} \tag{8.4f}$$

Substituting Eq. (8.4c) into Eq. (8.4f) results in

$$\frac{T_4}{T_1} = \left(\frac{v_3}{v_2}\right)^{\gamma} \tag{8.4g}$$

Substitution of Eqs. (8.4b), (8.4c), and (8.4g) into Eq. (8.4a) gives the final result

$$\eta = 1 - \frac{1}{\gamma}\frac{1}{(v_1/v_2)^{\gamma-1}}\left[\frac{(v_3/v_2)^{\gamma}-1}{(v_3/v_2)-1}\right] \tag{8.4}$$

Equation (8.4) shows that the theoretical Diesel cycle efficiency is a function of the ratio v_3/v_2, called the "cutoff ratio," in addition to the so-called compression ratio.

Another performance parameter frequently used in Diesel analysis is the per cent cutoff, defined by the relation

$$\text{cutoff} = \frac{v_3 - v_2}{v_1 - v_2} \tag{8.5}$$

Example 8.3:

A theoretical Diesel cycle has an initial pressure and temperature of 14 lb/in.^{2} and 70F. The compression ratio is 13, and the temperature at the end of heat addition is 2500F. Assuming $c_v = 0.171$, $c_p = 0.24$, and $R = 53.3$, what are the cutoff ratio, per cent cutoff and temperature at the end of expansion and thermal efficiency?

Solution:

From the statement of the example,

$$\frac{v_1}{v_2} = 13$$

and the temperature at the end of compression is determined from the isentropic relation

$$\frac{T_2}{T_1} = \left(\frac{v_1}{v_2}\right)^{\gamma-1} = (13)^{0.4} = 2.79$$

$$T_2 = 530(2.79) = 1480R$$

The temperature at the end of heat addition is 2960R, and from the relation for a constant pressure process

$$\frac{v_3}{v_2} = \frac{T_3}{T_2} = \frac{2960}{1480} = 2$$

The cutoff may be determined from Eq. (8.5),

$$\text{cutoff} = \frac{(v_3/v_2) - 1}{(v_1/v_2) - 1} = \frac{2 - 1}{13 - 1} = 0.0833$$

The volume ratio v_1/v_3 is determined from the relation

$$\frac{v_1}{v_3} = \frac{v_1}{v_2}\frac{v_2}{v_3} = 6.5$$

The temperature at the end of expansion is determined from the isentropic relation

$$\frac{T_3}{T_4} = \left(\frac{v_1}{v_3}\right)^{\gamma-1} = (6.5)^{0.4} = 2.11$$

$$T_4 = \frac{2960}{2.11} = 1402R$$

The thermal efficiency in this case is most easily determined from Eq. (8.3),

$$\eta = 1 - \frac{0.171}{0.24}\left[\frac{1402 - 530}{2960 - 1480}\right] = 54.8 \text{ per cent}$$

The mechanical arrangement of Diesel engines is similar to that of spark ignition engines except that in general the compression ratio is higher and fuel is injected into the cylinder near the end of the compression stroke rather than entering with the air. Actual Diesel engines do not operate on a true Diesel cycle in that the heat addition is not at constant pressure. A more realistic ideal cycle for modern Diesel engines would be one in which a part of the heat addition was at constant volume and the remainder of the heat addition was at constant pressure. Theoretical consideration of such a refinement is hardly justified, however, owing to the effect of the other approximations made in the air standard analysis.

8.4 Comparison of Otto and Diesel cycles

While actual Diesel engines in general have higher compression ratios than engines operating on the Otto cycle, it is interesting to compare the efficiences of the two cycles for the same compression ratio. Let it be assumed that an engine A operates on the Otto cycle while an engine B, having the same compression ratio as engine A, operates on the Diesel cycle and that both cycles have the same heat addition per pound. P–v and T–s diagrams for this case are shown in Fig. 8.4.

As shown in Fig. 8.4, cycle 1–2–3–4–1 is the Otto cycle, and cycle 1–2–5–6–1 is the Diesel cycle. Since both cycles have the same compression ratio, the compression process, 1–2, is identical for both cycles. Since the heat addition for both cycles is equal, the following relation exists:

$$c_v(T_3 - T_2) = c_p(T_5 - T_2)$$

From this relation it is apparent that T_5 is less than T_3 since c_p is greater than c_v. However, since the heat addition is equal for both cycles, the areas under the heat addition curves in the T–s plane

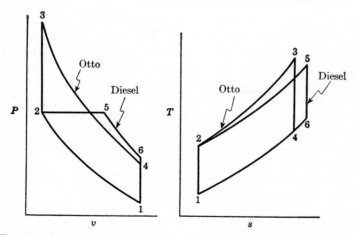

Fig. 8.4. Otto and Diesel cycles having same compression ratio and heat addition.

must be equal. Therefore, s_5 must be greater than s_3 as shown in Fig. 8.4. Since the initial volume for both cycles was the same, processes 6–1 and 4–1, which are constant volume processes, must occur at the same volume as shown in Fig. 8.4.

It is apparent in Fig. 8.4 that the heat rejected in the Diesel cycle, which is the area under the T–s curve 6–1, is greater than the heat rejected in the Otto cycle, which is the area under the T–s curve 4–1. Since the heat addition for both cycles was taken as the same value, from the definition of thermal efficiency, Eq. (8.1), it is established that the thermal efficiency of the Otto cycle is greater than that of the Diesel cycle for a given compression ratio and heat addition.

The compression ratio of Diesel engines is not limited by detonation as is the compression ratio of spark ignition engines. It is therefore possible to operate Diesel engines at higher compression ratios than similar spark ignition engines and hence realize greater efficiency than with the spark ignition engines. Improved fuels and engine design, however, are constantly raising the upper limits of compression ratio for spark ignition engines; and, as shown above, for equal compression ratios, the spark ignition engine is inherently more efficient than the Diesel, or compression ignition, engine.

8.5 The Brayton or gas turbine cycle

The preceding cycle discussions have dealt with nonflow cycles. That is, the important processes of compression, heat addition, and expansion have taken place in sequence in the same closed cylinder. The theoretical cycle which the gas turbine power plant approaches, called the Brayton cycle, is a steady-flow cycle. That is, compression, heat addition, and expansion occur under steady-flow conditions. These processes occur in separate components—compressor, burner, and turbine—rather than within the same cylinder. Figure 8.5 is a schematic diagram of a gas turbine power plant, showing these components.

The processes for the theoretical Brayton cycle are reversible adiabatic compression, constant pressure heat addition, reversible adiabatic expansion, and constant pressure heat rejection. These processes are shown in P–v and T–s diagrams in Fig. 8.6. Since all processes are steady flow, stagnation values will be used in the following analysis.

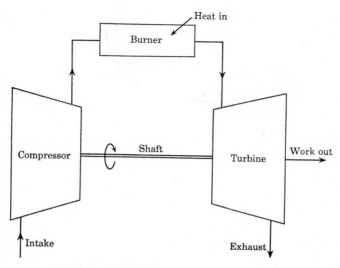

FIG. 8.5. COMPONENTS OF SIMPLE GAS TURBINE.

Process 1–2 in Fig. 8.6 is a reversible adiabatic compression for which the energy equation is

$$\frac{W_{1-2}}{J} = h_{t1} - h_{t2} = c_p(T_{t1} - T_{t2}) \tag{8.6a}$$

Process 2–3 is a constant pressure heat addition for which the energy equation is

$$Q_{2-3} = h_{t3} - h_{t2} = c_p(T_{t3} - T_{t2}) \tag{8.6b}$$

Process 3–4 is a reversible adiabatic expansion for which the energy equation is

$$\frac{W_{3-4}}{J} = h_{t3} - h_{t4} = c_p(T_{t3} - T_{t4}) \tag{8.6c}$$

Process 4–1 is a constant pressure heat rejection which occurs in the exhaust outside the engine for which the energy equation is

$$Q_{4-1} = h_{t1} - h_{t4} = c_p(T_{t1} - T_{t4}) \tag{8.6d}$$

Inspection of Eqs. (8.6a)–(8.6d) shows that the entire heat input is given by Eq. (8.6b) and the entire heat rejection is given by Eq. (8.6d). Making use of these equations and the definition of thermal

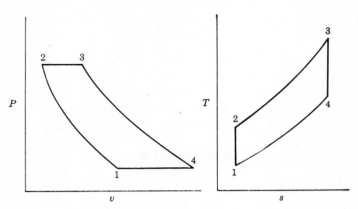

FIG. 8.6. THEORETICAL BRAYTON CYCLE.

efficiency, Eq. (8.1), results in

$$\eta = 1 - \frac{T_{t4} - T_{t1}}{T_{t3} - T_{t2}} \tag{8.6}$$

This expression may be further simplified by making use of the isentropic relation for the expansion and compression processes. For the compression process

$$\frac{T_{t2}}{T_{t1}} = \left(\frac{P_{t2}}{P_{t1}}\right)^{(\gamma-1)/\gamma} \tag{8.7a}$$

and for the expansion process

$$\frac{T_{t3}}{T_{t4}} = \left(\frac{P_{t3}}{P_{t4}}\right)^{(\gamma-1)/\gamma} \tag{8.7b}$$

However, $P_{t1} = P_{t4}$ (8.7c)

$$P_{t2} = P_{t3} \tag{8.7d}$$

so that Eqs. (8.7a) and (8.7b) may be combined to give

$$\frac{T_{t4}}{T_{t1}} = \frac{T_{t3}}{T_{t2}} \tag{8.7e}$$

Subtracting 1 from both sides of Eq. (8.7e), and rearranging, results in

$$\frac{T_{t1}}{T_{t2}} = \frac{T_{t4} - T_{t1}}{T_{t3} - T_{t2}} \tag{8.7f}$$

Substituting Eq. (8.7f) in Eq. (8.6) and making use of Eq. (8.7a) gives

$$\eta = 1 - \frac{1}{(P_{t2}/P_{t1})^{(\gamma-1)/\gamma}} \tag{8.7}$$

This equation shows that the theoretical efficiency of the Brayton cycle is a function of the ratio of the compressor outlet stagnation pressure to the compressor inlet stagnation pressure. This ratio will be called the "compressor pressure ratio" to avoid confusion with the "compression ratio" previously discussed in connection with piston engines.

Example 8.4:

A theoretical Brayton cycle gas turbine has a compressor pressure ratio of 6 with an inlet stagnation pressure and stagnation temperature of 14.7 lb/in.^{2} and 60F. The temperature at the end of heat addition is 1600F. Air in the amount of 60 lb$_m$/sec flows through the engine. What are the thermal efficiency and horsepower output, assuming $c_p = 0.24$ B/lb$_m$ F, $\gamma = 1.4$, and $R = 53.3$ ft-lb/lb$_m$ R?

Solution:

The stagnation temperature at the end of compression is found from the isentropic relation

$$\frac{T_{t2}}{T_{t1}} = \left(\frac{P_{t2}}{P_{t1}}\right)^{(\gamma-1)/\gamma} = (6)^{0.286} = 1.67$$

$$T_{t2} = 520(1.67) = 868R$$

The heat addition per pound is

$$Q = c_p(T_{t3} - T_{t2})$$
$$= 0.24(2060 - 868) = 286 \text{ B/lb}_m$$

From Eq. (8.7) the thermal efficiency is

$$\eta = 1 - \frac{1}{1.67} = 0.401$$

The output net work per pound is then

$$W = \eta J Q = 0.401 \ (778) \ 286$$
$$= 89{,}100 \text{ ft-lb/lb}_m$$

The horsepower output is

$$\dot{W} = \frac{\dot{w}W}{550} = \frac{60(89,100)}{550} = 9730 \text{ hp}$$

8.6 Actual gas turbine cycles

While the theoretical gas turbine cycles show the efficiency to be a function of the compressor pressure ratio and independent of temperature, owing to friction losses in the actual cycle the thermal efficiency is dependent on the maximum and minimum temperatures of the cycle.

The actual cycle can best be represented by an enthalpy-entropy diagram as shown in Fig. 8.7. The actual compressor process is not frictionless but occurs with an increase in entropy, and the compressor efficiency is given by

$$\eta = \frac{h_{t2s} - h_{t1}}{h_{t2} - h_{t1}} \tag{8.8}$$

The actual heat addition is not at constant stagnation pressure but occurs with some pressure loss $P_{t2} - P_{t3}$ as shown. The actual

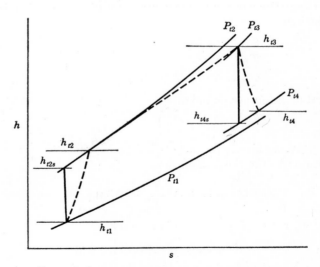

Fig. 8.7. *h-s* diagram for gas turbine cycle.

turbine process is not frictionless but occurs with an increase in entropy, and the turbine efficiency is given by

$$\eta = \frac{h_{t3} - h_{t4}}{h_{t3} - h_{t4s}} \tag{8.9}$$

A further loss occurs because the turbine exhaust stagnation pressure is slightly greater than the compressor inlet stagnation pressure.

As shown in Fig. 8.7, the turbine output, $h_{t3} - h_{t4}$, is less than in the theoretical cycle, while the compressor input, $h_{t2} - h_{t1}$, is greater than in the theoretical cycle. The result of these differences is that the net useful shaft work is considerably reduced from that of the ideal cycle.

Example 8.5:

A Brayton cycle gas turbine has a compressor pressure ratio of 6 with an inlet stagnation pressure and stagnation temperature of 14.7 lb/in.² and 60F. The compressor efficiency is 80 per cent. The stagnation pressure loss in the burner is 3 lb/in.² The turbine inlet stagnation temperature is 1600F, and the turbine outlet stagnation pressure is 15.6 lb/in.² with a turbine efficiency of 85 per cent. Air in the amount of 60 lb_m/sec flows through the engine. What are the thermal efficiency and horsepower output based on Table 6 of the Appendix?

Solution:

From Table 6 the initial conditions are

$$h_{t1} = 124.3, \qquad P_{rt1} = 1.215$$

For the isentropic compressor process shown in Fig. 8.7

$$P_{rt2s} = 6P_{rt1} = 7.290$$

and the corresponding enthalpy from Table 6 is

$$h_{t2s} = 207.6$$

From Eq. (8.8) the actual increase in enthalpy in the compressor is

$$h_{t2} - h_{t1} = \frac{207.6 - 124.3}{0.8}$$

$$= 104.1$$

and

$$h_{t2} = 228.4$$

From the stated conditions, at the turbine inlet

$$h_{t3} = 521.4$$

$$P_{rt3} = 196.2$$

$$P_{t3} = 6(14.7) - 3 = 85.2 \text{ lb/in.}^2$$

The pressure ratio across the turbine is

$$\frac{P_{t3}}{P_{t4}} = \frac{85.2}{15.6} = 5.46$$

and for the isentropic turbine process shown in Fig. 8.7

$$P_{rt4s} = \frac{P_{rt3}}{5.46} = 36$$

The corresponding enthalpy is, from Table 6,

$$h_{t4s} = 326.5$$

and from Eq. 8.9 the enthalpy drop in the turbine is

$$h_{t3} - h_{t4} = 0.85 \ (521.4 - 326.5)$$

$$= 164.6$$

The specific net output work is then

$$W = J[(h_{t3} - h_{t4}) - (h_{t2} - h_{t1})]$$

$$= 778(164.6 - 104.1)$$

$$= 47{,}100 \text{ ft-lb/lb}_m$$

The heat added per pound is

$$Q = h_{t3} - h_{t2}$$

$$= 293 \text{ B/lb}_m$$

The thermal efficiency is then

$$\eta = \frac{W}{JQ} = 0.206$$

The horsepower output is

$$\dot{W} = \frac{60(47{,}100)}{550} = 5140 \text{ hp}$$

(Compare these results with those of Example 8.4 for a theoretical cycle under similar operating limits.)

8.7 Regenerative gas turbine cycle

Some improvement in efficiency over the simple gas turbine cycle can be obtained by heating the air leaving the compressor with the exhaust gas leaving the turbine by means of a heat exchanger. The heating of the air leaving the compressor reduces the amount of heat added to the system in the burner with very little reduction in turbine output, thus increasing the thermal efficiency. This additional heat transfer process is termed "regeneration," and the cycle is referred to as the "regenerative" cycle. Figure 8.8 is a schematic diagram of the components necessary for a regenerative cycle.

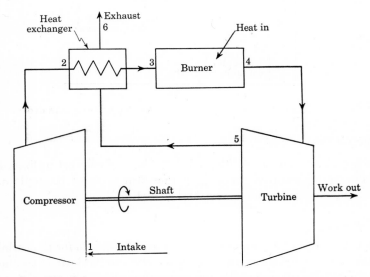

FIG. 8.8. SCHEMATIC DIAGRAM OF REGENERATIVE GAS TURBINE
POWER PLANT.

The theoretical air standard cycle for a regenerative gas turbine engine is shown in Fig. 8.9. It should be noted that the temperature of the exhaust gas leaving the heat exchanger would ideally be the same as the temperature of the compressor air leaving the heat exchanger. Actually the exhaust temperature will always be higher than that of the compressor air leaving the heat exchanger.

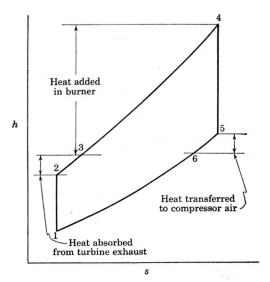

FIG. 8.9. h-s DIAGRAM FOR IDEAL REGENERATIVE GAS TURBINE CYCLE.

Example 8.6:

What improvement in thermal efficiency would be realized by employing regenerative heating in the ideal cycle of Example 8.4, assuming constant specific heat and $\gamma = 1.4$?

Solution:

For the cycle of Example 8.4, the temperature ratio for the turbine is the same as for the compressor since the specific heat is assumed constant. The turbine outlet temperature is then (refer to Fig. 8.9)

$$T_{t5} = \frac{T_{t4}}{1.67}$$

$$= \frac{2060}{1.67} = 1234\text{R}$$

The compressor outlet temperature is

$$T_{t2} = 868\text{R}$$

and the temperature rise in the heat exchanger would be

$$T_{t3} - T_{t2} = \frac{1234 - 868}{2}$$

$$= 183F$$

and $$T_{t3} = 868 + 183 = 1051R$$

The heat added with regeneration would then be

$$Q = c_p(T_{t4} - T_{t3})$$

$$= 0.24 \ (2060 - 1051)$$

$$= 242 \ B/lb_m$$

Since the work output is unchanged, the thermal efficiencies of the two cycles will be in the ratio of the heat added for each cycle. Therefore

$$\eta = \frac{286}{242} \ (0.401) = 0.473$$

This represents an improvement of 6.2 per cent in the over-all efficiency.

8.8 Gas turbine for jet propulsion

The gas turbine operating on the Brayton cycle is ideally suited for jet propulsion. Such a power plant, called a turbojet engine, represents the most important application of the gas turbine in volume of units produced. A discussion of the turbojet engine will be reserved for Chap. XI, where momentum principles are developed.

PROBLEMS

1. Plot a curve of theoretical Otto cycle efficiency versus compression ratio for compression ratios of 2, 4, 6, 8, 10, 15, and 20 based on a specific heat ratio of $\gamma = 1.35$.

2. A theoretical Otto cycle has a compression ratio of 7.5. The pressure and temperature prior to compression are 14.7 lb/in.^{2} and 60F. The temperature at the end of heat addition is 3100F. The specific heat ratios for compression, heat addition, and expansion are 1.39, 1.34, and 1.31, respectively. What is the specific net work for

the cycle? What is the thermal efficiency for the cycle? Sketch $P-v$ and $T-s$ diagrams.

3. Solve Prob. 2, using a constant specific heat ratio of 1.4 for all processes.

4. The engine of Prob. 2 operates on a four-stroke cycle, and has a bore of 3.5 in. and a stroke of 3.5 in. with eight cylinders, and operates at 3000 revolutions per minute. What is the theoretical horsepower output?

5. An Otto engine contains 0.1 lb_m of air at a pressure and temperature of 15 $lb/in.^2$ and 80F at the beginning of the compression stroke. The volume at the end of compression is 0.21 $ft.^3$ What is the compression ratio? What is the theoretical efficiency based on a specific heat ratio of 1.4? What is the work per cycle if the temperature at the end of heat addition is 2800F?

6. The engine of Prob. 5 turns at 2500 revolutions per minute and operates on a four-stroke cycle. What is the theoretical horsepower output?

7. A theoretical Diesel cycle has a compression ratio of 14 and a per cent cutoff of 15. What is the theoretical efficiency for a specific heat ratio of 1.4?

8. A theoretical Diesel cycle has a compression ratio of 12 and an efficiency of 50 per cent. What is the cutoff ratio if the specific heat ratio is 1.4?

9. Plot a curve of theoretical Diesel cycle efficiency versus compression ratio for compression ratios of 2, 4, 6, 8, 10, 15, and 20 based on a 15 per cent cutoff and a specific heat ratio of 1.35.

10. Repeat Prob. 9, using 20 per cent cutoff instead of 15 per cent.

11. A theoretical Diesel cycle has an initial pressure and temperature of 14 $lb/in.^2$ and 80F. The compression ratio is 14, and the temperature at the end of heat addition is 3100F. The specific heat ratios for compression, heat addition, and expansion are 1.37, 1.34, and 1.31, respectively. What is the thermal efficiency for the cycle? What is the specific work for the cycle? What is the entropy change for the heat addition process? Sketch $P-v$ and $T-s$ diagrams.

12. Solve Prob. 11, using a constant specific heat ratio of 1.4 for all processes.

13. Plot a curve of theoretical Brayton cycle efficiency versus compressor pressure ratio for pressure ratios of 2, 4, 6, 8, 10, 15, and 20 based on a specific heat ratio of 1.35. Compare with the results of Prob. 1.

14. A theoretical Brayton cycle gas turbine has a compressor pressure ratio of 5 with an inlet stagnation pressure and stagnation temperature of 14 lb/in.² and 60 F. The stagnation temperature at the end of the heat addition process is 1500F. The specific heat ratios for compression, heat addition, and expansion are 1.39, 1.35, and 1.33, respectively. What is the specific net work for the cycle? What is the thermal efficiency for the cycle? Sketch $P-v$ and $T-s$ diagrams.

15. The engine in Prob. 14 takes in 100 lb_m/sec. The fuel has a heating value of 19,000 B/lb_m. What is the net power output? What is the rate of heat addition? How many pounds of fuel per hour are required?

16. Solve Prob. 14, using a constant specific heat ratio of 1.4 for all processes.

17. Work Prob. 14, using turbine and compressor efficiencies of 85 per cent, all other data remaining unchanged.

18. What theoretical increase in efficiency could be realized by regeneration in the cycle of Prob. 14?

19. A theoretical regenerative gas turbine cycle has a compressor pressure ratio of 6 with a turbine inlet stagnation temperature of 1540F. Ambient temperature is 40F. What is the theoretical efficiency, using Table 6?

20. Solve Prob. 19, using a constant specific heat ratio of 1.4 for all processes.

21. A centrifugal compressor handles air at the rate of 3000 cubic feet per minute measured at intake, where $P = 14.7$ psia and $T = 80°F$. Determine the delivery temperature and the specific work if the process is an internally reversible polytropic with $n = 1.34$.

22. A compressor handles 400 lb_m/min of hydrogen. The stagnation pressures and temperatures at intake and discharge are 14.3 psia, 79°F, 30 psia, and 200°F. If the process is a reversible polytropic, determine the polytropic exponent, the work, and the heat transferred in this steady flow process.

Chapter IX

VAPOR POWER CYCLES

9.1 Introduction

In addition to engines that operate on the gas power cycles described in the preceding chapter are a class of power plants operating on a vapor cycle. The fluid used in most vapor cycles is steam, and stationary steam power plants generate most of the worlds' electric power.

While gas cycles involving combustion products as a working fluid must inherently operate in open cycles, vapor cycles may operate in either open or closed cycles and, in general, operate in closed cycles for increased efficiency. The processes of compression, heating, expansion, and cooling are necessary in vapor cycles as well as in gas cycles. One important difference exists: the compression process of a vapor cycle involves a liquid, while the compression process of a gas cycle involves a gas. Since the density of a liquid does not vary appreciably during compression, relatively little work is required for compression to high pressures. In fact, the work of compression in a vapor cycle represents such a small fraction of the total energy associated with the cycle that it may be neglected in calculations that do not require extreme accuracy. The work of compression in gas cycles represents a substantial part of the total energy associated with the cycle and cannot be neglected.

9.2 The Rankine cycle

The theoretical Rankine cycle, which is the basic cycle approached by steam power plants, is composed of four steady flow processes: reversible adiabatic compression of the liquid; constant pressure heat addition, in which the liquid undergoes a change of phase and is vaporized; reversible adiabatic expansion of the vapor, producing output work; and constant pressure cooling of the vapor until it is condensed and returned to its initial condition. As in the case of the gas turbine cycle, these processes occur in separate components—

176

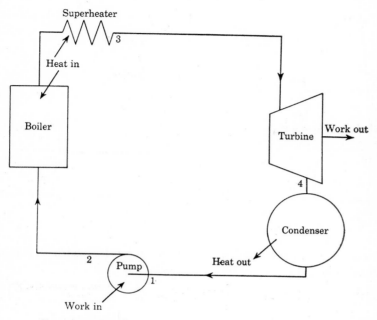

FIG. 9.1. SCHEMATIC DIAGRAM OF STEAM POWER PLANT.

pump, boiler (and superheater), turbine or steam engine, and condenser. Figure 9.1 is a schematic diagram showing these components.

The processes of the theoretical Rankine cycle are shown in P–v and T–s diagrams in Fig. 9.2. Process 1–2 in Fig. 9.1 is a reversible adiabatic compression for which the energy equation is

$$\frac{W_{1-2}}{J} = h_{t1} - h_{t2} \tag{9.1a}$$

The work input may also be found by evaluating $\int v_t \, dP_t$, where the specific volume may be considered constant for compression of the liquid. That is,

$$W_{1-2} = v_t(P_{t2} - P_{t1}) = P_{t2}v_{t2} - P_{t1}v_{t1} \tag{9.1b}$$

Process 2–3 is a constant pressure heat addition for which the energy equation is

$$Q_{2-3} = h_{t3} - h_{t2} \tag{9.1c}$$

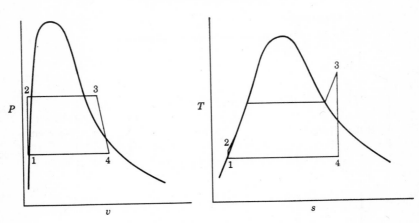

FIG. 9.2. THEORETICAL RANKINE CYCLE.

Process 3–4 is a reversible adiabatic expansion for which the energy equation is

$$\frac{W_{3-4}}{J} = h_{t3} - h_{t4} \qquad (9.1d)$$

Process 4–1 is a constant pressure heat rejection for which the energy equation is

$$Q_{4-1} = h_{t1} - h_{t4} \qquad (9.1e)$$

Inspection of Eqs. (9.1a)–(9.1e) shows that the entire heat input is given by Eq. (9.1c) and the entire heat rejection is given by Eq. (9.1e). Upon substitution of Eqs. (9.1c) and (9.1e) into Eq. (8.1) the thermal efficiency for the cycle is

$$\eta = 1 - \frac{h_{t4} - h_{t1}}{h_{t3} - h_{t2}} \qquad (9.1f)$$

where the sign of Eq. (9.1e) has been changed to make the heat rejection positive.

If it is assumed that the compressor work is negligibly small compared with the other energy terms, the following relation applies:

$$h_{t1} = h_{t2} \qquad (9.1g)$$

Substituting Eq. (9.1g) into Eq. (9.1f) results in

$$\eta = 1 - \frac{h_{t4} - h_{t1}}{h_{t3} - h_{t1}} \qquad \text{(compressor work} \atop \text{neglected)} \qquad (9.1)$$

In general, kinetic energy effects are small between components in steam power cycles, and stagnation conditions given above are closely approached by static conditions.

Example 9.1:

A steam power plant operates on a theoretical Rankine cycle. Steam is generated at stagnation conditions of 500 lb/in.² and 800F and expands through a turbine to a condenser at 1 lb/in.² What are the thermal efficiency and specific net work, (a) considering the pump work and (b) neglecting the pump work?

Solution:

From Table 3 of the Appendix the properties of the water entering the pump are

$$h_{t1} = 69.7, \qquad v_{t1} = 0.01614$$

The compressor work is

$$W_{1-2} = v_{t1}(P_{t2} - P_{t1}) = 0.01614(500 - 1)144$$
$$= 1162 \text{ ft-lb/lb}_m$$

$$\frac{W_{1-2}}{J} = h_{t2} - h_{t1} = 1.49 \text{ B/lb}_m$$

and the enthalpy entering the boiler is

$$h_{t2} = 69.7 + 1.5 = 71.2$$

From Table 4 of the Appendix the properties of the steam entering the turbine are

$$h_{t3} = 1412.1, \qquad s_3 = 1.6571$$

For an isentropic expansion to the condenser pressure the enthalpy of the steam entering the condenser may be found from the Mollier chart or from Table 3 of the Appendix by first determining the quality.

$$h_{t4} = 925.8$$

The turbine work, which is the net work, neglecting the pump, is then

$$\frac{W_{3-4}}{J} = h_{t3} - h_{t4} = 1412.1 - 925.8$$

$$= 486.3 \text{ B/lb}_m$$
$$W_{3-4} = 778(486.3) = 378,000 \text{ ft-lb/lb}_m$$

The net work, considering the pump work, is

$$W_{3-4} - W_{1-2} = 378,000 - 1160 = 376,840$$

Thus, the error in neglecting the pump work is approximately 0.3 per cent.

The thermal efficiency from Eq. (9.1f) is

$$\eta = 1 - \frac{925.8 - 69.7}{1412.1 - 71.2} = 0.361$$

while from Eq. (9.1)

$$\eta = 0.362$$

9.3 Actual steam power plant cycles

The preceding article has described the theoretical, or ideal, vapor power cycle. In actual power plant cycles losses occur which reduce the net work output for a given heat input.

For a closed cycle, heat must be added by combustion external to the working medium. Heat is transferred to the working medium from the combustion gases by means of heat exchangers. The two primary heat exchangers are the boiler and superheater. Not all the energy in the combustion gas is absorbed by the working medium, and the energy in the flue gas is lost to the cycle. This loss is not revealed in the cycle analysis as shown in $P-v$ or $T-s$ diagrams since the heat input in the cycle analysis is the heat added to the working medium and not the heat liberated by the fuel in the external combustion process. The efficiency of the heat transfer process, called the steam generator efficiency, is rarely over 80 per cent. That is, for every energy unit liberated by combustion, only 0.8 energy unit is added to the working medium. In many power plants without elaborate heat exchange equipment, this efficiency may be as low as 50 per cent. The over-all efficiency for the power plant is obtained by taking the product of the steam generator efficiency and the cycle efficiency.

Other sources of loss in actual power plants are pressure losses due to friction in the steam generating components, friction losses in the turbine, and friction losses in the pump and condenser. In general the losses in the pump and condenser are negligibly small compared with the other losses. As illustrated in the preceding chapter on the gas turbine cycle, anywhere a pressure drop or entropy increase due to friction occurs, the net work output and cycle efficiency are reduced.

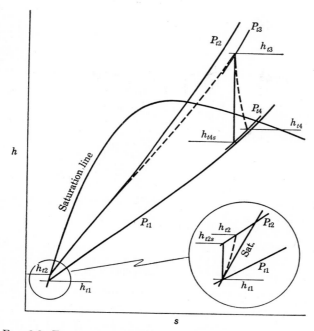

FIG. 9.3. ENTHALPY-ENTROPY DIAGRAM FOR RANKINE CYCLE
WITH LOSSES.

Figure 9.3 is an enthalpy-entropy diagram of a steam power plant
cycle with losses. The line for the steam generating process connecting points 2 and 3 is not intended to show where the pressure
losses occur but only to show that point 3, the turbine inlet, is at a
lower pressure than point 2, the pump discharge.

Example 9.2:

A steam power plant operates on a Rankine cycle under the following stagnation conditions: turbine inlet, 400 lb/in.^{2}, 800F; turbine
outlet, 1 lb/in.^{2}; condenser outlet, 1 lb/in.^{2}, 95F; boiler inlet, 500
lb/in.^{2} The component efficiencies are turbine 80 per cent, boiler and
superheater 80 per cent, and pump 75 per cent. What are the thermal
efficiency and specific net work?

Solution:

Referring to Fig. 9.3, the following values are obtained from the steam tables of the Appendix and the Mollier chart:

$$h_{t1} = 62.98, \qquad h_{t3} = 1416.4, \qquad h_{t4s} = 941.1$$
$$v_{t1} = 0.0161$$

The compressor work is

$$\frac{W_{1-2}}{J} = h_{t1} - h_{t2} = \frac{v_t(P_{t1} - P_{t2})}{0.75J}$$

$$= \frac{0.0161(1 - 500)144}{0.75(778)} = -1.98$$

from which

$$h_{t2} = 64.96$$

The heat supplied is

$$Q = \frac{h_{t3} - h_{t2}}{0.8} = 1690 \text{ B/lb}_m$$

The turbine work is

$$\frac{W_{3-4}}{J} = 0.8 \, (h_{t3} - h_{t4s}) = 381 \text{ B/lb}_m$$

The net work per pound of steam is then

$$W_{3-4} + W_{1-2} = J(381 - 2)$$
$$= 295,000 \text{ ft-lb/lb}_m$$

The thermal efficiency is

$$\eta = \frac{379}{1690} = 0.224$$

9.4 The reheat cycle

Near-isentropic expansion to low condenser pressures in the turbines of steam power plants may result in steam whose quality is so low that it contains a high moisture content. The presence of approximately 10 per cent or more of liquid particles in steam will cause serious erosion of turbine blades and should be avoided to maintain long turbine life and high performance.

The so-called reheat cycle has been developed to allow a large over-

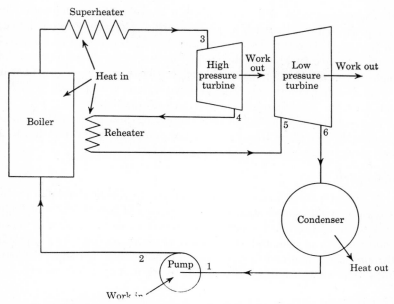

FIG. 9.4. SCHEMATIC DIAGRAM OF REHEAT CYCLE COMPONENTS.

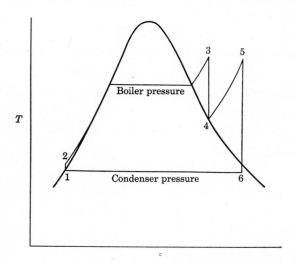

FIG. 9.5. THEORETICAL REHEAT CYCLE.

all expansion ratio and still maintain superheated or high-quality
steam throughout the turbine process with no loss in cycle efficiency.
In this cycle, two turbines are employed, a high-pressure turbine and
a low-pressure turbine as shown in Fig. 9.4. The steam leaving the
high-pressure turbine is passed through a heat exchanger in which it
is superheated before entering the low-pressure turbine, where it ex-
hausts to the condenser at near 100 per cent quality.

Figure 9.5 is a T–s diagram for the cycle, showing how the reheat
process by increasing the entropy allows an isentropic expansion to a
low pressure near the saturated vapor line.

Example 9.3:

A steam power plant operates on the theoretical reheat cycle.
Steam is generated at stagnation conditions of 500 lb/in.^{2} and 800F
and expands through the high-pressure turbine to the saturated vapor
condition. It is reheated at constant pressure to 800F and expands
through the low-pressure turbine to a condenser at 1 lb/in.^{2} Neglecting pump work, what are the specific work and cycle efficiency?

Solution:

From the steam tables of the Appendix the enthalpy of the water
entering the pump is

$$h_{t1} = 69.7$$

The enthalpy and entropy of the steam entering the turbine are

$$h_{t3} = 1412.1, \quad s_3 = 1.6571$$

From the Mollier chart the conditions following isentropic expansion
to saturated vapor are

$$h_{t4} = 1175, \quad P_{t4} = 52 \text{ lb/in.}^2$$

and the conditions following reheat to 800F are

$$h_{t5} = 1430, \quad s_5 = 1.917$$

Isentropic expansion from this condition to 1 lb/in.^{2} results in

$$h_{t6} = 1070, \quad X_6 = 0.966$$

The specific work is then

$$W_{3-4} + W_{5-6} = J[(1412.1 - 1175) + (1430 - 1070)]$$
$$= 464{,}000 \text{ ft-lb/lb}_m$$

The heat supplied is

$$Q_{2-3} + Q_{4-5} = (1412 - 69.7) + (1430 - 1175)$$
$$= 1597 \text{ B/lb}_m$$

The thermal efficiency is

$$\eta = \frac{W_{net}}{JQ_{in}} = 0.374$$

9.5 The regenerative cycle

A considerable improvement over the Rankine cycle efficiency can
be obtained if a part of the steam in the turbine is bled off before it is
completely expanded and is used to heat the condensate water before
it is introduced into the boiler. In this way a part of the energy supplied to the steam which would normally be rejected in the condenser
is used to reduce the amount of external heat required. Such a cycle
is called a regenerative cycle and is shown schematically in Fig. 9.6.

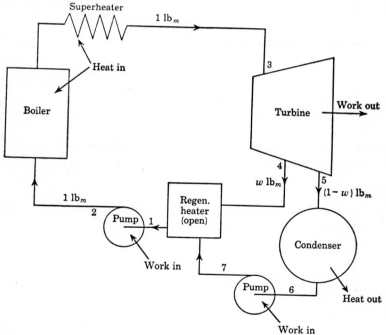

Fig. 9.6. Schematic diagram of regenerative cycle components.

In this cycle, only a part of the steam passes through the condenser, and a simple presentation with the conventional temperature-entropy or enthalpy-entropy diagrams is not possible since a single condition does not define the entire medium at all locations in the cycle. It is still possible to analyze the cycle, however, with the methods previously developed.

The amount of steam bled off for regeneration is determined by the pressure in the regenerative heater, which acts as a condenser for the steam being bled off. Regenerative heaters are of two types, open and closed. In the open heaters the steam is mixed with condensate water which has passed through a pump to come up to the heater operating pressure. Another pump is required to bring the heater discharge flow up to boiler pressure. In the closed heaters the steam condensed in the heater is discharged into the main condenser, with a corresponding drop in pressure, and the water from the condenser is passed through the heater in passages separated from the bleed-off steam. The closed heater system has the advantage that only one pump is required instead of two, but the pressure drop between the heater and condenser results in a slight loss in efficiency.

Example 9.4:

A steam power plant operates on a theoretical regenerative cycle as shown in Fig. 9.6. Steam is generated at stagnation conditions of 500 lb/in.^{2} and 800F. Part of the steam is bled at a pressure of 30 lb/in.^{2} into the regenerative heater, and the remainder is condensed at a pressure of 1 lb/in.^{2} Neglecting pump work, what are the specific work for the cycle and the cycle efficiency? Assume that the fluid leaving both the condenser and the heater is saturated liquid.

Solution:

From the steam tables and the Mollier chart in the Appendix the following stagnation values are determined:

$$h_{t1} = 218.82, \qquad h_{t3} = 1412.1$$

$$s_{t3} = s_{t4} = s_{t5} = 1.6571$$

$$h_{t4} = 1134.6, \qquad h_{t5} = 925.8, \qquad h_{t6} = 69.7$$

The quantity of steam bled to the heater is determined as follows: Let w be the fraction of a pound bled off for every pound supplied to the turbine. Application of the steady flow energy equation to the heater results in

$$wh_{t4} + (1 - w)h_{t6} = h_{t1}$$

which may be rewritten

$$w = \frac{h_{t1} - h_{t6}}{h_{t4} - h_{t6}}$$

Supplying the necessary enthalpy values gives

$$w = \frac{218.8 - 69.7}{1134.6 - 69.7} = 0.14 \text{ lb}_m/\text{lb}_m$$

The specific work is then

$$\frac{W}{J} = (h_{t3} - h_{t4}) + (1 - w)(h_{t4} - h_{t5})$$

$$= 277.5 + 0.86(208.8) = 457.3 \text{ B/lb}_m$$

$$W = 354{,}000 \text{ ft-lb/lb}_m$$

The heat supplied is

$$Q = h_{t3} - h_{t1} = 1193.1 \text{ B/lb}_m$$

and the efficiency is

$$\eta = \frac{457.3}{1193.3} = 0.383$$

If these values are compared with those of Example 9.1, it will be noted that the specific work is slightly smaller with regeneration while the cycle efficiency has been increased.

In many large, modern power plants it is common to employ one reheater and several regenerative heaters as shown schematically in Fig. 9.7. The steam supplying the heaters is bled at various stages of expansion in the turbine.

9.6 The binary vapor cycle

It has been shown that the ideal, or Carnot, cycle efficiency increases with an increase in the temperature at which heat is supplied. From a practical standpoint, heat can be supplied to water at constant temperature only below its critical temperature of 705F, and even this requires extremely high pressures. This thermodynamic limitation of the properties of water has led to the development of a compound, or binary, vapor cycle in which both mercury and water are used as thermodynamic media. Such a cycle is shown schematically in Fig. 9.8.

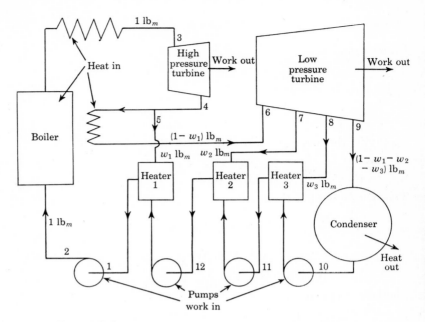

FIG. 9.7. SCHEMATIC DIAGRAM OF COMBINED REHEAT AND
REGENERATIVE CYCLE COMPONENTS.

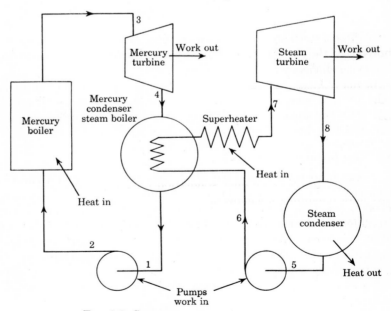

FIG. 9.8. SCHEMATIC BINARY VAPOR CYCLE.

Since mercury has an extremely high critical point, it is possible to add heat to mercury at constant temperature far in excess of that possible for water. The mercury may then be passed through a turbine, and the condenser for the mercury turbine can be used as the source of heat for a conventional steam power plant, where most of the heat added to the steam is at constant temperature. The resulting cycle efficiency is considerably higher than can be realized by using steam alone. Power plants operating on the binary vapor cycle have been successfully built and operated. The fact that mercury vapor is extremely poisonous makes handling difficult and has retarded development of this cycle.

PROBLEMS

1. A steam engine operates without a condenser on an open theoretical Rankine cycle. The inlet stagnation conditions are 200 lb/in.² and 500F, and the discharge stagnation pressure is 15 lb/in.² What is the thermal efficiency of the cycle?

2. The same as Prob. 1 except that the cycle is closed with a condenser pressure of 1 lb/in.²

3. The same as Prob. 1 except that the cycle is closed with a condenser pressure of 5 lb/in.²

4. Determine the cycle efficiency for Carnot engines operating between the temperature limits of those of Probs. 1, 2, and 3.

5. A theoretical Rankine cycle operates between stagnation conditions of 300 lb/in.², 700F, and 1 lb/in.² What rate of steam flow would be required for a net power output of 1000 horsepower, (a) neglecting pump work; (b) considering pump work?

6. Solve Prob. 5 if the inlet stagnation pressure is 600 lb/in.², all other data remaining unchanged.

7. Solve Prob. 5 if the inlet stagnation temperature is 1000F, all other data remaining unchanged.

8. Sketch T–s diagrams, and compare the thermal efficiencies and specific work of the following theoretical Rankine cycles, all of which have a turbine exhaust pressure of 1 lb/in.²:

Turbine Inlet Stagnation Conditions

(a)	300 lb/in.^{2}	600F
(b)	300 lb/in.^{2}	Saturated vapor
(c)	600F	Saturated vapor

9. A steam power plant operates on a Rankine cycle under the following stagnation conditions: turbine inlet 350 lb/in.^{2}, 700F; turbine outlet 1 lb/in.^{2}; condenser outlet 1 lb/in.^{2}, 100F; boiler inlet 425 lb/in.^{2} The component efficiencies are turbine 82 per cent, boiler and superheater 78 per cent, and pump 70 per cent. What are the thermal efficiency and specific net work?

10. Solve Prob. 9 if all component efficiencies are 100 per cent.

11. Steam enters the turbine of a theoretical reheat cycle at 2000 lb./in.^{2} and 900F. It expands in this turbine to a quality of 94 per cent and is reheated at constant pressure to 850F and expanded through another turbine to a pressure of 1 lb/in.^{2} What are the specific net work and cycle efficiency?

12. If no reheat had been employed in Prob. 11 and the first turbine had expanded to 1 lb./in.^{2} condenser pressure, what would be the quality of the steam leaving the turbine?

13. Steam enters the turbine of a theoretical reheat cycle at 400 lb/in.^{2} and 700F. It expands in this turbine to a quality of 94 per cent and is reheated at constant pressure to 650F and expanded through another turbine to 1 lb/in.^{2} What is the ratio of the work of the first turbine to that of the second?

14. If no reheat had been employed in Prob. 13 and the first turbine had expanded to 1 lb/in.^{2}, what would be the quality of the steam leaving the turbine?

15. A theoretical reheat cycle operates under the following stagnation conditions:

High-pressure turbine inlet 2500 lb/in.^{2}, 1000F
High-pressure turbine outlet 600 lb/in.^{2}
Low-pressure turbine inlet 600 lb/in.^{2}, 950F
Low-pressure turbine outlet 1.5 lb/in.^{2}

What are the heat added per pound of steam, specific net work, and cycle efficiency?

16. A theoretical regenerative cycle operates under the following stagnation conditions:

Turbine inlet 400 lb/in.^{2}, 800F

Turbine outlet 1 lb/in.^{2}

Reheater pressure 80 lb/in.^{2}

What is the cycle efficiency?

17. The same as Prob. 16 except that the reheater pressure is 50 lb/in.^{2}

18. A theoretical regenerative cycle operates with the following stagnation conditions:

Turbine inlet 600 lb/in.^{2}, 1000F

Turbine outlet 1 lb/in.^{2}

Reheater pressure 100 lb/in.^{2}

What are the specific net work and cycle efficiency?

19. Solve Prob. 18 if a second reheater is installed in the cycle operating at a pressure of 20 lb./in.^{2}, all other data remaining unchanged.

Chapter X

REFRIGERATION

Refrigeration is a process or group of processes which maintain the temperature of a body or system below the temperature of its surroundings. This chapter will deal primarily with mechanical refrigeration in which the cold body temperature is maintained by the expenditure of mechanical energy, that is, shaft work. In general, a refrigerating machine requires component processes of compression, expansion, heat addition, and heat removal similar to those of heat engines except that they operate in the reverse direction. A refrigerating machine removes energy (absorbs heat) from the cold body and by the expenditure of external energy, usually mechanical, rejects heat at a higher temperature than its surroundings. Thus refrigerating machines may be considered as heat engines in reverse.

10.1 Performance coefficients and units

The definition of thermal efficiency cannot be used for a refrigeration cycle, since the net work is into the cycle and the net heat flow is from the cycle. An efficient refrigerating machine is one in which a large quantity of heat is removed from the cold body at the expense of a small quantity of external energy. This has led to the concept of a performance coefficient, which is a measure of refrigerating efficiency, that is defined as the ratio of the heat removed from the cold body to the net external energy supplied. That is,

$$\beta = \frac{JQ_s}{W_{\text{net}}} \qquad (10.1a)$$

Since the net work of a cycle is equal to the difference between the heat supplied and the heat rejected, the performance coefficient may also be expressed as

$$\beta = \frac{Q_s}{Q_r - Q_s} \qquad (10.1)$$

Performance coefficients may be greater than unity, and the larger the performance coefficient, the more efficient is the refrigerating system.

The accepted unit of refrigerating capacity is called the "ton." A refrigerator has a capacity of one ton if it is capable of freezing one ton of water at 32F in one day. The latent heat of fusion of water is 144 B/lb_m. The energy absorbed in freezing 1 ton of water in 1 day is

$$1 \text{ ton} = 144(2000) = 288,000 \text{ B/day}$$

This is equivalent to

$$1 \text{ ton} = 3.33 \text{ B/sec}$$

Example 10.1:

A refrigerating unit has a capacity of 5 tons and is driven by a motor that delivers 10 horsepower. What is the coefficient of performance?

Solution:

From Eq. (10.1a) and the definition of the ton,

$$\beta = \frac{778(3.33)5}{10(550)} = 2.35$$

10.2 Reversed Carnot cycle

The Carnot cycle has been shown to be the most efficient theoretical heat engine cycle. Similarly, a Carnot cycle operating in reverse is the most efficient theoretical refrigeration cycle. The reversed Carnot cycle was discussed briefly in Chap. X in connection with *Carnot's Principle*. A temperature-entropy diagram for a reversed Carnot cycle is shown in Fig. 10.1.

The cycle is composed of four externally reversible processes—two constant temperature processes and two adiabatic processes. The thermodynamic medium undergoes a constant temperature expansion from condition 1 to condition 2 in which heat is absorbed from the cold body at temperature T_s. This process is followed by an isentropic compression to condition 3 at temperature T_r in which external work is supplied. The fluid is then compressed at constant temperature to condition 4, and heat is rejected to the surroundings. The

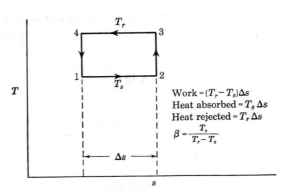

FIG. 10.1. REVERSED CARNOT CYCLE.

final process which returns the fluid to its original condition is an isentropic expansion in which work is done.

The performance coefficient for a Carnot refrigerating cycle is, from Eq. (10.1) and Fig. 10.1,

$$\beta = \frac{T_s}{T_r - T_s} \qquad \text{(Carnot refrigerator)} \qquad (10.2)$$

For a Carnot heat engine the efficiency increases as the difference between the source and receiver temperatures increases. For a Carnot refrigerating machine the reverse is true—the performance coefficient increases as the difference between the two temperatures decreases. As shown in Eq. (10.2) for a given cold body temperature T_s, the lower the temperature at which heat is rejected, the greater the performance coefficient. The lowest practical temperature at which heat can be rejected is, of course, atmospheric temperature.

10.3 The vapor compression cycle

The practical refrigerating cycle that most nearly approaches a Carnot cycle is the vapor compression cycle. The theoretical vapor compression cycle is similar to a reversed Rankine power cycle and is shown schematically in Fig. 10.2.

A saturated vapor at low temperature is compressed to a higher temperature and pressure in the superheat region. The fluid is then passed through a condenser and heat is removed until the fluid reaches the saturated liquid condition. It is then expanded to the cold body temperature and heat is absorbed at this temperature until the origi-

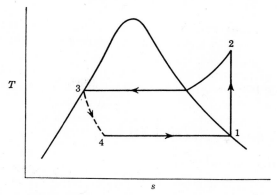

FIG. 10.2. *T-s* DIAGRAM FOR VAPOR COMPRESSION REFRIGERATING CYCLE.

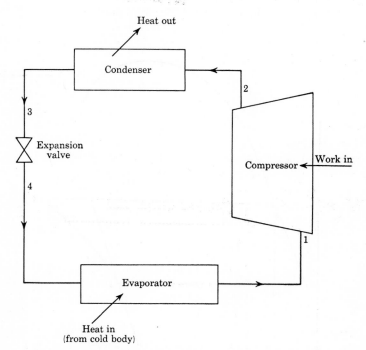

FIG. 10.3. SCHEMATIC DIAGRAM OF VAPOR COMPRESSION
REFRIGERATION CYCLE.

nal saturated vapor condition is reached, thus closing the cycle. The expansion process from 3–4 could be accompanied by shaft work output which would reduce the net work of the cycle. Since this is near the liquid region, a relatively small amount of work could be realized in expanding between pressures 3 and 4 and this process is usually accomplished by a throttle valve to avoid the complication of an additional mechanical engine. The components of a vapor compression cycle are shown schematically in Fig. 10.3.

10.4 Pressure-enthalpy chart

A useful thermodynamic chart for vapor refrigeration work is the pressure-enthalpy diagram for the refrigerating medium. Figure 10.4 is a schematic representation of a pressure-enthalpy diagram for a thermodynamic medium showing a theoretical vapor compression cycle. A pressure-enthalpy diagram for ammonia is given in the Appendix.

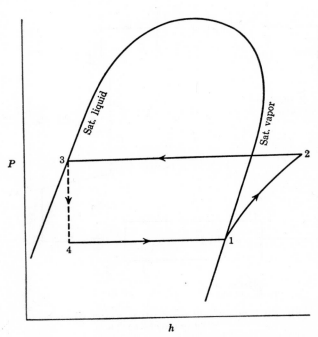

FIG. 10.4. PRESSURE-ENTHALPY DIAGRAM SHOWING THEORETICAL VAPOR-COMPRESSION CYCLE.

Example 10.2:

A theoretical vapor compression cycle for ammonia operates between stagnation pressures of 30 and 200 lb/in.² The capacity of the machine is 3 tons. Determine the coefficient of performance, evaporator temperature, and power required.

Solution:

From the pressure-enthalpy chart of the Appendix and Fig. 10.4 the following values are determined.

$$T_{t1} = -1\text{F}, \qquad h_{t1} = 612$$
$$s_{t1} = s_{t2} = 1.34, \qquad h_{t2} = 733$$
$$h_{t3} = h_{t4} = 150$$

The compressor work is

$$\frac{W}{J} = h_{t2} - h_{t1} = 121 \text{ B/lb}_m$$

The heat removed is

$$Q = h_{t1} - h_{t3} = 462 \text{ B/lb}_m$$

The coefficient of performance is

$$\beta = \frac{462}{121} = 3.82$$

The evaporator temperature for a saturation pressure of 30 lb/in.² is

$$T_{t1} = -1\text{F}$$

The capacity of the machine is

$$\dot{Q} = 3(3.33) = 10 \text{ B/sec}$$

The mass flow is

$$\dot{w} = \frac{10}{462} = 0.0217 \text{ lb}_m/\text{sec}$$

and the power is

$$\dot{W} = 0.0217(778)121 = 2040 \text{ ft-lb/sec}$$

or

$$\dot{W} = \frac{2040}{550} = 3.71 \text{ hp}$$

Actual vapor compression cycles will not be as efficient as the theoretical vapor cycle for several reasons. In the flow cycle itself pressure

losses and increase in entropy due to friction will reduce the heat removed and increase the work required as shown in Fig. 10.5. Further,
for efficient heat transfer to take place, the evaporator temperature
must be somewhat lower than the cold body temperature. For the

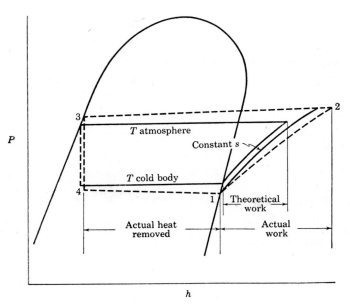

P

3

T atmosphere

Constant s

T cold body

4

1

Theoretical work

Actual heat removed

Actual work

2

h

Fig. 10.5. Pressure enthalpy diagram for actual
vapor-compression cycle.

same reason the condenser temperature must be somewhat higher
than that of the surroundings to which heat is rejected.

10.5 Refrigerating fluids

The thermodynamic requirements for fluids for vapor compression
refrigeration depend to a great extent on the particular type and cold
body temperature of the desired cycle. For household refrigeration a
nontoxic fluid having a relatively low melting point at ordinary pressures is desirable. Freon 12, CCl_2F_2, has been widely used for this
application, and a chart of properties is included in the Appendix.

Another widely used commercial refrigerant is ammonia, for which
tables and a pressure-enthalpy chart are given in the Appendix. Am-

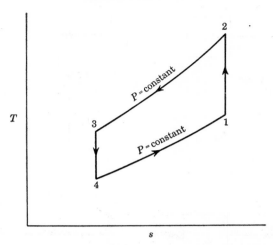

FIG. 10.6. *T-s* DIAGRAM OF THEORETICAL GAS REFRIGERATION CYCLE.

monia is toxic but has desirable characteristics and is relatively inexpensive. Other common refrigerants are carbon dioxide, propane sulfur dioxide, and, for some applications, water. Air or nitrogen can also be used in the gas cycle, which will be described in the next section.

10.6 Gas refrigeration cycle

The Brayton, or gas turbine, cycle can be reversed and used as a refrigeration cycle. The operating fluid is usually air or nitrogen, and, for air, an open cycle may be used. Since heat is not absorbed or rejected at constant temperature, this cycle is not as efficient as the vapor compression cycle. It is used to advantage, however, where large quantities of cold air are desired or as a part of a gas liquefaction system.

The theoretical cycle is shown in Fig. 10.6, and the components are shown schematically in Fig. 10.7. The gas is first compressed adiabatically, cooled at constant pressure, then expanded through a turbine or gas engine. The final process is a constant pressure heat absorption. For an open cycle used to produce cold air, the heater shown in Fig. 10.7 would not be necessary. The work of compression is, of course, greater than the turbine output, requiring a net work input to the cycle.

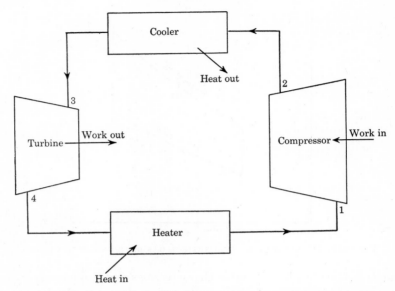

FIG. 10.7. SCHEMATIC DIAGRAM OF GAS REFRIGERATION SYSTEM.

Example 10.3:

A theoretical air refrigerating machine operates between stagnation pressures of 14 and 60 lb/in.[2] Air enters the compressor at 80F and leaves the turbine at −20F. The air flow required is 30 lb_m/sec. Determine the coefficient of performance and the net power required. (Assume $c_p = 0.24$.)

Solution:

From the isentropic gas relation the temperatures at the end of compression and before expansion are

$$\frac{T_{t2}}{T_{t1}} = \frac{T_{t3}}{T_{t4}} = \left(\frac{60}{14}\right)^{0.286} = 1.517$$

$$T_{t2} = 1.517(540) = 818R$$

$$T_{t3} = 1.517(440) = 666R$$

The compressor work is

$$\frac{W_{1-2}}{J} = 0.24(818 - 540) = 66.7 \text{ B/lb}_m$$

The turbine work is

$$\frac{W_{3-4}}{J} = 0.24(666 - 440) = 54.1 \text{ B/lb}_m$$

The heat absorbed is

$$Q_{4-1} = 0.24(540 - 440) = 24 \text{ B/lb}_m$$

The coefficient of performance is

$$\beta = \frac{24}{66.7 - 54.1} = 1.905$$

The net power is

$$\dot{W} = 30(778)(66.7 - 54.1)$$
$$= 294,000 \text{ ft-lb/sec}$$

or
$$\dot{W} = \frac{294,000}{550} = 534 \text{ hp}$$

The actual gas refrigeration cycle will not be as efficient as the theoretical cycle because of friction pressure loss in the heat transfer

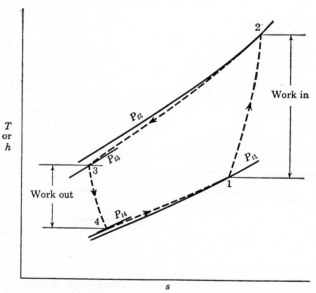

FIG. 10.8. *T-s* OR *h-s* DIAGRAM FOR ACTUAL GAS REFRIGERATION CYCLE.

processes and entropy increase in the compression and expansion processes. An enthalpy-entropy or temperature-entropy diagram for an actual cycle is shown schematically in Fig. 10.8.

10.7 The absorption refrigeration cycle

It is possible to operate a refrigeration cycle in which the primary external energy supplied is heat energy rather than mechanical work. A cycle has been developed which depends on the ability of liquids to absorb certain vapors. In this cycle the compression process is replaced essentially with a vapor generator, absorber, and small-capacity liquid pump. The components of an ammonia absorption cycle are shown schematically in Fig. 10.9.

The principles of operation are as follows: A strong ammonia solution is heated externally in the generator, driving off high-pressure

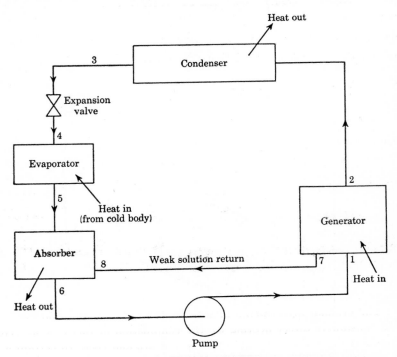

FIG. 10.9. SCHEMATIC DIAGRAM OF ABSORPTION REFRIGERATION SYSTEM.

ammonia vapor, which is liquefied in the condenser and expanded through a throttle valve to a condition of low temperature, low pressure vapor. This vapor absorbs heat from the cold body in an evaporator and is passed to the ammonia solution at low temperature. This weak solution absorbs ammonia, and the resulting strong solution is pumped back to the generator. The ammonia absorption process liberates heat which must be removed from the absorber to keep the temperature sufficiently low for absorption to take place. The absorber is fed by a weak solution which remains in the generator after the ammonia vapor has been driven off. The pump is necessary to overcome the pressure difference which occurs between the absorber and generator. Additional heat exchangers can be added to the cycle to improve its performance.

The absorption cycle can be operated without a pump, thus eliminating all moving parts. This can be accomplished by introducing an inert, insoluble gas into the system. This gas does not go into solution but has the effect of keeping the mixture pressure constant. The partial pressure of the ammonia vapor varies as in the previously described cycle, and circulation is accomplished by free convection, where the hot mixture in the generator, being less dense, rises and is replaced by the colder, more dense mixture from the absorber.

10.8 Heat pumps

A refrigeration machine is, in effect, a heat pump. The term heat pump, however, is used to describe a refrigerating cycle that is used for the purpose of heating rather than cooling. In this application the heat rejected by the cycle is of use rather than the maintenance of a cold body at a low temperature.

An essentially infinite low-temperature source is required such as the atmosphere, a large body of water or stream, or the earth. Heat is removed from the source by the expenditure of mechanical work and discharged at a higher temperature to the body being heated. Under favorable conditions the quantity of heat rejected can be many times the heat equivalent of the mechanical work.

The original investments in such units are large, and under most circumstances direct heating by the combustion of fuel is more economical in regard to both operating and original cost. In certain localities a heat pump can be used for air conditioning in the summer and heating in the winter, making a desirable combination.

PROBLEMS

1. Plot a curve of coefficient of performance versus cold body temperature for a Carnot refrigerating machine discharging heat at 80F for cold body temperatures from −100 to 60F.

2. Repeat Prob. 1 for a discharge temperature of 100F.

3. What horsepower would be required to operate a Carnot refrigerating machine whose capacity was 10 tons for a cold body temperature of 0F and a discharge temperature of 100F?

4. Solve Prob. 3 for a cold body temperature of 32F and a discharge temperature of 90F.

5. A theoretical vapor compression cycle using ammonia operates between stagnation pressures of 30 lb/in.^{2} and 190 lb/in.^{2} Determine the coefficient of performance, cold body temperature, horsepower per ton, and mass flow rate per ton.

6. Solve Prob. 5 if the operating pressures are 28 lb/in.^{2} and 170 lb/in.^{2}

7. A theoretical vapor compression cycle using Freon 12 operates between stagnation temperature limits of 120F and −10F. What is the condenser pressure? Determine the coefficient of performance, horsepower per ton, and mass flow rate per ton. *Freon Chart Inside back Cover.*

8. A theoretical vapor compression cycle using ammonia operates between stagnation pressures of 20 lb/in.^{2} and 200 lb/in.^{2} What is the quality of the ammonia entering the evaporator?

9. Solve Prob. 8 if the pressure limits are 30 lb/in.^{2} and 200 lb/in.^{2}

10. In Prob. 8 how much could the coefficient of performance be increased if the expansion process were isentropic and produced output work?

11. A vapor compression refrigeration machine using ammonia operates between compressor inlet and exit stagnation pressures of 30 lb/in.^{2} and 180 lb/in.^{2} There is a 5 per cent pressure drop in both the condenser and the evaporator, and the compressor efficiency is 70 per cent. Determine the coefficient of performance, horsepower per ton, and mass flow rate per ton. Compare with Prob. 5.

12. Solve Prob. 11 if the compressor efficiency is 85 per cent, all other data remaining unchanged.

13. A theoretical gas refrigerating cycle using air with a constant specific heat operates between stagnation pressures of 15 and 90 lb/in.^{2} The compressor inlet stagnation temperature is 80F, and the turbine inlet stagnation temperature is 90F. The mass flow rate is 5 lb/sec. What are the power required and the coefficient of performance?

14. Solve Prob. 13 if the compressor and turbine efficiencies are 80 per cent.

15. A theoretical gas refrigerating machine is used for air conditioning. The working fluid is air, and the stagnation pressures are 15 lb/in.^{2} and 75 lb/in.^{2} The compressor inlet stagnation temperature is 75F, and the turbine inlet stagnation temperature is 95F. The capacity of the machine is 10 tons. What is the power required?

16. Solve Prob. 15 if turbine and compressor efficiencies are 85 per cent, all other data remaining unchanged.

17. A house requiring 80,000 B/hr is heated by a theoretical ammonia refrigerating machine acting as a heat pump. The cold body is stream water at 40F, and the condenser temperature is 115F. What is the power required?

Chapter XI

NOZZLES AND JET PROPULSION

A nozzle is a flow channel whose purpose is to produce a high-velocity directed fluid jet. Nozzles have wide application in turbines and jet propulsion devices such as turbojets, ramjets, and rockets, and their study constitutes an important field in thermodynamics. Nozzles are of two general types—converging, and converging-diverging—as shown in Fig. 11.1. Converging nozzles are used for the flow of liquids and for the flow of gases and vapors for discharge velocities not exceeding sonic velocity. Where supersonic discharge flow of a gas is desired, the converging-diverging type—also called De Laval or simply Laval—is necessary, for reasons that will be discussed later.

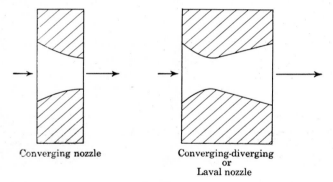

Converging nozzle

Converging-diverging
or
Laval nozzle

FIG. 11.1. NOZZLE TYPES.

11.1 Adiabatic flow through nozzles

Two basic relations are necessary in the study of flow through nozzles. These are the steady flow energy equation and the so-called "continuity equation," which states that the mass flow rate is constant throughout the nozzle.

It is generally assumed that the flow through a nozzle is adiabatic with respect to the nozzle walls. While finite heat transfer may take place, the flow through the nozzle is so rapid that the heat transfer per unit mass of fluid flowing is negligibly small compared with other types of energy involved. It is also assumed that potential energy changes are negligible and that there is no shaft work. The steady flow energy equation for adiabatic nozzle flow from station 1 to station 2 may be written

$$h_{t1} = h_2 + \frac{V_2^2}{2g_cJ} \qquad (11.1a)$$

from which $\qquad V_2 = \sqrt{2g_cJ(h_{t1} - h_2)} \qquad (11.1)$

It should be emphasized that the above equations apply to flows with friction since the assumption of reversibility has not been made. It should also be noted that the equation acts between the inlet stagnation condition and the exit static condition. Eq. 11.1 serves to illustrate the method used to obtain the exit velocity. The student, however, should start with the steady flow energy equation in such a solution. Thermodynamics becomes difficult when one attempts to memorize every specialized equation. Working from fundamentals is the secret of success.

Under steady flow conditions, mass is neither accumulated nor depleted from the system. Therefore, the mass flow rate at the nozzle inlet must equal the mass flow rate at the nozzle exit and at all intermediate points in the flow. If the fluid properties are uniform at any nozzle cross section, the volume flow rate at any section is given by the product of the cross-section area and the velocity at that location. That is,

$$\dot{v} = AV \qquad (11.2a)$$

The mass flow rate is found by dividing by the specific volume and is

$$\dot{w} = \frac{AV}{v} = \frac{A_1V_1}{v_1} = \frac{A_2V_2}{v_2} \qquad (11.2)$$

Equation (11.2) is known as the continuity equation for a one-dimensional flow. This equation combined with Eq. (11.1) is useful in the solution of nozzle problems.

Example 11.1:

Steam expands through a nozzle from stagnation conditions of 100 lb/in.² and 600F to static conditions of 14.7 lb/in.² and 300F. The nozzle exit area is 1 in.² What are the exit velocity and mass flow rate?

Solution:

From the steam tables of the Appendix the following values are determined:

$$h_{t1} = 1329.1, \qquad h_2 = 1192.8, \qquad v_2 = 30.53$$

From Eq. (11.1) the exit velocity is

$$V_2 = \sqrt{2g_cJ(1329.1 - 1192.8)} = 2620 \text{ ft/sec}$$

From Eq. (11.2) the mass flow rate is

$$\dot{w} = \frac{1(2620)}{144(30.53)} = 0.596 \text{ lb}_m/\text{sec}$$

11.2 Reversible adiabatic nozzle flow

The flow relations of the preceding article were based on the assumption of adiabatic flow for any medium. The case of reversible adiabatic, or isentropic, flow when the medium is an ideal gas is of importance in the study of nozzles, since many instances of nozzle flow approach this condition.

For an isentropic flow, the stagnation enthalpy, stagnation pressure, and stagnation temperature are constant at all points in the flow. That is,

$$\left.\begin{array}{l} h_{t1} = h_{t2} = h_t \\ P_{t1} = P_{t2} = P_t \\ T_{t1} = T_{t2} = T_t \end{array}\right\} \quad \begin{array}{l} \text{(isentropic} \\ \text{nozzle flow)} \end{array} \quad \text{(11.3a)}$$

If, in addition, the working fluid is an ideal gas with constant specific heat, the following isentropic relations exist at any point:

$$\frac{T_{t1}}{T} = \left(\frac{P_{t1}}{P}\right)^{(\gamma-1)/\gamma} \qquad \text{(isentropic)} \quad \text{(11.3b)}$$

From the steady flow energy equation, the velocity at any point in the flow may be determined from the relation

$$\frac{V^2}{2g_cJ} = h_{t1} - h \qquad (11.3c)$$

But for an ideal gas with constant specific heat

$$h_{t1} - h = c_p(T_{t1} - T) \qquad (11.3d)$$

Substituting Eq. (6.7) in this relation and rearranging gives

$$h_{t1} - h = \frac{R}{J} \frac{\gamma}{\gamma - 1} T_{t1} \left(1 - \frac{T}{T_{t1}} \right) \tag{11.3e}$$

Substituting Eq. (11.3e) in Eq. (11.3c) and making use of Eq. (11.3b) gives

$$V = \sqrt{\frac{2\gamma g_c R T_{t1}}{\gamma - 1} \left[1 - \left(\frac{P}{P_{t1}} \right)^{(\gamma-1)/\gamma} \right]} \qquad \begin{array}{l}\text{(Isentropic nozzle} \\ \text{flow, ideal gas)}\end{array} \tag{11.3}$$

Equation (11.3) gives the relation of the velocity at any point in an isentropic flow in terms of the inlet stagnation temperature, ratio of the pressure at the point to the inlet stagnation pressure, and specific heat ratio for a given gas.

The mass flow rate may be determined from Eqs. (11.2) and (11.3), making use of the specific volume relation for an ideal gas and Eq. (11.3b) in the following manner: From Eq. (11.2) and the specific volume relation for an ideal gas

$$\dot{w} = \frac{AVP}{RT} \tag{11.4a}$$

which may be written

$$\dot{w} = \frac{AVP_{t1}}{RT_{t1}} \frac{T_{t1}}{T} \frac{P}{P_{t1}} \tag{11.4b}$$

Making use of Eq. (11.3b), this becomes

$$\dot{w} = \frac{AVP_{t1}}{RT_{t1}} \left(\frac{P}{P_{t1}} \right)^{1/\gamma} \tag{11.4c}$$

Substituting Eq. (11.3) in this expression results in

$$\dot{w} = \frac{AP_{t1}}{\sqrt{RT_{t1}/g_c}} \sqrt{\frac{2\gamma}{\gamma - 1} \left[\left(\frac{P}{P_{t1}} \right)^{2/\gamma} - \left(\frac{P}{P_{t1}} \right)^{(\gamma+1)/\gamma} \right]}$$

$$\text{(Isentropic nozzle flow, ideal gas)} \tag{11.4}$$

Figure 11.2 is a dimensionless plot of Eqs. (11.3) and (11.4) showing the variation of velocity and nozzle area with pressure ratio for constant inlet conditions and mass flow rate. As shown in Fig. 11.2, the flow area first decreases, reaches a minimum, and then increases with decreasing pressure along the flow path. Also, as shown in Fig. 11.2, the velocity approaches a maximum as the downstream pressure approaches zero.

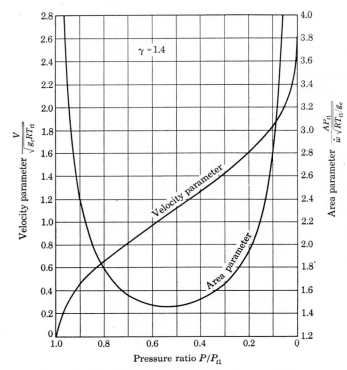

FIG. 11.2. ISENTROPIC NOZZLE FLOW CHARACTERISTICS.

Example 11.2:

Determine the exit velocity and mass flow rate for isentropic flow of air through a nozzle from inlet stagnation conditions of 100 lb/in.^{2} and 500F to an exit pressure of 15 lb/in.^{2} if the exit area is 1 in.^{2} Assume a constant specific heat ratio of 1.4.

Solution:

The pressure ratio in this case is

$$\frac{P_2}{P_{t1}} = \frac{15}{100} = 0.15$$

and the following exponential values are obtained:

$$\left(\frac{P_2}{P_{t1}}\right)^{(\gamma-1)/\gamma} = 0.582, \quad \left(\frac{P_2}{P_{t1}}\right)^{2/\gamma} = 0.066, \quad \left(\frac{P_2}{P_{t1}}\right)^{(\gamma+1)/\gamma} = 0.0385$$

$$T_2 = T_{t1} \left(\frac{P_2}{P_{t1}} \right)^{(\gamma-1)/\gamma}$$

$$= 960(0.582) = 559°R$$

and using the steady flow energy equation

$$Q = h_{t2} - h_{t1} + \frac{W}{J}$$

$$0 = h_2 + \frac{V_2^2}{2g_c J} - h_{t1} + 0$$

solving for the exit velocity with $h_{t1} - h_2 = c_p(T_{t1} - T_2)$

$$V_2 = \sqrt{2g_c J c_p(T_{t1} - T_2)}$$

$$= \sqrt{2(32.2)(778)(.24)(960 - 559)} = 2200 \text{ fps}$$

A solution for the mass rate of flow can now be obtained.

$$\dot{w} = \frac{A_2 V_2}{v_2} = \frac{A_2 V_2 P_2}{R T_2} = \frac{1(2200)(15)}{53.3(559)} = 1.108 \frac{\text{lb}_m}{\text{sec}}$$

11.3 Critical flow and sonic velocity

Inspection of Fig. 11.2, which is a plot of Eq. (11.4), shows a minimum value for some value of pressure ratio between 0 and 1. This value can be determined analytically by differentiating Eq. (11.4) with respect to the pressure ratio and equating the result to zero. This pressure ratio is called the critical pressure ratio and is

$$\frac{P^*}{P_{t1}} = \left(\frac{2}{\gamma + 1} \right)^{\gamma/(\gamma-1)} \tag{11.5}$$

where P^* is the pressure existing at the minimum flow area. The corresponding temperature ratio is, of course,

$$\frac{T^*}{T_{t1}} = \frac{2}{\gamma + 1} \tag{11.6}$$

It can also be shown that the velocity existing at this point is sonic. That is, the fluid at this location is moving with the same speed at which small pressure disturbances are propagated in the fluid. It can be shown that the speed of sound in an ideal gas depends on only the temperature, gas constant, and specific heat ratio. The well-known relation for the speed of sound in an ideal gas is

$$c = \sqrt{\gamma g_c R T} \tag{11.7}$$

where c is the speed of sound at a location where T is the fluid temperature.† Substituting Eq. (11.5) in Eq. (11.3) and making use of Eq. (11.6) gives the velocity at the minimum area, or throat,

$$V^* = \sqrt{\gamma g_c R T^*} \tag{11.8}$$

Comparing this relation with Eq. (11.7) shows that the velocity at the minimum area is indeed sonic since T^* is the temperature at the minimum area.

Since the velocity downstream of the throat is supersonic, provided the pressure is sufficiently low, pressure changes in the flow cannot be transmitted upstream and the flow from the inlet to the throat in a sense "does not know" what is happening downstream of the throat. For this reason the flow at the minimum area, or throat, is called "critical" since the mass flow is limited by the speed of sound at this point.

Example 11.3:

For the nozzle of Example 11.2 having the following flow data, determine the ideal throat area, pressure, temperature, and velocity:

$$P_{t1} = 100 \text{ lb/in.}^2$$

$$T_{t1} = 960 \text{ R}$$

$$P_2 = 15 \text{ lb/in.}^2$$

$$\dot{w} = 1.13 \text{ lb}_m/\text{sec}$$

Solution:

From Eqs. (11.5) and (11.6)

$$P^* = 100 \left(\frac{2}{1 + 1.4} \right)^{3.5} = 52.8 \text{ lb/in.}^2$$

$$T^* = 960 \left(\frac{2}{1 + 1.4} \right) = 800 \text{ R}$$

From Eq. (11.8)

$$V^* = \sqrt{1.4(32.2)53.3(800)} = 1387 \text{ ft/sec}$$

† See, for example, M. W. Zemansky, *Heat and Thermodynamics*, McGraw-Hill Book Company, Inc., New York, 1943, p. 110, for a derivation of this expression.

The throat specific volume is

$$v^* = \frac{53.3(800)}{144(52.8)} = 5.6 \text{ ft}^3/\text{lb}_m$$

From Eq. (11.2) the throat area is

$$A^* = \frac{1.13(5.6)144}{1387} = 0.658 \text{ in.}^2$$

11.4 Ideal nozzle flow phenomena

The relations of the preceding two sections apply to reversible adiabatic (isentropic) flow of an ideal gas having constant specific heat. These relations offer a basis for the study of actual nozzle flow, since the effects of friction should be minimized in nozzle design and the actual flow should approach the ideal flow. The following discussion is an analysis of nozzle flow based on the relations derived in the preceding sections.

The mass flow rate through a nozzle is limited by the inlet stagnation conditions and the throat area. Equation (11.4) and Art. 11.3 show that, for a nozzle of fixed geometry and fixed inlet conditions, the mass flow rate will increase as the downstream pressure is decreased until the throat pressure is that necessary to give sonic velocity. A further decrease in downstream pressure increases the exit velocity but has no effect on the flow from the inlet to the throat. The mass flow rate is a direct function of the inlet stagnation conditions so that increasing the inlet pressure results in a proportional increase in mass flow rate, even though increasing the inlet pressure does not alter the throat velocity, which is sonic.

Figure 11.2 and Art. 11.3 also show that, for a nozzle to be designed for supersonic exit velocity when the inlet velocity is subsonic, the flow area must first decrease and then increase. Such nozzles are called Laval nozzles, and the minimum area section where sonic velocity occurs is called the throat. Equation (11.3) shows that the maximum exit velocity would be obtained for a nozzle discharging into a vacuum, that is, when $P_2 = 0$. Figure 11.2 and Eq. (11.4) show, however, that the nozzle exit area in this case should be infinitely large—a condition that is obviously impractical. Figure 11.3 shows a typical plot of flow characteristics versus flow length for a supersonic Laval nozzle.

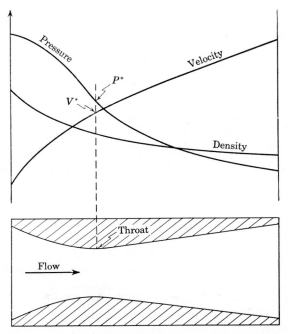

Fig. 11.3. Typical Laval Nozzle Characteristics vs. Length.

11.5 Actual nozzle flow and efficiency

The flow through actual nozzles may be considered adiabatic, but it is not frictionless. The effect of friction is to increase the entropy, and this is shown in Fig. 11.4, which is an enthalpy-entropy diagram for a nozzle flow, showing both the actual and ideal flow processes acting between the same pressures.

The energy equation for the actual process is given by Eq. (11.1a), which may be written

$$\frac{V_2^2}{2g_cJ} = h_{t1} - h_2 \qquad (11.9a)$$

The energy equation for the ideal flow may be written similarly as

$$\frac{V_{2s}^2}{2g_cJ} = h_{t1} - h_{2s} \qquad (11.9b)$$

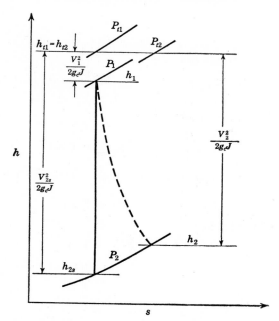

FIG. 11.4. *h-s* DIAGRAM FOR NOZZLE PROCESS.

where the subscript *s* has been used to denote the result of an isentropic process. Nozzle efficiency is usually defined as a velocity ratio —the ratio of the actual exit velocity to the velocity that would have been realized from frictionless flow to the same pressure. The efficiency is then

$$\eta = \frac{V_2}{V_{2s}} \qquad (11.9c)$$

which, from Eqs. (11.9a) and (11.9b), becomes

$$\eta = \sqrt{\frac{h_{t1} - h_2}{h_{t1} - h_{2s}}} \qquad \begin{array}{c}\text{(nozzle velocity} \\ \text{efficiency}\end{array} \qquad (11.9)$$

Example 11.4:

Determine the efficiency of the nozzle of Example 11.1.

Solution:

From the steam tables of the Appendix the following values are found for the isentropic process:

$$h_{t1} = 1329.1, \quad s_{t1} = s_{2s} = 1.7581, \quad h_{2s} = 1151.4$$

The actual values are given in Example 11.1.

The efficiency would then be

$$\eta = \sqrt{\frac{1329.1 - 1192.8}{1329.1 - 1151.4}} = 0.87$$

For an ideal gas having constant specific heat the numerator of Eq. (11.9) is

$$h_{t1} - h_2 = c_p(T_{t1} - T_2) \qquad (11.10a)$$

and the denominator is

$$h_{t1} - h_{2s} = c_p(T_{t1} - T_{2s}) \qquad (11.10b)$$

The ratios of these quantities may be written

$$\frac{h_{t1} - h_2}{h_{t1} - h_{2s}} = \frac{1 - (T_2/T_{t1})}{1 - (T_{2s}/T_{t1})} \qquad (11.10c)$$

However, the ratio T_{2s}/T_{t1} is isentropic so that Eq. (11.3b) may be used and Eq. (11.10c) becomes

$$\eta = \sqrt{\frac{1 - (T_2/T_{t1})}{1 - (P_2/P_{t1})^{(\gamma-1)/\gamma}}} \qquad \text{(ideal gas)} \quad (11.10)$$

Example 11.5:

A nozzle using an ideal gas (air) has inlet stagnation conditions of 100 lb/in.^{2} and 500F and an exit pressure of 15 lb/in.^{2} The nozzle exit area is 1 in.^{2}, and the nozzle efficiency is 95 per cent. The specific heat ratio is 1.4. What are the exit velocity and mass flow rate?

Solution:

Using the values of Example 11.2, the isentropic exit velocity is 2200 ft/sec. From Eq. (11.9c) the actual exit velocity is

$$V_2 = 0.95(2200) = 2090 \text{ ft/sec}$$

From Eq. (11.10) the actual exit temperature is

$$T_2 = 960\{1 - (0.95)^2[1 - (0.15)^{0.286}]\}$$
$$= 598 \text{ R}$$

The specific volume at the exit is

$$v = \frac{53.3(598)}{144(15)} = 14.3 \text{ ft}^3/\text{lb}_m$$

From Eq. (11.2) the mass flow is

$$\dot{w} = \frac{1(2090)}{144(14.3)} = 1.012 \text{ lb}_m/\text{sec}$$

Comparing these values with those of Example 11.2 shows that both the velocity and mass flow rate for a given area are reduced by friction.

Laval nozzles are designed to operate with a fixed over-all pressure ratio. If the pressure ratio is such that the exit pressure is greater than that for which it was designed, shock waves are formed in the flow, causing the fluid velocity to decrease with additional losses and increased entropy. If the discharge pressure is less than that for which the nozzle was designed, the flow within the nozzle will be smooth and additional expansion will occur outside the nozzle.

The effect of friction from the inlet to the throat of a nozzle is slightly to lower the pressure at the throat. The velocity at the throat is still sonic, however, and can be determined from Eqs. (11.6) and (11.8). Nozzle efficiencies of 90 to 95 per cent are attainable in practice with smooth nozzles whose exit semiangles do not exceed 15°, and no appreciable errors will result if it is assumed that the nozzle efficiency at any point along the axis is the same as the over-all nozzle efficiency.

11.6 Diffusers

While nozzles are defined as flow channels whose purpose is to accelerate a fluid with a corresponding reduction in pressure, diffusers are defined as flow channels whose purpose is to increase the fluid pressure with a corresponding decrease in velocity. A diffuser, then, is a nozzle in reverse. Unfortunately, diffusers are inherently not as efficient as nozzles since diffusers, in compressing the flow, are causing the fluid to do what it does not "want" to do, while nozzles, in expanding, are allowing the fluid to do what it "wants" to do. The efficiency of diffusers whose inlet velocity is subsonic can be fairly high. The efficiency of diffusers whose inlet velocity is supersonic is poor owing to the formation of shock waves and boundary layer growth.

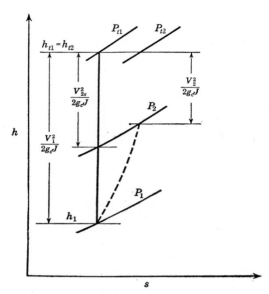

FIG. 11.5. *h-s* DIAGRAM FOR DIFFUSER PROCESS.

While diffusers, in general, increase the static pressure in the fluid, there is a loss in stagnation pressure resulting from the increase in entropy caused by fluid friction. Diffuser efficiency is expressed as the ratio of the outlet stagnation pressure to the inlet stagnation pressure. That is,

$$\eta = \frac{P_{t2}}{P_{t1}} \qquad (11.11)$$

The energy equations for the actual and ideal processes are

$$h_1 + \frac{V_1{}^2}{2g_cJ} = h_{t2} \qquad \text{(actual)} \quad (11.12a)$$

$$h_1 + \frac{V_1{}^2}{2g_cJ} = h_{t1} \qquad \text{(isentropic)} \quad (11.12b)$$

These processes are shown in Fig. 11.5, which is an enthalpy-entropy diagram for a gas.

For an ideal gas having constant specific heat, Eq. (11.12b) may be written in a manner similar to Eq. (11.3e) as

$$\frac{V_1^2}{2g_cJ} = h_{t1} - h_1 = \frac{R}{J}\frac{\gamma}{\gamma - 1}T_1\left(\frac{T_{t1}}{T_1} - 1\right) \qquad (11.12c)$$

Since this is an isentropic process, Eq. (11.3b) applies. Substituting Eq. (11.3b) and rearranging gives

$$\frac{P_{t1}}{P_1} = \left(1 + \frac{(\gamma - 1)V_1^2}{2\gamma g_c R T_1}\right)^{\gamma/(\gamma-1)} \qquad (11.12d)$$

The exit stagnation pressure may now be found by eliminating P_{t1} between Eqs. (11.11) and (11.12d) as

$$P_{t2} = \eta P_1\left(1 + \frac{(\gamma - 1)V_1^2}{2\gamma g_c R T_1}\right)^{\gamma/(\gamma-1)} \qquad \text{(ideal gas)} \quad (11.12)$$

Also, for an ideal gas, since enthalpy is a function of temperature only, from Eqs. (11.12a) and (11.12b) it is apparent that

$$T_{t1} = T_{t2} \qquad \text{(ideal gas)} \quad (11.13)$$

Example 11.6:

Air enters a diffuser at a velocity of 500 ft/sec at static conditions of 14.7 lb/in.² and 60F. The diffuser efficiency is 85 per cent. What is the exit stagnation condition? Assume $c_p = 0.24$, $\gamma = 1.4$.

Solution:

Substituting into Eq. (11.12) gives

$$P_{t2} = 0.85(14.7)\left[1 + \frac{(1.4 - 1)500^2}{2(1.4)32.2(53.3)520}\right]^{3.5}$$

$$= 14.3 \text{ lb/in.}^2$$

Solving for the temperature ratio from Eq. (11.12c) and making use of Eq. (11.13), the exit stagnation temperature is

$$\frac{T_{t1}}{T_1} = 1 + \frac{(1.4 - 1)500^2}{2(1.4)32.2(53.3)520}$$

$$= 1.04$$

$$T_{t2} = T_{t1} = 520(1.04) = 541 \text{ R}$$

11.7 Momentum principles and jet thrust

The fact that nozzles can be used to accelerate a fluid has been used to advantage in the field of jet propulsion. The basic relations for jet propulsion are based on two laws of Sir Isaac Newton—force equals mass times acceleration, and every action causes an equal and opposite reaction.

Newton's Second Law states that the summation of forces acting on a body is equal to the product of the mass and acceleration of the body. That is,

$$\sum F = m\frac{dV}{dt} \tag{11.14a}$$

Consider now that m is a mass of fluid passing through a steady flow system. Equation (11.14a) may be written

$$\sum F\, dt = m\, dV \tag{11.14b}$$

which, when integrated for a steady flow in one direction, becomes

$$\sum F\, \Delta t = m(V_2 - V_1) \tag{11.14c}$$

where Δt is the time interval required for the mass m to pass through the system. The quantity $m/\Delta t$ is, in this case, the mass flow rate since every quantity of mass requires the same time interval to pass through the system, and Eq. (11.14c) may be written

$$\sum F = \overset{\bullet}{m}(V_2 - V_1) \tag{11.14d}$$

where $\sum F$ is the summation of forces acting on the fluid undergoing acceleration and the right-hand member is the rate of change of momentum.

Newton's Third Law states that for every action there is an equal and opposite reaction. Thus, the summation of forces on the fluid in Eq. (11.14) would be positive in the direction of flow if the exit velocity were greater than the inlet velocity, and this would produce a reaction of equal magnitude and opposite direction on the apparatus that is causing the flow to accelerate.

Figure 11.6 is a schematic diagram of the forces acting on the fluid in a jet engine. Fluid enters with a velocity V_1 through area A_1 at pressure P_1. Energy is added to the medium within the engine, and it leaves with a velocity V_2 through area A_2 at pressure P_2. The reaction force is shown as F_i. The internal thrust the fluid exerts on the engine will then be equal and opposite to F_i. The summation of forces acting on the fluid as shown in Fig. 11.6 is then

$$\sum F = F_i + A_1 P_1 - A_2 P_2 \qquad (11.14e)$$

Solving for the internal thrust from Eqs. (11.14d) and (11.14e) gives

$$F_i = \frac{\dot{w}}{g_c} (V_2 - V_1) + A_2 P_2 - A_1 P_1 \qquad (11.14)$$

The external, or net, thrust of a jet engine is defined as the internal thrust minus the external static pressure force opposing the internal thrust. If P_a is ambient pressure surrounding the engine, the net static pressure force opposing the internal thrust is, from Fig. 11.6, $P_a(A_2 - A_1)$ and the external net thrust becomes

$$F_n = \frac{\dot{w}}{g_c} (V_2 - V_1) + A_2(P_2 - P_a) - A_1(P_1 - P_a) \qquad (11.15a)$$

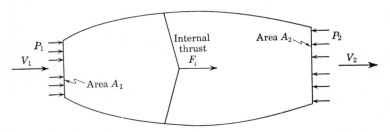

Ambient pressure P_a

FIG. 11.6. SCHEMATIC DIAGRAM OF FORCES ON FLUID IN A JET ENGINE.

In many instances of jet propulsion engines the entering pressure, exit pressure, and ambient pressure are approximately equal. For these cases the thrust equation becomes

$$F_n = \frac{\dot{w}}{g_c} (V_2 - V_1) \qquad \begin{array}{l}\text{(thrust of a jet}\\ \text{engine, } P_1 = P_2 = P_a)\end{array} \qquad (11.15)$$

The above equations consider only a single fluid to be accelerated within the engine. For more than one fluid the thrust would be obtained as the sum of the reaction forces for all the fluids. In turbojet engines the fuel flow is quite small compared with the air flow and may be neglected for approximate calculations.

Equation (11.15) shows that it is possible to develop a propulsive

V_1 & V_2 are velocitys of the fluid relative to the engine

force if a fluid can be accelerated within an engine with no loss in pressure. This may be accomplished by first compressing the fluid, then adding heat, and finally expanding the fluid from the elevated pressure back to the initial pressure to obtain a high exit velocity.

Example 11.7:

An ideal gas enters the exhaust nozzle of a jet engine with stagnation conditions of 30 lb/in.^{2} and 1000F. The discharge pressure is 14.7 lb/in.^{2} The mass flow rate is 60 lb$_m$/sec. The nozzle efficiency is 95 per cent. The engine is on a test stand. The gas characteristics are $R = 53.3$, $\gamma = 1.35$, $c_p = 0.264$. What is the thrust of the engine?

Solution:

From Eq. (11.3), the isentropic exit velocity would be

$$V_{2s} = \sqrt{\frac{2(1.35)32.2(53.3)1460}{1.35 - 1}\left[1 - \left(\frac{14.7}{30}\right)^{0.259}\right]}$$

$$= 1800 \text{ ft/sec}$$

The actual jet speed is then

$$V_2 = 0.95(1800) = 1710 \text{ ft/sec}$$

The jet thrust from Eq. (11.15) with $V_1 = 0$ is

$$F_n = \frac{60}{32.2}(1710 - 0) = 3180 \text{ lb}$$

11.8 Turbojet engine cycle

The theoretical gas turbine cycle was discussed in Chap. VIII. The basic components of this cycle were the compressor, burner, and turbine. This cycle is ideally suited to jet propulsion by the addition of two processes—an inlet diffuser ram compression process, and a jet nozzle expansion process. The components for a turbojet engine are shown schematically in Fig. 11.7. As shown in this figure the turbine does not produce external work but does produce the work necessary to drive the compressor.

The processes for the theoretical turbojet cycle are reversible adiabatic inlet diffuser compression, reversible adiabatic mechanical compression, constant pressure heat addition, reversible adiabatic turbine expansion, and reversible adiabatic jet nozzle expansion. These processes are shown in an enthalpy-entropy diagram in Fig. 11.8. For an ideal gas with constant specific heat these processes are as follows:

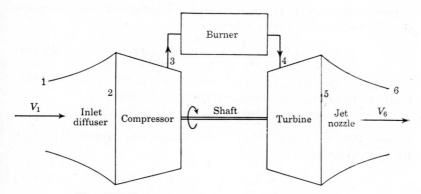

FIG. 11.7. SCHEMATIC DIAGRAM OF TURBOJET ENGINE.

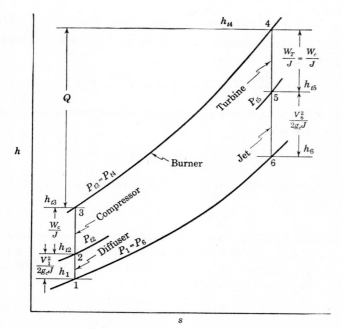

FIG. 11.8. *h-s* DIAGRAM FOR THEORETICAL TURBOJET CYCLE.

Assume negligible Velocities
At points 2, 3, 4, 5

Process 1–2 in Fig. 11.8 is a reversible adiabatic diffuser compression for which the energy equation is

$$\frac{V_1^2}{2g_cJ} = h_{t2} - h_1 = c_p(T_{t2} - T_1) \tag{11.16a}$$

It can be seen from Fig. 11.8 that point 2 in the cycle also represents the stagnation condition for point 1. Therefore,

$$T_{t1} = T_{t2} \quad \text{and} \quad P_{t1} = P_{t2}$$

Process 2–3 is a reversible adiabatic compressor process for which the energy equation is

$$\frac{W_{2-3}}{J} = h_{t2} - h_{t3} = c_p(T_{t2} - T_{t3}) \tag{11.16b}$$

Process 3–4 is a constant pressure heat addition for which the energy equation is

$$Q_{3-4} = h_{t4} - h_{t3} = c_p(T_{t4} - T_{t3}) \tag{11.16c}$$

Process 4–5 is a reversible adiabatic turbine process for which the energy equation is

$$\frac{W_{4-5}}{J} = h_{t4} - h_{t5} = c_p(T_{t4} - T_{t5}) \tag{11.16d}$$

Process 5–6 is a reversible adiabatic jet nozzle process for which the energy equation is

$$\frac{V_6^2}{2g_cJ} = h_{t5} - h_6 = c_p(T_{t5} - T_6) \tag{11.16e}$$

Process 6–1 is a constant pressure heat rejection for which the energy equation is

$$Q_{6-1} = h_1 - h_6 = c_r(T_1 - T_6) \tag{11.16f}$$

Inspection of Eqs. (11.16a)–(11.16f) shows that the entire heat input is given by Eq. (11.16c) and the entire heat rejection is given by Eq. (11.16f). Making use of these equations and the definition of thermal efficiency, Eq. (8.1), results in

$$\eta = 1 - \frac{T_6 - T_1}{T_{t4} - T_{t3}} \tag{11.16}$$

This expression may be further simplified by making use of the isentropic gas relation for the compression and expansion processes. For the compression processes

$$\frac{T_{c}}{T_1} = \left(\frac{P_c}{P_i}\right)^{(\gamma-1)/\gamma}$$ (11.17a)

and for the expansion processes

$$\frac{T_{t4}}{T_3} = \left(\frac{P_{t4}}{P_3}\right)^{(\gamma-1)/\gamma}$$ (11.17b)

However, $$P_{t3} = P_{t4}$$ (11.17c)

$$P_1 = P_2$$ (11.17d)

so that Eqs. (11.17a) and (11.17b) may be combined to give

$$\frac{T_3}{T_1} = \frac{T_{t4}}{T_{t3}}$$ (11.17e)

Subtracting 1 from both sides and rearranging results in

$$\frac{T_1}{T_{t3}} = \frac{T_c - T_1}{T_{t4} - T_{t3}}$$ (11.17f)

Substituting Eq. (11.17f) in Eq. (11.16) and making use of Eq. (11.17a) gives

$$\eta = 1 - \frac{1}{(P_{t3}/P_1)^{(\gamma-1)/\gamma}}$$ (11.17)

This equation is similar to Eq. (8.7) and shows the theoretical cycle efficiency to be a function of the over-all compression pressure ratio.

The thermal efficiency may be expressed in different terms that are more convenient in some circumstances. Since the work of the turbine is equal to the work of the compressor, the net useful energy developed by the cycle is the difference between the kinetic energy leaving the engine and the kinetic energy entering the engine. The thermal efficiency is then the ratio of this difference to the heat supplied. That is,

$$\eta = \frac{V_6^2 - V_1^2}{2g_cJ(h_{t4} - h_{t3})}$$ (11.18)

The equivalence of this expression and Eq. (11.16) is easily proved and is left as an exercise for the student.

Equation 11.18 can also be worked out by considering the steady flow energy equation written from point 1 to point 6.

$$h_1 + \frac{V_1^2}{2g_cJ} + Q_{3-4} = h_6 + \frac{V_6^2}{2g_cJ}$$

Rearranging and substituting "Q_{6-1}" for "$h_6 - h_1$".

$$Q_{3-4} = Q_{6-1} + \frac{V_6^2 - V_1^2}{2g_c J}$$

For the cycle $Q_{3-4} = Q_s$ and $Q_{6-1} = Q_r$

Therefore $$Q_s - Q_r = \frac{V_6^2 - V_1^2}{2g_c J}$$

$$\eta = \frac{Q_s - Q_r}{Q_s} = \frac{V_6^2 - V_1^2}{2g_c J (h_{t4} - h_{t3})}$$

Example 11.8:

A theoretical turbojet is moving through the air at a speed of 600 ft/sec. The static air temperature and pressure are 60F and 14.7 lb/in.^{2} The compressor pressure ratio is 6, and the turbine inlet stagnation temperature is 1540F. Based on an average specific heat ratio of 1.35 ($c_p = 0.264$), what are the thermal efficiency and thrust per pound of air per second?

Solution:

$$P_{t1} = P_{t2}, \text{ from Eq. (11.11) for } \eta = 100\%$$

Therefore, inlet diffuser pressure ratio is, from Eq. (11.12d),

$$\frac{P_{t2}}{P_1} = \left[1 + \frac{0.35(600)^2}{2(1.35)32.2(53.3)520} \right]^{3.86} = 1.21$$

The over-all pressure ratio is then

$$\frac{P_{t3}}{P_1} = \frac{P_{t2}}{P_1}\frac{P_{t3}}{P_{t2}} = 1.21(6) = 7.26$$

From Eq. (11.17) the theoretical efficiency is

$$\eta = 1 - \frac{1}{(7.26)^{0..59}} = 0.41$$

The temperature at the end of compression is

$$T_{t3} = T_1 \left(\frac{P_{t3}}{P_1} \right)^{(\gamma - 1)/\gamma}$$

$$= 520(1.67) = 869 \text{ R}$$

The heat supplied is then, from Eq. (11.16c),

$$Q = 0.264(2000 - 869) = 299 \text{ B/lb}_m$$

From Eq. (11.18) the exit velocity is

$$V_6 = \sqrt{0.41(2)32.2(778)299 + (600)^2}$$
$$= 2545 \text{ ft/sec}$$

The thrust developed by a mass flow of 1 lb_m/sec would be, from Eq. 11.15,

$$F_n = \frac{1(2545 - 600)}{32.2} = 60.4 \text{ lb}$$

Losses occur in the actual turbojet cycle which greatly reduce the thrust that could be realized theoretically. Figure 11.9 is a schematic diagram of an actual turbojet cycle (dashed lines) with the corresponding theoretical cycle shown as solid lines. It should be noted that the thermal efficiency of the actual cycle is given by Eq. (11.18) since no isentropic flow or constant specific heat assumptions have been used in its development.

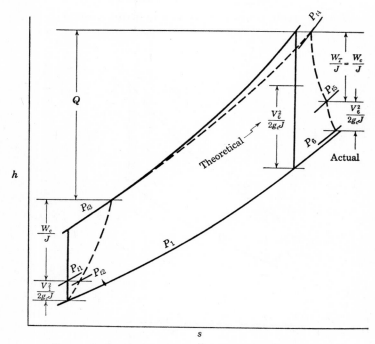

FIG. 11.9. h-s DIAGRAM FOR ACTUAL TURBOJET CYCLE.

11.9 Ramjet engines

For high-speed flight it is possible to obtain sufficient compression from the inlet diffuser process so that mechanical compression is no longer necessary. Since the function of the turbine in a turbojet engine is to drive the compressor, elimination of the compressor also removes the necessity for a turbine. The resulting engine is called a ramjet engine and is shown schematically in Fig. 11.10. The theoretical cycle is similar to the turbojet cycle and is shown in Fig. 11.11.

While ramjet engines are best suited to supersonic air speeds, the inlet diffuser efficiency falls off rapidly in this region, causing losses in

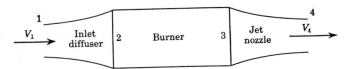

FIG. 11.10. SCHEMATIC DIAGRAM OF RAMJET ENGINE.

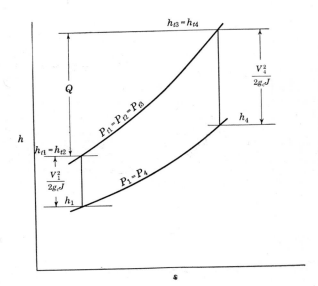

FIG. 11.11. h-s DIAGRAM OF THEORETICAL RAMJET CYCLE.

cycle efficiency. At present the upper limit for efficient operation of these engines is two or three times the speed of sound.

Example 11.9:

What is the theoretical cycle efficiency for a ramjet engine whose air speed is 1000 miles per hour in standard air at 14.7 lb/in.^{2} and 60F?

Solution:

The air speed is

$$V_1 = 1000 \left(\frac{88}{60}\right) = 1467 \text{ ft/sec}$$

From Eq. (11.12d) the over-all pressure ratio is

$$\frac{P_{t1}}{P_1} = \left[1 + \frac{0.4(1467)^2}{2(1.4)32.2(53.3)520}\right]^{3.5} = 2.82$$

The cycle efficiency is then

$$\eta = 1 - \frac{1}{(2.82)^{0..86}} = 0.256$$

11.10 The rocket motor

Another type of jet propulsion device is the rocket. Unlike the turbojet and ramjet, whose propulsive medium is atmospheric air, the rocket carries the entire mass that is accelerated with it. The rocket motor consists essentially of a combustion chamber and nozzle, although for liquid propellant rockets a feed pump is necessary to force the propellant into the combustion chamber. A schematic rocket motor is shown in Fig. 11.12, and the theoretical rocket cycle

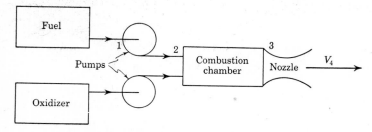

Fig. 11.12. Schematic diagram of liquid propellant rocket motor.

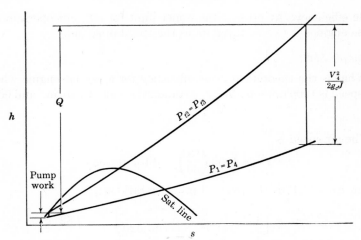

Fig. 11.13. h-s DIAGRAM OF THEORETICAL ROCKET CYCLE.

is shown in Fig. 11.13. For a rocket motor, no external medium is brought into the system, and the entering area A_1 and initial velocity V_1 in the thrust Eqs. (11.14), (11.15a), and (11.15) are zero.

Example 11.10:

Gas enters the nozzle of an ideal rocket motor at stagnation conditions of 300 lb/in.^{2} and 4540F. It expands isentropically to 14.7 lb/in.^{2} The mass flow rate is 100 lb$_m$/sec. The specific heat ratio for the gas is 1.25, and its molecular weight is 30. Neglecting the pump work, what is the rocket thrust?

Solution:

The gas constant is

$$R = \frac{1544}{30} = 51.5$$

The pressure ratio is

$$\frac{P_4}{P_{t3}} = \frac{14.7}{300} = 0.049$$

From Eq. (11.3) the exit velocity is

$$V_4 = \sqrt{\frac{2(1.25)32.2(51.5)5000}{1.25 - 1} [1 - (0.049)^{0.2}]}$$

$$= 6140 \text{ ft/sec}$$

The thrust is then

$$F_n = \frac{100}{32.2} (6140) = 19,050 \text{ lb}$$

PROBLEMS

1. Steam expands through a nozzle from stagnation conditions of 200 lb/in.^{2} and 800F to static conditions of 30 lb/in.^{2} and 400F. The mass flow rate is 3 lb$_m$/sec. (a) What is the exit velocity? (b) What is the exit area?

2. Steam expands isentropically through a nozzle from stagnation conditions of 200 lb/in.^{2} and 800F to a static pressure of 30 lb/in.^{2} The mass flow rate is 3 lb/sec. (a) What is the exit velocity? (b) What is the exit area? (c) From these data, what is the efficiency of the nozzle in Prob. 1?

3. For the conditions of Prob. 2 determine the throat area from a plot of area versus static pressure. (*Hint:* Investigate pressures of 100, 110, and 120 lb/in.^{2})

4. Air expands isentropically through a nozzle from stagnation conditions of 200 lb/in.^{2} and 800F to a static pressure of 30 lb/in.^{2} The mass flow rate is 3 lb/sec. Assume a constant specific heat ratio for the process of 1.39. (a) What is the exit velocity? (b) What is the exit area? Compare these results with those of Prob. 2.

5. For the data of Prob. 4 determine the throat area, pressure, temperature, and velocity.

6. Solve Prob. 4 if the nozzle efficiency is 95 per cent rather than being isentropic.

7. The throat area for an air nozzle is 1 in.^{2}, and the inlet stagnation conditions are 80 lb/in.^{2} and 100F. The exit static pressure is 14.7 lb/in.^{2} If the flow is isentropic, determine (a) the mass flow; (b) the exit velocity; (c) the exit area.

8. The nozzle ring for a steam turbine requires a flow of 30 lb$_m$/sec with inlet stagnation conditions of 300 lb/in.^{2} and 700F. The exit static pressure is 100 lb/in.^{2} What is the required throat area, assuming isentropic flow and a specific heat ratio of 1.33?

9. What are the exit velocity and required exit area for Prob. 8?

10. An air nozzle has a throat diameter of 0.5 in. and a mass flow rate of 2.3 lb_m/sec. The nozzle inlet stagnation temperature is 100F. Assuming isentropic flow and a constant specific heat ratio of 1.4, what is the inlet stagnation pressure?

11. The nozzle of Prob. 10 has an exit diameter of 1 in. If the flow is isentropic, what is the exit velocity?

12. An air nozzle has sonic exit velocity. The nozzle inlet stagnation conditions are 40 $lb/in.^2$ and 800F. The mass flow rate is 100 lb_m/sec. For isentropic flow what are the exit area, pressure, and velocity, based on a specific heat ratio of 1.35?

13. Solve Prob. 12, using Table 6 of the Appendix.

14. The inlet stagnation conditions for an air nozzle are 200 $lb/in.^2$ and 200F. The ratio of the exit area to the throat area is 3. If the flow is isentropic, determine the exit pressure.

15. Air enters a diffuser at a velocity of 600 ft/sec at static conditions of 14.7 $lb/in.^2$ and 60F. The exit stagnation pressure is 16.5 $lb/in.^2$ What is the diffuser efficiency?

16. A jet engine is flying at 600 miles per hour, and the jet velocity is 2000 ft/sec. The mass flow is 100 lb/sec. What is the net thrust?

17. A turbojet engine is moving through the air at 700 ft/sec. The ambient air pressure and temperature are 8 $lb/in.^2$ and 0F. The compressor pressure ratio is 5, and the turbine inlet stagnation temperature is 1540F. The mass flow is 100 lb_m/sec. For a theoretical cycle what are the thermal efficiency and net thrust based on an average specific heat ratio of 1.35?

18. What is the theoretical cycle efficiency for a ramjet engine whose air speed is 1500 miles per hour in air at 8 $lb/in.^2$ and 0F?

19. If the nozzle inlet stagnation temperature in Prob. 18 is 3000F and the mass flow is 80 lb_m/sec, what is the net thrust?

20. A theoretical rocket motor has a combustion chamber stagnation pressure and stagnation temperature of 320 $lb/in.^2$ and 5000F. The specific heat ratio is 1.25. The molecular weight of the gas is 26. The thrust is 50,000 lb for a nozzle exit pressure of 14 $lb/in.^2$ What is the nozzle throat area? What is the nozzle exit area?

Chapter XII

MIXTURES

Mixtures of gases and mixtures of gases and vapors play important roles as thermodynamic media, and their study deserves special attention. Dry atmospheric air is a mixture of nitrogen and oxygen, while atmospheric air under ordinary conditions contains varying small amounts of water vapor. The gaseous products of combustion from internal combustion engines are a mixture of gases, as are the combustion products from steam powerplants. Many other examples of mixtures of gases could be given that are of thermodynamic importance. It is usually possible to treat a mixture of gases as though it were a pure substance. It is frequently desirable, however, to consider the constituents of a mixture individually in order to determine their effects on the mixture as a whole.

12.1 Partial pressure and rules for mixtures

It has been demonstrated experimentally that the constituents of a mixture of gases behave as though each occupied the total volume and each contributes to the resulting mixture pressure as though the other constituents of the mixture were not present. This is possible since the molecules in gases are spaced far apart and when gases are mixed the molecules of the mixture are equally far apart if the resulting pressure is not increased. The calculated pressure of each constituent, assumed to occupy the entire volume, is called the partial pressure. Dalton's Law states that the total pressure exerted by a mixture of gases, or a mixture of gas and vapor, is equal to the sum of the partial pressures of the constituents of the mixture. Since mixtures reach thermal equilibrium after mixing, the temperatures of all constituents are equal and equal to the temperature of the mixture.

Consider a mixture of three gases or gases and vapors, *a*, *b*, and *c*. The above stated properties of mixtures may be summarized in equation form as follows:

1. The volume of the mixture is equal to the volume of each constituent in the mixture.

$$\bar{v}_m = \bar{v}_a = \bar{v}_b = \bar{v}_c \tag{12.1}$$

2. The temperature of the mixture is equal to the temperature of each constituent.

$$T_m = T_a = T_b = T_c \tag{12.2}$$

3. The pressure of the mixture is equal to the sum of the partial pressures of the constituents.

$$P_m = P_a + P_b + P_c \tag{12.3}$$

4. The mass of the mixture is equal to the sum of the masses of the constituents.

$$w_m = w_a + w_b + w_c \tag{12.4}$$

12.2 Mixtures of ideal gases

The preceding rules may be easily applied to mixtures of ideal gases. As would be expected, a mixture of ideal gases behaves as though it were itself an ideal gas. Consider a mixture of three ideal gases, a, b, and c. The equation of state for each of these gases is

$$P_a \bar{v}_a = w_a R_a T_a \tag{12.5a}$$

$$P_b \bar{v}_b = w_b R_b T_b \tag{12.5b}$$

$$P_c \bar{v}_c = w_c R_c T_c \tag{12.5c}$$

Solving for the partial pressures and making use of Eqs. (12.1) and (12.2),

$$P_a = \frac{w_a R_a T_m}{\bar{v}_m} \tag{12.5d}$$

$$P_b = \frac{w_b R_b T_m}{\bar{v}_m} \tag{12.5e}$$

$$P_c = \frac{w_c R_c T_m}{\bar{v}_m} \tag{12.5f}$$

and the mixture pressure is, from Eq. 12.3,

$$P_m = (w_a R_a + w_b R_b + w_c R_c) \frac{T_m}{\bar{v}_m} \tag{12.5g}$$

If the mixture is to behave as an ideal gas, the following equation of state must exist,

$$P_m \bar{v}_m = w_m R_m T_m \qquad (12.5h)$$

and the gas constant for the mixture is determined from Eqs. (12.5g) (12.5h), and (12.4) to be

$$R_m = \frac{w_a R_a + w_b R_b + w_c R_c}{w_a + w_b + w_c} \qquad (12.5)$$

Example 12.1:

A mixture of gases contains 2 lb_m of CO_2 and 1 lb_m of N_2. The pressure and temperature of the mixture are 30 $lb/in.^2$ and 60F. Determine the gas constant for the mixture, volume of the mixture, and partial pressure of the constituents.

Solution:

The gas constants for CO_2 and N_2 are

$$CO_2: \quad R = 35.1$$
$$N_2: \quad R = 55.1$$

From Eq. (12.5) the gas constant of the mixture is

$$R_m = \frac{2(35.1) + 1(55.1)}{2 + 1} = 41.8 \text{ ft-lb/lb}_m \text{ R}$$

From Eq. (12.5h) the volume is

$$\bar{v}_m = \frac{(2 + 1)41.8(520)}{144(30)} = 15.1 \text{ ft}^3$$

From Eq. (12.5d) the partial pressures are

$$CO_2: \quad P = \frac{2(35.1)520}{144(15.1)} = 16.8 \text{ lb/in.}^2$$

$$N_2: \quad P = \frac{1(55.1)520}{144(15.1)} = 13.2 \text{ lb/in.}^2$$

Other properties of mixtures that are of interest are internal energy, enthalpy, and entropy. Since these are all extensive quantities, the properties for the mixture are equal to the sum of the quantities for the constituents. Thus, for a mixture of gases a, b, and c

$$\tilde{u}_m = \tilde{u}_a + \tilde{u}_b + \tilde{u}_c \tag{12.6a}$$

$$\tilde{h}_m = \tilde{h}_a + \tilde{h}_b + \tilde{h}_c \tag{12.6b}$$

$$\tilde{s}_m = \tilde{s}_a + \tilde{s}_b + \tilde{s}_c \tag{12.6c}$$

On a specific basis these equations become

$$u_m = \frac{w_a u_a + w_b u_b + w_c u_c}{w_a + w_b + w_c} \tag{12.6d}$$

$$h_m = \frac{w_a h_a + w_b h_b + w_c h_c}{w_a + w_b + w_c} \tag{12.6e}$$

$$s_m = \frac{w_a s_a + w_b s_b + w_c s_c}{w_a + w_b + w_c} \tag{12.6f}$$

Similarly the specific heat can be found as

$$c_{pm} = \frac{w_a c_{pa} + w_b c_{pb} + w_c c_{pc}}{w_a + w_b + w_c} \tag{12.6}$$

12.3 Volumetric analysis

Mixtures are frequently analyzed on what is termed a volumetric basis. This type of analysis gives the percentage by volume of each of the constituents of a mixture that would exist if the constituent gases in the mixture could be separated from each other, each maintaining the same pressure and temperature as that of the mixture. Such a separation is shown schematically in Fig. 12.1 for gases a, b, and c having a volumetric analysis of $a = 0.25$, $b = 0.25$, $c = 0.50$.

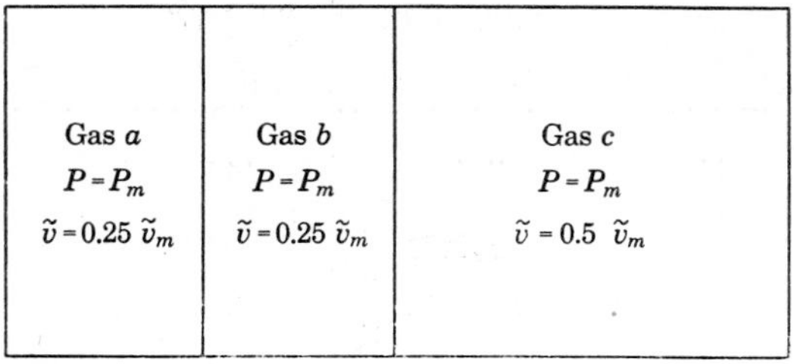

Gas a	Gas b	Gas c
$P = P_m$	$P = P_m$	$P = P_m$
$\tilde{v} = 0.25\ \tilde{v}_m$	$\tilde{v} = 0.25\ \tilde{v}_m$	$\tilde{v} = 0.5\ \tilde{v}_m$

FIG. 12.1. SCHEMATIC DIAGRAM FOR MIXTURE HAVING VOLUMETRIC ANALYSIS OF $a = 25\%$, $b = 25\%$, $c = 50\%$.

From Avogadro's law, which was discussed in Chap. 3, it was shown that equal volumes of gases at the same pressure and temperature contain the same number of molecules, and, hence, their masses are proportional to their molecular weights. Since the volumetric analysis assumes all the constituent gases to be at the same temperature and pressure, the number of molecules in each constituent volume is proportional to the percentage that the volume represents of the total mixture volume. The relative mass of each constituent is then found as the product of its molecular weight and per cent volume. This relation between the volumetric analysis and the molecular weight of the constituents is the primary advantage of the concept of volumetric analysis.

12.4 Gravimetric analysis

In addition to the volumetric basis referred to in the previous article, mixtures are also analyzed on a mass, or gravimetric, basis in which the per cents by mass of the gaseous constituents are stated. The gravimetric basis is useful in determining the extensive properties of mixtures. A simple conversion is possible between the volumetric and gravimetric analyses, as indicated in the preceding article.

Example 12.2:

The volumetric analysis of a certain gas mixture is 30 per cent carbon dioxide, 50 per cent nitrogen, and 20 per cent helium. Determine the gravimetric analysis.

Solution:

Such problems are best solved in tabular form as follows:

① Gas	② Molecular Weight	③ Volumetric Analysis	④ Relative Mass = ② × ③	Gravimetric Analysis ④ ÷ ⑤
CO_2	44	0.3	13.2	0.471
N_2	28	0.5	14.0	0.500
He	4	0.2	0.8	0.029
Total ⑤ (apparent molecular weight)			28.0	1.000

The apparent molecular weight of the mixture, which is shown in this example to be the sum of the relative masses of the constituents, could also be found from the relation

$$M_m = \frac{1544}{R_m} \tag{12.7}$$

where the gas constant for the mixture is determined from Eq. (12.5).

Example 12.3:

The mixture of Example 12.2 is heated at constant pressure from a temperature of 60F to 400F. What are the heat added per pound of mixture, specific work, and change in entropy for a nonflow process if the specific heat at constant pressure for the constituents are $CO_2 = 0.199$, $N_2 = 0.248$, He $= 1.251$?

Solution:

The properties of the mixture are best determined in tabular form, based on Eqs. (12.6) and (12.5).

① Gas	② Gravimetric Analysis	③ Specific Heat c_p	④ Gas Constant	⑤ Relative Specific Heat ② × ③	⑥ Relative Gas Constant ② × ④
CO_2	0.471	0.199	35.1	0.0937	16.52
N_2	0.500	0.248	55.2	0.1240	27.60
He	0.029	1.251	386.0	0.0363	11.19
				$c_{pm} = 0.2540$	$R_m = 55.32$

The energy equation is

$$dQ = du + \frac{dW}{J}$$

However, for a constant pressure process of an ideal gas

$$dQ = c_{pm} \, dT = dh$$

Also for an ideal gas

$$du = c_{vm} \, dT$$

So the energy equation becomes

$$c_{pm} \, dT = c_{vm} \, dT + \frac{dW}{J}$$

When integrated this is

$$c_{pm}(T_2 - T_1) = c_{vm}(T_2 - T_1) + \frac{W}{J}$$

The specific heat at constant volume is

$$c_{vm} = c_{pm} - \frac{R_m}{J}$$

$$= 0.2540 - 0.0711 = 0.1829$$

The heat supplied is then

$$Q = 0.2540(340) = 86.4 \text{ B/lb}_m$$

and

$$W = 778(0.0711)340 = 18,810 \text{ ft-lb/lb}_m$$

and the entropy change is

$$s_2 - s_1 = \int_{T_1}^{T_2} c_{pm} \frac{dT}{T} = 0.2540 \ln \frac{860}{520}$$

$$= 0.1281 \text{ B/lb}_m \text{ R}$$

12.5 Mixtures of gases and vapors

The rules of Art. 12.1 apply to mixtures of gases and vapors as well as to mixtures of gases. The distinction between gases and vapors is, in fact, arbitrary as discussed in Chap. I; and highly superheated vapors approach the characteristics of the ideal gas. While the vapor in a mixture may be treated as an ideal gas, the vapor properties are usually determined from tables, if available.

Atmospheric air under ordinary conditions contains superheated water vapor of very low partial pressure. Under certain conditions the water vapor will condense, and at this point the vapor is at the saturated vapor state. Under saturated conditions it should be remembered that the temperature of the mixture vapor automatically fixes the partial pressure of the water vapor. The treatment of problems involving mixtures of gases and vapors can be illustrated by examples.

Example 12.4:

Water vapor is mixed with air until the water vapor becomes saturated. The temperature and pressure of the mixture are 80F and 14.7 lb/in.^{2} Determine the partial pressures of the constituents and the gravimetric analysis, treating air as a pure substance.

Solution:

From the steam table of the Appendix the properties of saturated water vapor at 80F are

$$P = 0.5069 \text{ lb/in.}^2, \qquad v = 633.1 \text{ ft}^3/\text{lb}_m$$

The partial pressure of the water vapor is then

$$P = 0.5069 \text{ lb/in.}^2$$

and the partial pressure of the air is

$$P = 14.7 - 0.5 = 14.2 \text{ lb/in.}^2$$

From the ideal gas relation the specific volume for the air is

$$v = \frac{53.3(540)}{144(14.2)} = 14.1 \text{ ft}^3/\text{lb}_m$$

Since the volume of the water vapor is equal to the volume of air in the mixture,

$$\tilde{v}_m = w_{\text{air}}(14.1) = w_{\text{H}_2\text{O}}(633.1)$$

and

$$w_m = w_{\text{air}} + w_{\text{H}_2\text{O}}$$

From these relations

$$w_{\text{H}_2\text{O}} = 0.0223 w_{\text{air}}$$

$$w_m = w_{\text{air}} + 0.0223 w_{\text{air}}$$

$$= 1.0223 w_{\text{air}}$$

The gravimetric analysis is then

$$\text{Air:} \quad \frac{1.000}{1.0223} = 0.9782$$

$$\text{Water:} \quad \frac{0.0223}{1.0223} = 0.0218$$

Example 12.5:

Solve Example 12.4 for the gravimetric analysis, assuming the saturated water vapor to be an ideal gas having a partial pressure of 0.5069 lb/in.², and compare the results with those of Example 12.4.

Solution:

The gas constant for water vapor is

$$R = \frac{1544}{18} = 85.7$$

The specific volume would then be

$$v = \frac{85.7(540)}{144(0.5069)} = 634 \text{ ft}^3/\text{lb}_m$$

The gravimetric analysis is then

$$\text{Air:} \quad \frac{1.000}{1.0225} = 0.9787$$

$$\text{Water:} \quad \frac{0.0225}{1.0225} = 0.0213$$

This example shows negligible difference between the steam table values and those obtained by treating the water vapor as an ideal gas. In general, it is permissible to treat water vapor as an ideal gas for partial pressures of less than 1 lb/in.^{2}, for in this region as shown on the Mollier chart the enthalpy is a function of temperature alone.

12.6 Relative humidity

The degree of saturation of the water vapor in air is measured by a quantity called the relative humidity. The relative humidity is defined as the ratio of the partial pressure of the water vapor in air to the saturation pressure of water vapor at the mixture temperature. That is,

$$\varphi = \frac{P_{wv}}{P_g} \tag{12.8}$$

where P_{wv} = partial pressure of water vapor

P_g = saturation pressure at mixture temperature.

The relation of these pressures in a T–s diagram is shown in Fig. 12.2.

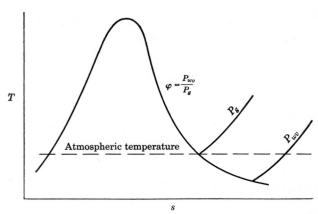

FIG. 12.2. RELATION OF PRESSURES FOR RELATIVE HUMIDITY.

Example 12.6:

Atmospheric air has a relative humidity of 62 per cent and a temperature of 80F. What is the partial pressure of the water vapor.

Solution:

From the steam tables, at 80F the saturation pressure is $P_g = 0.5069$. The partial pressure is then

$$P_{wv} = \varphi P_g = 0.62(0.5069) = 0.3143 \text{ lb/in.}^2$$

12.7 Specific humidity, humidity ratio

In addition to relative humidity, another quantity, called the specific humidity, or humidity ratio, is important in dealing with mixtures of air and water vapor. The specific humidity is defined as the ratio of the mass of water vapor in a mixture to the mass of dry air in the mixture. Thus

$$\text{specific humidity} = \frac{w_{wv}}{w_{\text{air}}} \tag{12.9}$$

If the water vapor is treated as an ideal gas, a relation can be developed between specific humidity and relative humidity. As shown in Example 12.4, the following relation exists

$$\frac{w_{wv}}{w_{\text{air}}} = \frac{v_{\text{air}}}{v_{wv}} \tag{12.10a}$$

For an ideal gas the following relations may be written:

$$v_{wv} = \frac{R_{wv} T_m}{P_{wv}} \tag{12.10b}$$

$$v_g = \frac{R_{wv} T_m}{P_g} \tag{12.10c}$$

$$v_{\text{air}} = \frac{R_{\text{air}} T_m}{P_{\text{air}}} \tag{12.10d}$$

Making use of Eq. (12.8) and dividing Eq. (12.10b) by (12.10c) gives

$$v_{wv} = \frac{1}{\varphi} v_g \tag{12.10e}$$

Substituting this relation in Eq. (12.10a) results in

$$\frac{w_{wv}}{w_{\text{air}}} = \varphi \frac{v_{\text{air}}}{v_g} \tag{12.10}$$

Substituting Eqs. (12.10c) and (12.10d) in Eq. (12.10) and the numerical values for R gives the alternate form

$$\frac{w_{wv}}{w_{\text{air}}} = 0.622\varphi \frac{P_g}{P_{\text{air}}} \tag{12.11}$$

Example 12.7:

Atmospheric air at 14.5 lb/in.^{2} and 70F has a relative humidity of 0.34. What is the specific humidity?

Solution:

From the steam tables, for 70F

$$P_g = 0.3631 \text{ lb/in.}^2$$

The mixture pressure is 14.5 lb/in.^{2}, and

$$P_{\text{air}} = 14.50 - (0.34)(0.36) = 14.38 \text{ lb/in.}^2$$

From Eq. (12.11) the specific humidity is

$$\frac{w_{wv}}{w_{\text{air}}} = 0.622(0.34) \frac{0.363}{14.38}$$

$$= 0.00535 \text{ lb}_m/\text{lb}_m$$

12.8 Dew point

Another quantity of interest in mixtures of air and water vapor is the dew point. The dew point is defined as the temperature at which

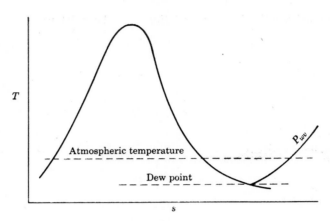

FIG. 12.3. *T-s* DIAGRAM SHOWING DEW POINT.

the water vapor in a mixture will start to condense if the mixture is cooled with no change in pressure or specific humidity. Cooling a mixture without changing either the mixture pressure or the specific humidity causes no change in the partial pressures of the mixture, and the water vapor is thus cooled at constant pressure. This process for the water vapor is shown in Fig. 12.3.

Example 12.8:

Air at 100F has a relative humidity of 60 per cent. What is the dew point?

Solution:

From the steam tables, for 100F

$$P_g = 0.9492 \text{ lb/in.}^2$$

The partial pressure of the water vapor is

$$P_{wv} = 0.6(0.9492) = 0.5695$$

From the same table, by interpolation, for a saturation pressure of 0.5695 the dew point temperature is

$$T = 83F$$

12.9 Adiabatic saturation

Up to this point in the discussion of air and water vapor, no mention has been made of a method for determining the relative humidity.

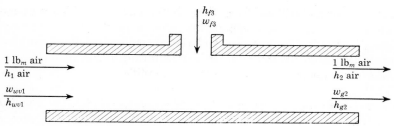

FIG. 12.4. SCHEMATIC DIAGRAM FOR ADIABATIC SATURATION.

This can be accomplished with a device called a psychrometer which makes use of the principle of adiabatic saturation.

Consider the insulated thermodynamic system shown in Fig. 12.4 in which dry air and water vapor enter at the left. Additional liquid water is introduced into the system until the resulting mixture leaving the system contains saturated water vapor and air. For convenience let $w_{air} = 1$ lb$_m$ and the corresponding amounts of water vapor be

$$w_{wv1} = \text{mass of water vapor entering with air}$$

$$w_{f3} = \text{additional water added to system}$$

$$w_{g2} = \text{mass of saturated water vapor leaving system}$$

Assume that potential and kinetic energy effects are negligible.

Application of the First Law of Thermodynamics for a steady flow system yields the following energy balance,

$$h_{\text{air } 1} + w_{wv1}h_{wv1} + w_{f3}h_{f3} = h_{\text{air } 2} + w_{g2}h_{g2} \qquad (12.12a)$$

where
$$w_{wv1} + w_{f3} = w_{g2} \qquad (12.12b)$$

Solving Eq. (12.12a) for w_{wv1} and making use of Eq. (12.12b) and the enthalpy-temperature relation for an ideal gas

$$w_{wv1} = \frac{c_p(T_2 - T_1)_{air} + w_{g2}(h_{g2} - h_{f3})}{h_{wv1} - h_{f3}} \qquad (12.12)$$

The temperature T_1 is known as the dry-bulb temperature and the temperature T_2 is known as the thermodynamic wet-bulb temperature. T_1 is, of course, equal to the temperature of the dry air–water vapor mixture. T_2 can be determined approximately by wrapping the bulb of a thermometer with a wick of porous gauze, dipping this gauze in water, and allowing atmospheric air to pass through the gauze. The air, in passing through the gauze, will absorb water vapor and will approach the point of saturation. The temperature read by this thermometer will then approach the thermodynamic wet-bulb temperature, and the water is introduced into the air at the same temperature when equilibrium is reached. That is, for a psychrometer $T_3 = T_2$, which simplifies the solution of Eq. (12.12). In the familiar sling psychrometer, air is passed through the wet-bulb wick by whirling the psychrometer, which contains the wet-bulb and dry-bulb thermometers, rapidly through the air. It should be noted that w_{wv1} in Eq. (12.12) represents the specific humidity, since 1 lb of dry air has been assumed. The following example illustrates the method in which a psychrometer can be used to determine specific humidity and relative humidity.

Example 12.9:

The wet- and dry-bulb readings from a sling psychrometer are 80 and 90F when the barometric pressure is 14.5 lb/in.^{2} What are the values of the specific humidity and relative humidity?

Solution:

In this case $h_{f3} = h_{f2}$, and from the steam tables for a saturation temperature of 80F

$$h_{g2} = 1096.6, \qquad h_{f3} = 48.02, \qquad P_{g2} = 0.5069$$

The partial pressure of air at the wet-bulb conditions is

$$P_{\text{air}} = 14.5 - 0.5069 = 13.99$$

and the relative humidity at saturation is, of course, 100 per cent. From Eq. (12.11) for 1 lb of dry air

$$w_{g2} = 0.622 \left(\frac{0.5069}{13.99}\right) = 0.0225 \ \text{lb}_m/\text{lb}_m$$

Since steam at very low pressures may be considered an ideal gas, its enthalpy is a function of temperature alone and

$$h_{wv1} = h_{g1}$$

which, for a temperature of 90F, is

$$h_{wv1} = 1100.9$$

The specific heat at constant pressure for air at these temperatures is 0.24. Substituting all these values in Eq. (12.12) gives the specific humidity

$$w_{wv1} = \frac{0.24(80 - 90) + 0.0225(1096.6 - 48.02)}{1100.9 - 48.02}$$

$$= 0.0201 \ \text{lb}_m/\text{lb}_m$$

From the steam tables, for a temperature of 90F

$$P_g = 0.6982$$

Solving Eq. (12.11) for the relative humidity,

$$\varphi = \frac{0.0201}{0.622}\left(\frac{14.5 - 0.698}{0.698}\right)$$

$$= 0.639$$

12.10 Psychrometric charts

For air at constant barometric pressure it is possible to construct a chart, known as a psychrometric chart, from which the specific humidity and relative humidity can be found for any given wet- and dry-bulb temperatures. Such a chart for 14.7 lb/in.² pressure is shown in the Appendix as Chart V. The chart is constructed from the results of a large number of calculations similar to the preceding example. In addition to lines of constant specific humidity and relative humidity, lines are shown for constant specific volume of dry air and enthalpy per pound of dry air. The specific humidity is given in units of grains, where

$$1 \ \text{lb}_m = 7000 \ \text{grains}$$

and the enthalpy is labeled as "total heat."

The use of psychrometric charts greatly simplifies the determination of the properties of air and water vapor mixtures. However, they apply at only one barometric pressure. If the barometric pressure deviates appreciably from 14.7 lb/in.², the use of Chart V may lead to serious error. The use of the chart will be illustrated by the following example.

Example 12.10:

The wet- and dry-bulb temperatures taken from a sling psychrometer are 69 and 84F. Barometric pressure is 14.7. What are (a) the specific humidity; (b) relative humidity; (c) partial pressure of the water vapor; (d) dew point; (e) enthalpy per pound of dry air?

Solution:

From Chart V of the Appendix the intersection of 69F wet-bulb and 84F dry-bulb temperatures is located. For this point

(a) The specific humidity is

$$\frac{w_{wv}}{w_{\text{air}}} = 82 \text{ grains/lb}_m$$

$$= \frac{82}{7000} = 0.0117 \text{ lb}_m/\text{lb}_m$$

(b) The relative humidity, by interpolation, is

$$\varphi = 47 \text{ per cent}$$

(c) The partial pressure of the water vapor from the scale at the left is

$$P_{wv} = 0.27 \text{ lb/in.}^2$$

(d) The dew point is found as the wet-bulb temperatures at the intersection of the specific humidity and saturation line and is

$$T = 62F$$

(e) The enthalpy is found by projecting the wet-bulb line to the enthalpy scale and is

$$h = 33.3 \text{ B/lb}_m \text{ dry air}$$

12.11 Evaporative cooling

In dry, hot climates a system similar to adiabatic saturation can be used for air conditioning. Figure 12.4 can be used to represent a schematic evaporative cooler with the exception that the water vapor leaving the system would not be completely saturated under desirable operating conditions. The process is adiabatic, however, and an enthalpy balance similar to Eq. (12.12a) applies.

As shown in Chart V of the Appendix, if the air is hot with a low relative humidity, a large difference exists between the dry-bulb and wet-bulb temperatures. This indicates that considerable cooling of the air can take place before the water vapor becomes saturated. Cooling the air to the saturation point is not desirable, however, since relative humidities approaching 100 per cent are physically uncomfortable. If the original humidity is low, it is possible to reduce the air temperature by increasing the humidity to some reasonable level below saturation.

Evaporative coolers are inexpensive and do not require an elaborate installation. They are ineffective, however, in locations where the relative humidity is normally high.

12.12 Mixing

This chapter has discussed mixtures as such without attention to mixing or diffusion processes. Simple cases of adiabatic mixing can be handled by the methods developed in this and previous chapters.

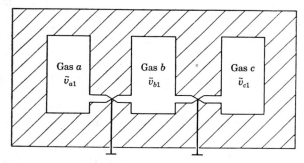

Fig. 12.5. Schematic diagram for adiabatic mixing.

Consider an insulated system containing three gases, a, b, and c, connected by valves as shown in Fig. 12.5. The gases are originally at different pressures and temperatures. After opening all the valves, the gases are assumed to mix completely and arrive at an equilibrium mixture condition. Since the process is adiabatic and no external work is done, the energy equation for the process is that the internal energy of the system remains constant. That is,

$$\tilde{u}_{a1} + \tilde{u}_{b1} + \tilde{u}_{c1} = \tilde{u}_{az2} + \tilde{u}_{bz2} + \tilde{u}_{cz2}$$
$$= \tilde{u}_m \tag{12.13a}$$

In terms of specific internal energy this equation becomes

$$w_a(u_{a2} - u_{a1}) + w_b(u_{b2} - u_{b1}) + w_c(u_{c2} - u_{c1}) = 0 \tag{12.13b}$$

For ideal gases with constant specific heat the change in internal energy is a function of temperature, and Eq. (12.13b) may be written

$$w_a c_{va}(T_{a2} - T_{a1}) + w_b c_{vb}(T_{b2} - T_{b1}) + w_c c_{vc}(T_{c2} - T_{c1}) = 0 \tag{12.13c}$$

However, for the gases after mixing

$$T_{a2} = T_{b2} = T_{c2} = T_m \tag{12.13d}$$

Solving Eqs. (12.13c) and (12.13d) for the mixture temperature gives

$$T_m = \frac{w_a c_{va} T_{a1} + w_b c_{vb} T_{b1} + w_c c_{vc} T_{c1}}{w_a c_{va} + w_b c_{vb} + w_c c_{vc}} \tag{12.13}$$

The mixture pressure is found as the sum of the partial pressures after mixing, using Eqs. (12.5g) and the relation

$$\tilde{v}_m = \tilde{v}_{a1} + \tilde{v}_{b1} + \tilde{v}_{c1} \tag{12.14a}$$

The change in entropy for the system is found as the sum of the entropy changes for the constituents, assuming each to expand from its initial conditions to the mixture conditions T_m and $\tilde{v}_m$. From Eq. (6.12)

$$\tilde{s}_{a2} - \tilde{s}_{a1} = w_a \left(c_{va} \ln \frac{T_m}{T_{a1}} + \frac{R_a}{J} \ln \frac{\tilde{v}_m}{\tilde{v}_{a1}} \right) \tag{12.14b}$$

$$\tilde{s}_{b2} - \tilde{s}_{b1} = w_b \left(c_{vb} \ln \frac{T_m}{T_{b1}} + \frac{R_b}{J} \ln \frac{\tilde{v}_m}{\tilde{v}_{b1}} \right) \tag{12.14c}$$

$$\tilde{s}_{c2} - \tilde{s}_{c1} = w_c \left(c_{vc} \ln \frac{T_m}{T_{c1}} + \frac{R_c}{J} \ln \frac{\tilde{v}_m}{\tilde{v}_{c1}} \right) \tag{12.14}$$

The entropy change for the process is obtained as the sum of Eqs. (12.14b), (12.14c), and (12.14).

Example 12.11:

Three gases are contained in a system similar to Fig. 12.5. The gases and their properties before mixing are tabulated below:

Gas	Mass-lb	Pressure lb/in.^{2}	Temperature R	Gas Constant	Specific Heat, c_v
CO_2	0.489	100	700	35.1	0.154
N_2	0.483	15	600	55.2	0.177
He	0.028	30	500	386.0	0.754

After the valves are opened and the gases thoroughly mixed, determine the pressure and temperature of the mixture and the change in entropy for the process.

Solution:

The volumes of the constituent gases prior to mixing are

$$CO_2: \quad \tilde{v} = \frac{0.489(35.1)700}{100(144)} = 0.837 \text{ ft}^3$$

$$N_2: \quad \tilde{v} = \frac{0.483(55.2)600}{15(144)} = 7.43 \text{ ft}^3$$

$$He: \quad \tilde{v} = \frac{0.028(386)500}{30(144)} = 1.25 \text{ ft}^3$$

The total volume after mixing is then

$$\tilde{v}_m = 0.84 + 7.43 + 1.25 = 9.52 \text{ ft}^3$$

From Eq. (12.13) the mixture temperature is

$$T_m = \frac{0.489(0.154)700 + 0.483(0.177)600 + 0.028(0.754)500}{0.489(0.154) + 0.483(0.177) + 0.028(0.754)}$$

$$= 624 \text{ R}$$

From Eq. (12.5g) the mixture pressure is

$$P_m = [0.489(35.1) + 0.483(55.2) + 0.028(386)] \frac{624}{9.52(144)}$$

$$= 24.9 \text{ lb/in.}^2$$

The entropy change for the constituents, from Eqs. (12.14b)–(12.14), is

$$CO_2: \quad \tilde{s}_2 - \tilde{s}_1 = 0.489 \left(0.154 \ln \frac{624}{700} + \frac{35.1}{778} \ln \frac{9.52}{0.837} \right)$$

$$= 0.0400$$

$$N_2: \quad \tilde{s}_2 - \tilde{s}_1 = 0.483 \left(0.177 \ln \frac{624}{600} + \frac{55.2}{778} \ln \frac{9.52}{7.43} \right)$$

$$= 0.0222$$

$$He: \quad \tilde{s}_2 - \tilde{s}_1 = 0.028 \left(0.754 \ln \frac{624}{500} + \frac{386}{778} \ln \frac{9.52}{1.25} \right)$$

$$= 0.0329$$

The entropy change for the process is then

$$\Delta\tilde{s} = 0.0400 + 0.0222 + 0.0329$$

$$= 0.0951 \text{ B/R}$$

This example shows an appreciable increase in entropy for the adiabatic mixing process, indicating that the process is irreversible, since a reversible adiabatic process is isentropic. An increase in entropy is characteristic of all adiabatic mixing processes of dissimilar gases. Adiabatic mixing of identical gases initially at the same pressure and temperature does not result in an increase in entropy, however, even though Eqs. (12.14b)–(12.14) would indicate an increase. This has been called *Gibbs paradox.*† Therefore, Eqs. (12.14b)–(12.14) do not apply to mixing processes for identical gases.

12.13 Air conditioning

Air conditioning as a general term implies the effective control of the physical and chemical properties of air to produce (1) comfort air conditioning—the maintenance of the air surrounding human beings in a condition most suitable for their comfort and health—or (2) industrial air conditioning—the maintenance of the air surrounding a material or product in process of manufacture or storage so as best to preserve the physical stability of the material throughout its manufacturing or storage period.

Industrial air conditioning makes it possible to produce better products at a higher rate in such diversified fields as book and newspaper printing, textile and precision instrument manufacturing, fuze and explosive manufacturing, and candy making. Air conditioning has been applied to the air for blast furnaces. Furthermore, it is used extensively for drying in various industrial processes.

Air conditioning for comfort is becoming very common, particularly in the southern part of the United States in stores, hotels, theaters, and restaurants. The gain in business, employee morale, and customer good-will usually is so great that air conditioning more than pays for itself. In the home, where there is no such financial gain possible, summer air conditioning has lagged. Perhaps the most important reason for the small demand for household air conditioning is the high initial cost.

The factors which affect human comfort from the viewpoint of air conditioning are, in the order of their importance: (1) temperature, (2) humidity, (3) air motion and distribution, and (4) purity. These factors represent the basic items which must be controlled by a *com-*

---

† See, for example, M. W. Zemansky, *Heat and Thermodynamics*, McGraw-Hill Book Company, Inc., New York, 2nd ed., p. 312.

plete air-conditioning system. Many installed systems do not operate to control all these factors and yet are reasonably effective.

Temperature and humidity have been defined before and their effect on human comfort is well understood. Air motion and distribution include the design and placement of ducts, deflectors, and fans. Purification covers the elimination or reduction of odors, dust particles, toxic gases, and bacteria. Normally dust and dirt are removed by circulating the air through mechanical filters (such as Fiberglas) but in more elaborate systems the air is passed through liquid baths or sprays (oil or water) which removes smoke, odors, and gases as well as dirt and dust particles.

There can be considerable variation in the placement of the component parts of the air-conditioning unit. For instance, the heating

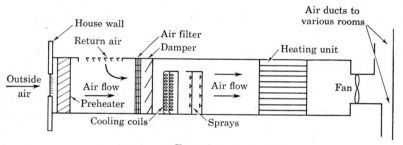

Fig. 12.6.

unit included in the schematic diagram might well consist of steam or hot water radiators in the various rooms of the house, and the filter and damper might be placed in various positions. A unit containing the elements shown is capable of maintaining constant temperature and constant humidity the year round, regardless of the condition of the entering air. Under certain conditions one or more pieces of the equipment are not used because the entering air often does not require all the processes. For instance, if the outside air is moist the entire year, the spray could be eliminated; if the outside air is hot and dry, the preheater could be eliminated; etc. For moderate climates, however, all the elements are necessary, and the unit cannot properly be called an "air-conditioning" unit unless it does contain all the component parts.

In connection with conditioning air for human beings, it is common to use a defined area on the psychrometric chart, which is called the *human comfort zone.* The extent of this zone depends on several factors, including the locality, the season of the year, the state of the air received by the air conditioner at a particular time, and the degree of activity of the persons in the conditioned space. Normally, the human comfort zone for a majority of people lies within the area enclosed by the 30% and 70% relative humidity lines and the 65°F and 85°F dry-bulb temperature lines.

Summary of functions of some air-conditioning components. "Water sprays" and an "evaporative cooler" do the same thing; i.e., they increase the moisture content at constant wet-bulb temperature. A "cooling coil," however, reduces the dry-bulb temperature at constant moisture content. If a cooling coil lowers the dry-bulb temperature to the dew point (saturation state) and continues to cool, then some moisture will condense out of the air and the state of the water vapor remaining in the air will proceed down along the saturation temperature curve of the psychrometric chart. This process involving condensation is called a *cooling and dehumidifying process.* A "heating unit" increases dry-bulb temperature at constant moisture content.

Example 12.13:

The air-conditioning equipment for an instrumented assembly and calibration depot in the midwest must be capable of the following operation: 8500 cfm of air at 45.0°F dry-bulb and 37.0°F wet-bulb is to be preheated, passed through water sprays until the relative humidity is 100%, and reheated to a final condition of 85.0°F dry-bulb and 30% relative humidity. What is the required capacity in B/min

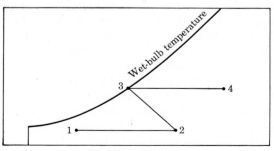

Dry-bulb temperature

Fig. 12.7.

of (a) the preheater, and (b) the reheater? (c) How many pounds of water must be added to the air per minute by the water sprays?

Solution:

On Chart V of the Appendix the processes described above can be plotted as in Fig. 12.7. Points 1 and 4 can be plotted immediately from the information above. Point 3 must lie to the left of point 4 on a line of constant moisture content. Point 3 must also lie on the 100% relative humidity line. Point 2 must lie to the right of point 1 on a line of constant moisture content and must also connect with a line of constant wet-bulb temperature passing through point 3. All properties of the four points in question can now be obtained from Chart V.

(a) $$\dot{w} = \frac{\dot{v}_1}{v_1} = \frac{8500}{12.775} = 665 \text{ lb}_m/\text{min}$$

$$Q_{1-2} = h_2 - h_1 = 20.3 - 13.85 = 6.45 \text{ B/lb}_m$$

$$Q_{1-2} = 665(6.45) = 4290 \text{ B/min}$$

(b) $$Q_{3-4} = h_4 - h_3 = 29.0 - 20.3 = 8.70 \text{ B/lb}_m$$

$$Q_{3-4} = 665(8.70) = 5790 \text{ B/min}$$

(c) The water content of the air at points 2 and 3 can be obtained from the vertical axis on the extreme right of the psychrometric chart.

$$\omega_2 = \frac{20}{7000} = 0.00286 \text{ lb}_m \text{ H}_2\text{O}/\text{lb}_m \text{ d.a.}$$

$$\omega_3 = \frac{54}{7000} = 0.00772 \text{ lb}_m \text{ H}_2\text{O}/\text{lb}_m \text{ d.a.}$$

Therefore the water added by the sprays would be

$$\omega_3 - \omega_2 = 0.00486 \text{ lb}_m \text{ H}_2\text{O}/\text{lb}_m \text{ d.a.}$$

or

$$\text{rate of water addition} = 665(0.00486) = 3.23 \text{ lb}_m/\text{min}$$

PROBLEMS

1. The volumetric analysis of a gas is as follows: CO_2, 40%; N_2, 40%; O_2, 20%. What are the partial pressures if the mixture pressure and temperature are 14.7 lb/in.^{2} and 60F?

2. What are the gas constant and apparent molecular weight of the mixture of Prob. 1?

3. What is the gravimetric analysis of the mixture of Prob. 1?

4. A mixture contains 1 lb_m of carbon monoxide and 1 lb_m of helium. The mixture is contained in a volume of 5 ft^3 at a temperature of 90F. What is the mixture pressure?

5. What is the volumetric analysis for the mixture of Prob. 4?

6. How much heat is required per pound to raise the temperature of the mixture of Prob. 1 to 240F under constant volume conditions? (Use the specific heats of Table 7 of the Appendix.)

7. What is the change in entropy in heating the mixture of Prob. 1 to 240F at constant pressure?

8. A mixture of nitrogen and water vapor has the following gravimetric analysis: N_2, 90%; H_2O, 10%. What are the partial pressures at 100F if the mixture pressure is 30 lb/in.^{2}?

9. What are the gravimetric and volumetric analyses of a mixture of air and saturated water vapor at 100F and 14.7 lb/in.^{2}?

10. Plot a curve of specific humidity versus air temperature from $-20F$ to 100F for saturated water vapor and a barometric pressure of 12.2 lb/in.^{2}

11. What is the specific humidity when the relative humidity is 70 per cent at 80F and 13 lb/in.^{2} barometric pressure?

12. The wet- and dry-bulb temperatures obtained from a sling psychrometer were 70 and 85F. Barometric pressure was 12 lb/in.^{2} What was the relative humidity?

13. What is the dew point in Prob. 11?

14. What is the dew point in Prob. 12?

15. Under standard sea level atmospheric pressure the wet- and dry-bulb temperatures are 70 and 80F. What are (a) the specific humidity; (b) relative humidity; (c) partial pressure of the water vapor; (d) dew point; (e) enthalpy per pound of dry air?

16. When atmospheric conditions are as follows, pressure, 14.7 lb/in.^{2}; temperature, 110F; relative humidity, 20 per cent, what temperature could be realized from an evaporative cooler if the relative humidity of the cooled air were increased to 70 per cent?

17. Work Example 12.11, interchanging the masses of carbon dioxide and helium.

18. One pound of nitrogen at 70F and 20 lb/in.^{2} is mixed adiabatically with 1 lb of hydrogen at 80F and 300 lb/in.^{2} (a) What are the resulting mixture pressure and temperature? (b) What is the change in entropy for the process?

Chapter XIII

GAS DYNAMICS

13.1 Introduction

The field of thermodynamics of high speed flow of an ideal gas has increased in importance in recent years with the development of jet propulsion, gas turbine power plants, and high-speed aerodynamics. This field is called gas dynamics and deals with the relations between fluid properties under high-speed flow conditions.

The introduction to thermodynamics presented in the early chapters of this book offers a suitable background for the development of these gas dynamic relations for a one-dimensional steady flow of an ideal gas. The assumptions upon which the following developments are based are then:

1. All flows to be analyzed are steady.

2. The flow is one-dimensional; that is, fluid properties vary only along the direction of flow and not transverse to the flow axis.

3. The thermodynamic medium is an ideal gas with constant specific heat.

13.2 Mach number

The dependence of fluid properties on the flow velocity may best be shown by the introduction of a dimensionless velocity ratio, called the Mach number. The Mach number is, by definition, the ratio of the velocity of the flow to the speed of sound at the point in question. That is,

$$N_M = \frac{V}{c} \tag{13.1a}$$

For an ideal gas, however, the speed of sound is given by the relation

$$c = \sqrt{\gamma g_c R T} \tag{13.1b}$$

which was expressed in Chap. XI and is repeated here for convenience. The Mach number for an ideal gas is then

$$N_M = \frac{V}{\sqrt{\gamma g_c R T}} \tag{13.1}$$

It will be shown in the following sections that fluid properties in high-speed gas flows are dependent on the Mach number and not on the velocity directly.

13.3 Stagnation condition

Stagnation enthalpy is defined by the relation

$$h_t = h + \frac{V^2}{2g_cJ} \qquad \text{(isentropic)} \quad (13.2a)$$

For an ideal gas with constant specific heat this may be written

$$c_p(T_t - T) = \frac{V^2}{2g_cJ} \qquad (13.2b)$$

Dividing by T, making use of Eq. (6.7), and rearranging gives

$$\frac{T_t}{T} - 1 = \frac{(\gamma - 1)V^2}{\gamma 2g_cRT} \qquad (13.2c)$$

Combining this relation with Eq. (13.1) gives the stagnation temperature ratio in terms of Mach number and specific heat ratio.

$$\frac{T_t}{T} = 1 + \frac{\gamma - 1}{2} N_M{}^2 \qquad (13.2)$$

Since the relation between stagnation and static conditions is isentropic, the stagnation pressure ratio becomes

$$\frac{P_t}{P} = \left(1 + \frac{\gamma - 1}{2} N_M{}^2\right)^{\gamma/(\gamma-1)} \qquad (13.3)$$

Stagnation pressure and temperature ratios are plotted versus Mach number in Fig. 13.1 for specific heat ratios of 1.4 and 1.3.

Example 13.1:

Air leaves a nozzle with a velocity of 2000 ft/sec at a pressure and temperature of 14.7 lb/in.^{2} and 10F. Assuming $\gamma = 1.4$, what are the stagnation pressure and temperature?

Solution:

Sonic velocity is

$$c = \sqrt{1.4(32.2)53.3(470)} = 1064$$

The Mach number is

$$N_M = \frac{2000}{1064} = 1.88$$

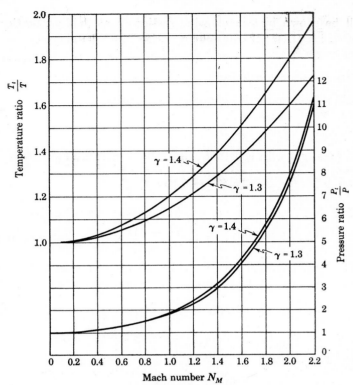

Fɪɢ. 13.1. Sᴛᴀɢɴᴀᴛɪᴏɴ ᴘʀᴇssᴜʀᴇ ᴀɴᴅ ᴛᴇᴍᴘᴇʀᴀᴛᴜʀᴇ ʀᴀᴛɪᴏs ᴠs. Mᴀᴄʜ ɴᴜᴍʙᴇʀ.

From Eq. (13.2) the stagnation temperature ratio is

$$\frac{T_t}{T} = 1 + 0.2(1.88)^2 = 1.702$$

and $$T_t = 1.702(470) = 801 \text{ R}$$

The stagnation pressure ratio is

$$\frac{P_t}{P} = (1.702)^{3.5} = 6.43$$

and $$P_t = 6.43(14.7) = 94.4 \text{ lb/in.}^2$$

13.4 The continuity equation

The continuity equation given by Eq. (11.2) may be usefully expressed in terms of flow area, stagnation conditions, and Mach number in the following way: For an ideal gas the continuity equation becomes

$$\dot{w} = \frac{AVP}{RT} \tag{13.4a}$$

Substituting for P and T from Eqs. (13.2) and (13.3) gives

$$\dot{w} = \frac{AVP_t}{RT_t}\left(1 + \frac{\gamma - 1}{2} N_M{}^2\right)^{1/(\gamma-1)} \tag{13.4b}$$

Multiplying and dividing by $\sqrt{\gamma g_c R T}$ and making use of Eqs. (13.1) and (13.2) and rearranging results in

$$\frac{\dot{w}\sqrt{RT_t}}{AP_t} = \sqrt{\gamma g_c} N_M\left(1 + \frac{\gamma - 1}{2} N_M{}^2\right)^{(\gamma+1)/(2-2\gamma)} \tag{13.4}$$

Figure 13.2 is a plot of the mass flow parameter of Eq. (13.4) versus Mach number for specific heat ratios of 1.4 and 1.3. It will be noted that the maximum value occurs at a Mach number of unity, which is consistent with the discussion of nozzle flow in Chap. XI.

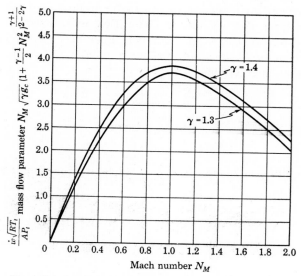

Fig. 13.2. Mass flow parameter vs. Mach number.

Example 13.2:

Air is flowing through a duct having an area of 0.3 ft². At one point in the duct the stagnation conditions are 30 lb/in.² and 160F.

The Mach number at this point is 0.82. What is the mass flow, assuming $\gamma = 1.4$?

Solution:

From Eq. (13.4) the mass flow rate is

$$\dot{w} = \frac{0.3(144)30}{\sqrt{53.3(620)}} \sqrt{1.4(32.2)} (0.82)[1 + 0.2(0.82)^2]^{-3}$$

$$= 26.8 \ \mathrm{lb}_m/\mathrm{sec}$$

13.5 Reversible adiabatic flow

The preceding relations developed in this chapter apply at any point in a flow and are based on the assumptions listed in Art. 13.1. If the flow itself is reversible adiabatic, these relations may also be applied between any two points in the flow since both the stagnation pressure and stagnation temperature are constant for a reversible adiabatic (isentropic) flow. For reversible adiabatic flows in which the area is changing it is convenient to refer all flow conditions to the critical, or sonic, flow condition. The critical pressure and temperature ratios were developed in Chap. XI. They may also be obtained by substituting a Mach number of unity in Eqs. (13.2) and (13.3); these relations then become

$$\frac{T_t}{T^*} = \frac{\gamma + 1}{2} \tag{13.5}$$

$$\frac{P_t}{P^*} = \left(\frac{\gamma + 1}{2}\right)^{\gamma/(\gamma-1)} \tag{13.6}$$

The minimum flow area, from Eq. (13.4), with a Mach number of unity is

$$A^* = \frac{\dot{w}\sqrt{RT_t}}{P_t\sqrt{\gamma g_c}} \left(\frac{\gamma + 1}{2}\right)^{(\gamma+1)/(2\gamma-2)} \tag{13.7a}$$

while the area at any other point in the flow is

$$A = \frac{\dot{w}\sqrt{RT_t}}{P_t\sqrt{\gamma g_c} N_M} \left(1 + \frac{\gamma - 1}{2} N_M{}^2\right)^{(\gamma+1)/(2\gamma-2)} \tag{13.7b}$$

The ratio of the area at any point to the minimum area is then, since the stagnation pressure, stagnation temperature, and mass flow rate are constant,

$$\frac{A}{A^*} = \frac{1}{N_M}\left(\frac{2}{\gamma+1} + \frac{\gamma-1}{\gamma+1} N_M{}^2\right)^{(\gamma+1)(2\gamma-2)} \tag{13.7}$$

Figure 13.3 is a plot of this area ratio versus Mach number for specific heat ratios of 1.4, 1.3, and 1.2.

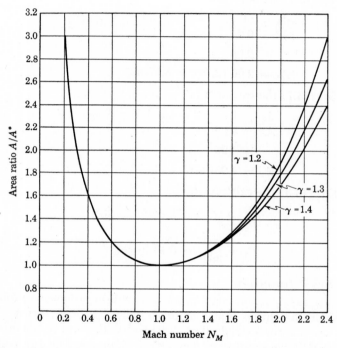

Fɪɢ. 13.3. Aʀᴇᴀ ʀᴀᴛɪᴏ ᴠs. Mᴀᴄʜ ɴᴜᴍʙᴇʀ ғᴏʀ ɪsᴇɴᴛʀᴏᴘɪᴄ ғʟᴏᴡ.

Example 13.3:

A supersonic air nozzle is to be designed for an exit Mach number of 3 and an inlet Mach number of 0.2 with a mass flow rate of 10 $lb_m/$ sec. Assuming isentropic flow with a specific heat ratio of 1.4 and inlet stagnation conditions of 200 lb/in.^{2} and 400F, what are the areas at the inlet, throat, and exit? What is the exit pressure?

Solution:

From Eq. (13.7a) the throat area is

$$A^* = \frac{10\sqrt{53.3(860)}}{200\sqrt{1.4(32.2)}} \left(\frac{1.4 + 1}{2}\right)^3$$

$$= 2.76 \text{ in.}^2$$

From Eq. (13.7) the inlet area is

$$\frac{A_1}{A^*} = \frac{1}{0.2}\left[\frac{2}{1.4 + 1} + \frac{1.4 - 1}{1.4 + 1}(0.2)^2\right]^3$$

$$= 2.96$$

$$A_1 = 2.96 \ (2.76) = 8.17 \text{ in.}^2$$

From Eq. (13.7) the exit area is

$$\frac{A_2}{A^*} = \frac{1}{3}\left[\frac{2}{1.4 + 1} + \frac{1.4 - 1}{1.4 + 1}(3)^2\right]$$

$$= 4.25$$

$$A_2 = 4.25(2.76) = 11.73 \text{ in.}^2$$

From Eq. (13.3) the exit pressure is

$$\frac{P_t}{P_2} = [1 + 0.2(3)^2]^{3.5} = 36.8$$

$$P_2 = \frac{200}{36.8} = 5.43 \text{ lb/in.}^2$$

13.6 Thrust function

Another gas dynamic relation that is useful in propulsion problems is that for the thrust function, or so called "stream thrust." The thrust function for a steady flow is defined as the sum of the momentum rate and the product of flow area and pressure at any point in the flow. That is,

$$F = \frac{\dot{w}}{g_c} V + AP \qquad (13.8a)$$

Where F is the thrust function and has the units of force. It will be noted that Eq. (11.14) for the internal thrust of a jet engine could be written as

$$F_i = F_2 - F_1 \qquad (13.8b)$$

Equation (11.15a) for net thrust is

$$F_n = F_2 - F_1 - P_a(A_2 - A_1) \qquad (13.8c)$$

For an ideal gas

$$\dot{w} = \frac{AVP}{RT} \tag{13.8d}$$

and Eq. (13.8a) may be written

$$F = \frac{V^2 AP}{g_c RT} + AP \tag{13.8e}$$

Multiplying and dividing the first term by γ, making use of Eq. (13.1), and factoring gives

$$F = (1 + \gamma N_M{}^2)AP \tag{13.8f}$$

Eliminating P between Eqs. (13.3) and (13.8e) results in

$$F = \frac{(1 + \gamma N_M{}^2)AP_t}{\left(1 + \dfrac{\gamma - 1}{2} N_M{}^2\right)^{\gamma/(\gamma-1)}} \tag{13.8g}$$

For a reversible adiabatic flow the sonic value of this function would be

$$F^* = (\gamma + 1)\left(\frac{2}{\gamma + 1}\right)^{\gamma/(\gamma-1)} A^* P_t \tag{13.8h}$$

The ratio of the thrust function to the sonic thrust function, from Eqs. (13.8g) and (13.8h), is

$$\frac{F}{F^*} = \frac{(1 + \gamma N_M)^2/(\gamma + 1)}{\left(\dfrac{2}{\gamma + 1} + \dfrac{\gamma - 1}{\gamma + 1} N_M{}^2\right)^{\gamma(\gamma-1)}} \frac{A}{A^*} \tag{13.8i}$$

Eliminating the area ratio between Eqs. (13.7) and (13.8i) gives the thrust ratio as a function of Mach number.

$$\frac{F}{F^*} = \frac{1 + \gamma N_M{}^2}{N_M \sqrt{2(\gamma + 1) + (\gamma^2 - 1)N_M{}^2}} \tag{13.8}$$

Figure 13.4 is a plot of this thrust ratio versus Mach number for specific heat ratios of 1.4, 1.3, and 1.2.

The net thrust of a jet engine in terms of F^* is, from Eqs. (13.8c) and (13.8h),

$$F_n = F_2{}^*\left[\frac{F_2}{F_2{}^*} - \frac{1}{\gamma + 1}\left(\frac{\gamma + 1}{2}\right)^{\gamma/(\gamma-1)} \frac{P_a}{P_{t2}} \frac{A_2}{A_2{}^*}\right]$$
$$- F_1{}^*\left[\frac{F_1}{F_1{}^*} - \frac{1}{\gamma + 1}\left(\frac{\gamma + 1}{2}\right)^{\gamma/(\gamma-1)} \frac{P_a}{P_{t1}} \frac{A_1}{A_1{}^*}\right] \tag{13.9}$$

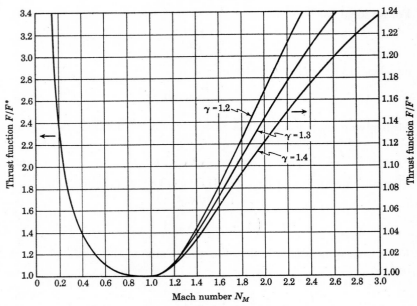

Mach number N_M

FIG. 13.4. THRUST FUNCTION VS. MACH NUMBER.

where the subscripts 1 and 2 refer to the locations at which fluid enters and leaves the system. For a rocket motor no external fluid enters the system; hence both F_1 and A_1 are zero.

Example 13.4:

An ideal rocket motor has a ratio of nozzle exit area to throat area of 3. The nozzle inlet stagnation pressure is 750 lb/in.², the throat area is 2 in.², and the specific heat ratio is 1.25. What is the internal rocket thrust? What is the external rocket thrust, assuming the nozzle exit pressure is equal to ambient pressure?

Solution:

From Eq. (13.8h) the sonic thrust function is

$$F^* = 225 \left(\frac{2}{1.25 + 1} \right)^5 2(300)$$

$$= 1873$$

From Fig. 13.3 for an area ratio of 3 and a specific heat ratio of 1.25 the exit Mach number is 2.45. From Eq. (13.8) or Fig. 13.4 the thrust function ratio is

$$\frac{F_2}{F_2{}^*} = \frac{1 + 1.25(2.45)^2}{2.45 \sqrt{4.5 + (1.25^2 - 1)2.45^2}}$$
$$= 1.239$$

The internal thrust, from Eq. (13.8b), since $F_1 = 0$, is

$$F_i = F_2 = 1.239(1873) = 2340 \text{ lb}$$

The net thrust is found from Eq. (13.9) with F_1 and A_1 equal to zero. From the statement of the problem, $P_a = P_2$, and from Eq. (13.3)

$$\frac{P_{t2}}{P_a} = [1 + 0.2(2.45)^2]^5 = 51.5$$

Substituting the above values in eq. (13.9),

$$\frac{F_n}{F^*} = 1.238 - \frac{1}{2.25}\left(\frac{1.25 + 1}{2}\right)^5 \frac{1}{51.3}(3) = 1198$$
$$F_n = 1198(1873) = 2240 \text{ lb}$$

13.7 *Momentum relation for constant area flow*

Many steady flows of practical importance approach constant area conditions. Such flows are the flow of gases in pipes and ducts and the flow of gases in constant-area combustion chambers. In order to apply gas dynamic theory to constant area flows, a force balance on a fluid element is useful. Figure 13.5 shows the forces acting on a fluid element under steady flow conditions in a constant area duct.

The forces acting on the element in the x direction are pressure forces on the right and left and a friction force around the peripheral area. From Newton's Second Law, equating the sum of the forces to

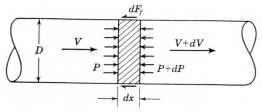

FIG. 13.5. CONSTANT AREA FLOW DIAGRAM.

the mass times acceleration, the following relation exists:

$$\frac{\pi D^2}{4}[P - (P + dP)] - dF_f = m\frac{dV}{dt} \qquad (13.10\text{a})$$

The mass of the element is

$$m = \rho\frac{\pi D^2}{4}dx \qquad (13.10\text{b})$$

where ρ is the density.

Since the flow is one-dimensional, the velocity is a function of x and

$$\frac{dV}{dt} = \frac{dV}{dx}\frac{dx}{dt} = V\frac{dV}{dx} \qquad (13.10\text{c})$$

Substituting Eqs. (13.10c) and (13.10b) in (13.10a) gives

$$dP = -\rho V\, dV - \frac{4\, dF_f}{\pi D^2} \qquad (13.10\text{d})$$

The friction factor f is defined as

$$f = \frac{F_f}{(1/2)\rho V^2 A} \qquad (13.10\text{e})$$

where F_f is the friction force acting on area A. Thus

$$dF_f = f\tfrac{1}{2}\rho V^2\pi D\, dx \qquad (13.10\text{f})$$

Substituting Eq. (13.10f) in Eq. (13.10d) gives

$$dP = -\rho V\, dV - \frac{4f}{D}\frac{1}{2}\rho V^2\, dx \qquad (13.10)$$

This is the general expression for the pressure drop in a fluid; two important cases will be analyzed—heat addition in the absence of friction and adiabatic flow with friction.

13.8 Constant area flow with heat addition

In the absence of friction Eq. (13.10) becomes

$$dP = -\rho V\, dV \qquad (13.11\text{a})$$

For a constant area flow the continuity equation shows the product ρV to be constant, and Eq. (13.11a) may be integrated between stations 1 and 2 in the flow to yield

$$P_2 - P_1 = \rho_1 V_1^2 - \rho_2 V_2^2 \qquad (13.11\text{b})$$

The density ρ is

$$\rho = \frac{1}{g_c v} \qquad (13.11c)$$

and for an ideal gas

$$\rho = \frac{P}{g_c R T} \qquad (13.11d)$$

Substituting Eq. (13.11d) in Eq. (13.11b) and simplifying,

$$P_1\left(1 + \frac{V_1^2}{g_c R T_1}\right) = P_2\left(1 + \frac{V_2^2}{g_c R T_2}\right) \qquad (13.11e)$$

Multiplying and dividing both sides by the specific heat ratio and making use of the Mach number relation,

$$P_1(1 + \gamma N_{M1}^2) = P_2(1 + \gamma N_{M2}^2) \qquad (13.11)$$

This relation is known as the equation of a Rayleigh line. In terms of stagnation pressures, from Eq. (13.3) it becomes

$$\frac{P_{t1}}{P_{t2}} = \frac{1 + \gamma N_{M2}^2}{1 + \gamma N_{M1}^2}\left(\frac{1 + \dfrac{\gamma - 1}{2} N_{M1}^2}{1 + \dfrac{\gamma - 1}{2} N_{M2}^2}\right)^{\gamma/(\gamma-1)} \qquad (13.12)$$

Figure 13.6 is a plot of the Mach number function from Eq. (13.12) versus Mach number for specific heat ratios of 1.4 and 1.3. As shown in Fig. 13.6 and Eq. (13.12), the stagnation pressure decreases with an increase in Mach number. The Mach number will increase with heat addition since the fluid density is reduced. A relation between stagnation temperature and Mach number may be easily obtained from Eqs. (13.4) and (13.12). From Eq. (13.4), which applies to any steady flow

$$\frac{P_{t1}}{P_{t2}} = \sqrt{\frac{T_{t1}}{T_{t2}}} \frac{N_{M2}}{N_{M1}} \frac{\left(1 + \dfrac{\gamma - 1}{2} N_{M2}^2\right)^{(\gamma+1)/(2-2\gamma)}}{\left(1 + \dfrac{\gamma - 1}{2} N_{M1}^2\right)^{(\gamma+1)/(2-2\gamma)}} \qquad (13.13a)$$

Eliminating P_{t1}/P_{t2} between Eqs. (13.13a) and (13.12) and squaring gives

$$\frac{T_{t2}}{T_{t1}} = \left(\frac{N_{M2}}{N_{M1}}\right)^2 \frac{1 + \dfrac{\gamma - 1}{2} N_{M2}^2}{1 + \dfrac{\gamma - 1}{2} N_{M1}^2}\left(\frac{1 + \gamma N_{M1}^2}{1 + \gamma N_{M2}^2}\right)^2 \qquad (13.13)$$

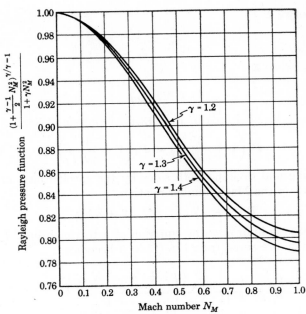

FIG. 13.6. RAYLEIGH LINE STAGNATION PRESSURE FUNCTION VS. MACH NUMBER.

Figure 13.7 is a plot of the Mach number function

$$\frac{N_M{}^2 \left(1 + \frac{\gamma - 1}{2} N_M{}^2\right)}{(1 + \gamma N_M{}^2)^2}$$

versus Mach number for specific heat ratios of 1.4 and 1.3.

Example 13.5:

Air is heated in a constant area duct. The initial stagnation conditions are 40 lb/in.^{2} and 60F. The initial Mach number is 0.2. The final stagnation temperature is 1620F. What are the final stagnation pressure and Mach number? Assume $\gamma = 1.35$.

Solution:

From the statement of the problem

$$\frac{T_{t2}}{T_{t1}} = \frac{2060}{520} = 4$$

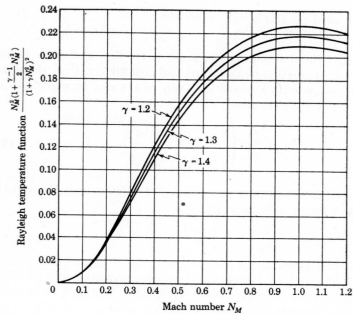

FIG. 13.7. RAYLEIGH LINE STAGNATION TEMPERATURE FUNCTION VS. MACH NUMBER.

For a Mach number of 0.2 from Fig. 13.7 the Mach number function is 0.036. The final Mach number function is

$$4(0.036) = 0.144$$

and from Fig. 13.7

$$N_{M2} = 0.49$$

From Fig. 13.6 the Mach number functions for 0.2 and 0.49 are 0.98 and 0.885. From Eq. (13.12) the pressure ratio is

$$\frac{P_{t1}}{P_{t2}} = \frac{0.98}{0.885} = 1.108$$

and

$$P_{t2} = \frac{40}{1.108} = 36.2 \text{ lb/in.}^2$$

13.9 Constant area flow with friction

For an adiabatic flow with friction in a constant area duct the energy equation between any two stations in the flow is

$$h_{t1} = h_{t2} \tag{13.14a}$$

For an ideal gas this is equivalent to

$$T_{t1} = T_{t2} \qquad (13.14b)$$

Equation (13.4) applies to any point in the flow and since the mass flow rate, stagnation temperature, and area are constant, the stagnation pressure ratio between any two points can be expressed as a function of Mach number. That is,

$$\frac{P_{t1}}{P_{t2}} = \frac{N_{M2}}{N_{M1}} \left(\frac{1 + \dfrac{\gamma - 1}{2} N_{M1}^2}{1 + \dfrac{\gamma - 1}{2} N_{M2}^2} \right)^{(\gamma+1)/(2\gamma-2)} \qquad (13.14)$$

This relation is known as the equation of a Fanno line. Figure 13.8 is a plot of the Mach number function

$$\frac{1}{N_M} \left(1 + \frac{\gamma - 1}{2} N_M^2 \right)^{(\gamma+1)/(2\gamma-2)}$$

versus Mach number for specific heat ratios of 1.4 and 1.3. As shown in Fig. 13.8 and Eq. (13.14) the stagnation pressure decreases with an increase in Mach number. Since the effect of friction is to reduce the pressure, it will also increase the Mach number.

For most high-speed duct flow problems the friction factor f is a constant, and a relation between the friction factor, duct length, and inlet and exit Mach numbers can be obtained by integrating Eq. (13.10) after first reducing it to a function of Mach number and flow length. The derivation of this relation is somewhat involved, and only the result will be given here.†

$$\frac{4fL}{D} = \left(\frac{\gamma + 1}{2\gamma} \ln \frac{N_{M1}^2}{1 + \dfrac{\gamma - 1}{2} N_{M1}^2} + \frac{1}{\gamma N_{M1}^2} \right)$$

$$- \left(\frac{\gamma + 1}{2\gamma} \ln \frac{N_{M2}^2}{1 + \dfrac{\gamma - 1}{2} N_{M2}^2} + \frac{1}{\gamma N_{M2}^2} \right) \qquad (13.15)$$

where L is the duct length. Figure 13.9 is a plot of the function

$$\frac{\gamma + 1}{2\gamma} \ln \frac{N_M^2}{1 + \dfrac{\gamma - 1}{2} N_M^2} + \frac{1}{\gamma N_M^2}$$

† See F. P. Durham, *Aircraft Jet Powerplants*, Prentice-Hall, Inc., New York, 1951, p. 113, for a derivation of this expression.

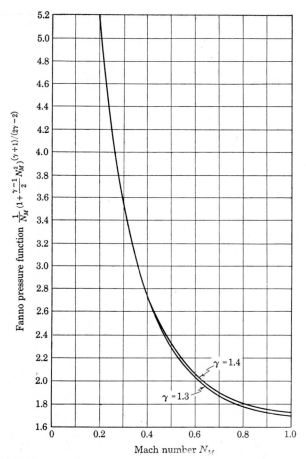

FIG. 13.8. FANNO PARAMETER VS. MACH NUMBER.

versus Mach number for specific heat ratios of 1.4 and 1.3. As shown in Fig. 13.9 and Eq. (13.15), the Mach number increases with increasing flow length and constant friction factor up to a Mach number of unity. Increasing the flow length beyond that necessary for sonic exit velocity would have the effect of choking the flow and reducing the inlet Mach number and mass flow rate.

Example 13.6:

Air enters a constant area duct with a Mach number of 0.4. The duct length is 10 ft, and the diameter is 3 in. The inlet stagnation con-

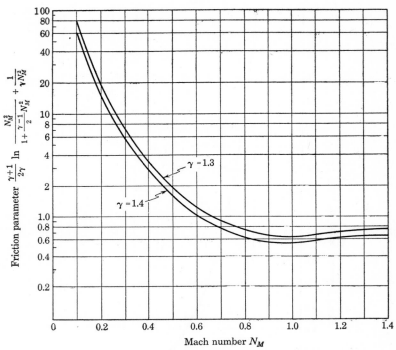

FIG. 13.9. FRICTION PARAMETER VS. MACH NUMBER.

ditions are 50 lb/in.^{2} and 100F. The friction factor is 0.008. What is the exit total pressure?

Solution:

The value of $4fL/D$ is

$$\frac{4fL}{D} = \frac{4(0.008)10(12)}{3} = 1.28$$

From Fig. 13.9 the Mach number function for the inlet Mach number is 2.9. The exit Mach number function is then

$$2.9 - 1.28 = 1.62$$

and the exit Mach number from Fig. 13.9 is

$$N_{M2} = 0.5$$

From Fig. 13.8 the Mach number functions for the inlet and exit Mach numbers are 2.73 and 2.3. And from Eq. (13.14) the stagnation pressure ratio is

$$\frac{P_{t1}}{P_{t2}} = \frac{2.73}{2.3} = 1.188$$

Thus, the duct exit pressure is

$$P_{t2} = \frac{50}{1.188} = 42.1 \text{ lb/in.}^2$$

PROBLEMS

1. The stagnation pressure in a wind tunnel is 16 lb/in.^{2} and the static pressure is 14 lb/in.^{2} The stagnation temperature is 100F. The specific heat ratio is 1.4. (a) What is the Mach number? (b) What is the velocity?

2. The Mach number of the air leaving a compressor rotor in a jet engine is 1.05. The stagnation pressure is 50 lb/in.^{2} What is the static pressure?

3. An airplane is flying at 600 mph at an altitude where the static temperature is 0 F. What is the stagnation temperature of the air entering the engine?

4. Combustion gas leaves the nozzle of a rocket motor with a Mach number of 4. The pressure at this point is 10 lb/in.^{2} The specific heat ratio is 1.25. What is the nozzle inlet stagnation pressure for isentropic flow?

5. Combustion gas enters the nozzle of a rocket motor at stagnation conditions of 300 lb/in.^{2} and 5000R. The area and static pressure at this point are 2 in.^{2} and 270 lb/in.^{2} The molecular weight of the gas is 30, and the specific heat ratio is 1.25. (a) What is the mass flow rate? (b) What is the throat area for isentropic flow?

6. A turbojet nozzle is to be designed for an inlet Mach number of 0.4 and an exit Mach number of 1. The gas constant is 53 ft-lb/lb$_m$ R, and the specific heat ratio is 1.3. The mass flow rate is 100 lb$_m$/sec. The nozzle inlet stagnation conditions are 30 lb/in.^{2} and 1000F. (a) What is the nozzle exit area for isentropic flow? (b) What is the nozzle inlet area? (c) What is the nozzle exit pressure for isentropic flow?

7. A test of a turbojet engine gave the following data:

Ambient pressure	14 lb/in.^{2}
Ambient temperature	60F
Inlet static pressure	15 lb/in.^{2}
Inlet Mach number	0.4
Inlet specific heat ratio	1.4
Inlet area	2 ft^2
Exit static pressure	15 lb/in.^{2}
Exit Mach number	1.0
Exit specific heat ratio	1.3
Exit area	2 ft^2

(a) What is the internal thrust? (b) What is the net thrust?

8. An ideal rocket motor is designed for an exit Mach number of 4. The nozzle inlet stagnation conditions are 600 lb/in.^{2} and 5000F. The specific heat ratio is 1.2, and the nozzle throat area is 5 in.^{2} Ambient pressure is 5 lb/in.^{2} What is the net thrust?

9. Air is heated in a constant area duct. The inlet Mach number is 0.2, and the exit Mach number is 0.8. The inlet stagnation conditions are 30 lb/in.^{2} and 200F. Neglecting friction, what are the exit stagnation conditions? (Assume $\gamma = 1.35$.)

10. Air is heated in a constant area duct from stagnation conditions of 60 lb/in.^{2} and 300F and a Mach number of 0.23 to a temperature of 2000F. Neglecting friction, what are the exit stagnation pressure and Mach number? (Assume $\gamma = 1.35$.)

11. Air is flowing in an insulated duct. The inlet Mach number is 0.25. The friction factor is 0.01. The duct diameter is 6 in. (a) What length of pipe would give a 10 per cent loss in stagnation pressure? (b) What would be the exit Mach number in this case?

Chapter XIV

HEAT TRANSFER

14.1 Introduction

In preceding chapters the flow of heat has been considered in energy balances without regard to the means by which heat can actually be transferred. It has been stated that a temperature difference is necessary for heat transfer to occur between two bodies and that heat will flow in the direction of decreasing temperature. Nothing has been given, however, regarding the mechanism of heat transfer.

The field of heat transfer is becoming increasingly important to engineers who are concerned with problems relating to thermodynamics, and a brief introduction to the study of heat transfer will be presented in this chapter. While many problems of heat transfer in the unsteady, or transient, state, involving irregular geometries, are complex and beyond the scope of this book, simple cases of steady heat transfer can be easily handled and will be presented here.

The three principal types of heat transfer are conduction, convection, and radiation. In steady state heat transfer, the rate of heat flow being considered is constant at all times. If energy sources are not involved, an energy balance on the system under consideration will yield the result that the rate of heat entering the system by all types of heat transfer is equal to the rate of heat leaving the system by all types of heat transfer. That is,

$$(\dot{Q}_k + \dot{Q}_c + \dot{Q}_r)_{in} = (\dot{Q}_k + \dot{Q}_c + \dot{Q}_r)_{out} \quad \begin{array}{c} \text{(steady heat} \\ \text{transfer)} \end{array} \quad (14.1)$$

where the subscripts k, c, and r refer to conduction, convection, and radiation, respectively. These three types of heat transfer will be described in the following articles.

14.2 Conduction

The method by which heat is transferred within a substance at rest is called conduction and is a series type of energy transfer between adjacent molecules. The basic relation for the one-dimensional conduction of heat is

$$\dot{Q} = -kA\frac{dT}{dx} \tag{14.2}$$

where k is a property of the material called the thermal conductivity, A is the area normal to the direction of heat flow, and dT/dx is the rate of change of temperature with respect to the thickness of the material. The negative sign is used to indicate a positive heat flow in the direction of decreasing temperature. The conventional units for thermal conductivity in engineering heat transfer are B/hr-ft-F.

In general, the thermal conductivity is dependent on temperature for homogeneous materials. The variation of conductivity with temperature is not great for moderate temperature differences, and the conductivity will be considered constant for the applications shown in this chapter. Table 14-1 lists thermal conductivities for a variety of materials at normal temperatures.

TABLE 14-1

THERMAL CONDUCTIVITIES OF SOLIDS AT TEMPERATURES NEAR 100F

Material	Conductivity B/hr-ft-F
Cotton wool	0.01
Corkboard	0.025
Mineral wool	0.026
Balsa	0.040
Asbestos fiber	0.044
White pine	0.065
Fir	0.090
Gypsum plaster	0.30
Common brick	0.40
Concrete (average house construction)	0.80
Porcelain	0.95
Mild steel	26
Wrought iron	34.5
Yellow brass	52
Aluminum	118
Copper	220
Silver	242

14.3 Conduction through a plane wall

The simplest case of steady state heat conduction is that of heat transfer through a plane homogeneous wall. The notation for this

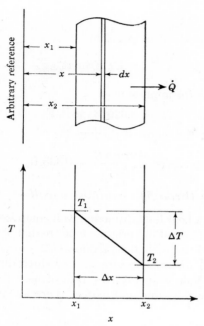

FIG. 14.1. CONDUCTION THROUGH PLANE WALL.

case is shown in Fig. 14.1. Heat is flowing in the direction shown, and the distances x_1 and x_2 are from an arbitrary reference.

The quantities $\dot{Q}$, k, and A in Eq. (14.2) are constant, and separation of the variables x and T gives

$$\dot{Q} \, dx = -kA \, dT \qquad (14.3a)$$

Integrating this expression between the limits x_1 and x_2 on the left and T_1 and T_2 on the right yields

$$\dot{Q}(x_2 - x_1) = -kA(T_2 - T_1) \qquad (14.3b)$$

This equation can be rearranged to give

$$\dot{Q} = -kA \frac{\Delta T}{\Delta x} \qquad \begin{array}{l} \text{(steady heat flow,} \\ \text{plane wall)} \end{array} \qquad (14.3)$$

where ΔT and ΔX are as shown in Fig. 14.1.

Example 14.1:

What thickness of mineral wool would be required to transmit 3.9 B/hr-ft² with a temperature drop of 50F?

Solution:

From the statement of the problem

$$\frac{\dot{Q}}{A} = 3.9 \text{ B/hr-ft}^2$$

From Table 14.1 for mineral wool

$$k = 0.026 \text{ B/hr-ft-F}$$

From Eq. (14.3) the required thickness is

$$\Delta x = \frac{0.026(50)}{3.9} = 0.333 \text{ ft}$$

14.4 Conduction through a composite wall

The steady-state heat flow through a wall composed of two or more parallel layers of different materials can be treated by first considering each of the layers individually. Figure 14.2 shows a temperature-thickness diagram for a composite wall of three different materials.

Since the heat flow is steady, the rate of heat flow through each of the materials is the same and perfect thermal contact is assumed

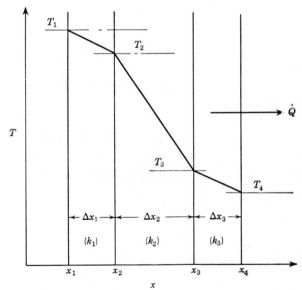

Fig. 14.2. Conduction through composite plane wall.

between adjacent materials. The heat balance is then

$$\dot{Q} = \dot{Q}_1 = \dot{Q}_2 = \dot{Q}_3 \tag{14.4a}$$

From Eq. (14.3) the temperature drop for each of the materials is

$$T_1 - T_2 = \frac{\dot{Q}(\Delta x)_1}{k_1 A} \tag{14.4b}$$

$$T_2 - T_3 = \frac{\dot{Q}_2(\Delta x)_2}{k_2 A} \tag{14.4c}$$

$$T_3 - T_4 = \frac{\dot{Q}_3(\Delta x)_3}{k_3 A} \tag{14.4d}$$

Making use of Eq. (14.4a), the sum of Eqs. (14.4b–14.4d) is

$$T_1 - T_4 = \frac{\dot{Q}}{A}\left[\frac{(\Delta x)_1}{k_1} + \frac{(\Delta x)_2}{k_2} + \frac{(\Delta x)_3}{k_3}\right] \tag{14.4e}$$

This equation may be rearranged to give

$$\dot{Q} = \frac{A(T_1 - T_4)}{[(\Delta x)_1/k_1] + [(\Delta x)_2/k_2] + [(\Delta x)_3/k_3]} \tag{14.4f}$$

For *n* materials Eq. (14.4f) would become

$$\dot{Q} = \frac{A(T_1 - T_{n+1})}{(\Delta x/k)_1 + (\Delta x/k)_2 + \cdots + (\Delta x/k)_n} \quad \begin{array}{l}\text{(steady heat flow} \\ \text{through com-} \\ \text{posite wall)}\end{array} \tag{14.4}$$

Example 14.2:

What is the rate of heat flow per square foot through a composite wall composed of 1 in. of gypsum plaster and 4 in. of mineral wool if the inner and outer surface temperatures are 85F and 30F?

Solution:

Using values of conductivity from Table 14.1 and Eq. (14.4), the heat flow is

$$\frac{\dot{Q}}{A} = \frac{12(85 - 30)}{(1/0.30) + (4/0.026)}$$

$$= 4.2 \text{ B/hr-ft}^2$$

14.5 Conduction through cylindrical walls

The steady state heat transfer through the walls of a circular cylinder may be analyzed by using the basic conduction equation

(14.2), replacing the variable x by the radius r, and making use of the relation between the area A and the radius at any distance from the center. Figure 14.3 is a diagram for the conduction through a homogeneous cylindrical wall.

The area normal to the heat flow in terms of the radius r is

$$A = 2\pi r L \tag{14.5a}$$

where L is the length of the cylinder. Substituting Eq. (14.5a) into Eq. (14.2) and changing variables gives

$$\dot{Q} = -2\pi L k r \frac{dT}{dr} \tag{14.5b}$$

Separating variables in this relation results in

$$\dot{Q} \frac{dr}{r} = -2\pi L k \; dT \tag{14.5c}$$

Integrating Eq. (14.5c) between the limits r_1 and r_2 on the left and T_1 and T_2 on the right, and rearranging, gives

$$\dot{Q} = \frac{2\pi L k(T_1 - T_2)}{\ln (r_2/r_1)} \tag{14.5}$$

Equation (14.5) shows that the temperature distribution in a cylinder is a logarithmic function of the radius, rather than a linear function of distance, which was the case with a plane wall.

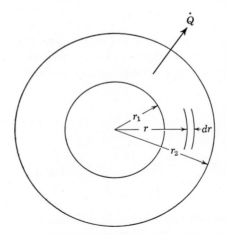

FIG. 14.3. CONDUCTION THROUGH CYLINDRICAL WALL.

Example 14.3:

Determine the rate of heat flow per foot of length for a 6.5-in. outside-diameter steam pipe jacketed with a 1-in. thickness of insulation having a conductivity of 0.06 B/hr-ft-F. The inner and outer surface temperatures of the insulation are 350F and 110F.

Solution:

From Eq. (14.5) the heat flow per unit length is

$$\frac{\dot{Q}}{L} = \frac{2\pi(0.06)(350 - 110)}{\ln(4.25/3.25)}$$

$$= 336 \text{ B/hr-ft}$$

The steady state heat flow through a composite cylindrical wall of n layers can be derived from Eq. (14.5) in a manner analogous to that leading up to Eq. (14.4) for a composite plane wall. The result is

$$\dot{Q} = \frac{2\pi L(T_1 - T_{n+1})}{\frac{1}{k_1}\ln\frac{r_2}{r_1} + \frac{1}{k_2}\ln\frac{r_3}{r_2} + \cdots \frac{1}{k_n}\ln\frac{r_{n+1}}{r_n}} \tag{14.6}$$

A typical temperature distribution for a composite cylindrical wall composed of three materials is shown in Fig. 14.4.

Example 14.4:

A jacketed, wrought-iron steam pipe has a wall thickness of 0.25 in. and an inside diameter of 5.5 in. The insulating jacket is 0.5 in. thick and has an outer surface temperature of 100F. The conductivities for the pipe and insulation are 34.5 and 0.05 B/hr-ft-F, respectively. The heat flow through 10 ft of pipe is 2000 B/hr. What is the inner surface temperature of the pipe?

Solution:

Solving Eq. (14.6) for the temperature drop gives

$$T_1 - T_3 = \frac{2000}{2\pi(10)}\left(\frac{1}{34.5}\ln\frac{3.00}{2.75} + \frac{1}{0.05}\ln\frac{3.5}{3.0}\right)$$

$$= 98.4\text{F}$$

The inner surface temperature is then

$$T_1 = 100 + 98.4 = 198.4\text{F}$$

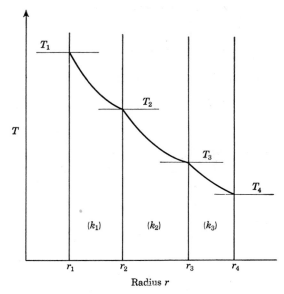

FIG. 14.4. TEMPERATURE DISTRIBUTION IN COMPOSITE CYLINDRICAL
WALL.

It will be noted in this example the pipe wall gives a negligible contribution to the total temperature drop.

14.6 Convection

The method by which heat is transferred from or to a solid body by a liquid or gas that is in motion relative to the solid body is called convection. Two types of convective heat transfer are recognized: natural, or free, convection, and forced convection. In free convection the motion of the fluid is caused by differences in density which occur in different regions of the fluid. In forced convection the motion of the fluid is caused by a mechanical fan or pump; or the relative motion between the solid body and the fluid may be caused by moving the solid body through the fluid as in the case of an airplane in flight.

The accepted relation for expressing heat transfer by convection is

$$\dot{Q} = HA(T_f - T_s) \tag{14.7}$$

where H = quantity called the convective heat transfer coefficient, or film coefficient

T_f = representative fluid temperature

T_s = surface temperature of solid body

The conventional units of the film coefficient H are B/hr-ft^2-F.

Equation (14.7) appears to be quite simple. The factors involved in the determination of the film coefficient H, however, are complex and depend on many fluid properties as well as the flow velocity, nature of the flow, and geometry and orientation of the solid body. For free convection, it has been found that the film coefficient can usually be determined from a relation of the form.[†]

$$H = C \frac{k}{L} \left(\frac{\rho V L}{\mu} \right)^a \left(\frac{L^3 \rho^2 \alpha g \, \Delta T}{\mu^2} \right)^b \qquad \text{(free convection)} \quad (14.8)$$

and for forced convection it has been found that the film coefficient can be obtained from a relation of the form

$$H = C \frac{k}{L} \left(\frac{\rho V L}{\mu} \right)^a \left(\frac{c_p \mu}{k} \right)^b \qquad \text{(forced convection)} \quad (14.9)$$

where C, a, and b = experimentally determined constants

k = thermal conductivity of the fluid

L = some characteristic dimension of the solid body

ρ = characteristic fluid density

μ = fluid viscosity

c_p = specific heat of the fluid

α = coefficient of thermal expansion of the fluid

g = acceleration due to gravity

ΔT = temperature difference given in Eq. (14.7).

The dimensionless quantities

$$\frac{HL}{k}, \quad \frac{\rho V L}{\mu}, \quad \frac{c_p \mu}{k}, \quad \frac{L^3 \rho^2 \alpha g \, \Delta T}{\mu^2}$$

are called Nusselt number, Reynolds number, Prandtl number, and Grashof number, respectively. These quantities occur in many problems of convective heat transfer.

A detailed study of convection is beyond the intended purpose of this chapter. Equations (14.8) and (14.9) have been introduced to

[†] See for example, M. Jakob and G. A. Hawkins, *Elements of Heat Transfer and Insulation*, 2nd ed., John Wiley & Sons, Inc., New York, 1950, Chaps VI, VII, VIII.

indicate the complexity and interrelation of the quantities upon which the film coefficient H depends.

Example 14.5:

The wall in Example 14.2 is heated by free convection of air at 90F. What is the film coefficient on the high-temperature side of the wall?

Solution:

Since the heat flow is steady, the rate of convective heat transfer must be equal to the rate of heat transfer by conduction. From Eq. (14.7) and the data of Example 14.2, the film coefficient is

$$H = \frac{4.2}{90 - 85}$$
$$= 0.84 \text{ B/hr-ft}^2\text{-F}$$

14.7 *Combined convection and conduction*

A great many cases of steady state heat transfer involve both convection and conduction, where a surface is heated or cooled by convection and heat is transferred internally to or from the surface by conduction. Heat transfer through the wall of a house is an example: heat enters the wall by free convection from air in the room, is transferred through the composite wall by conduction, and is transferred to the outside air by convection. Another example is the heat transfer in a power plant boiler: heat is transferred from the combustion gases to the boiler tubes by convection, either free or forced; it is transferred through the metal of the tubes by conduction; and it is transferred to the water within the tubes by forced convection. Devices such as steam power plant boilers and superheaters, automobile radiators, and refrigeration cooling coils are called heat exchangers and in general involve both convection and conduction.

The simplest case of combined convection and conduction is that of a plane wall with convection on both sides as shown in Fig. 14.5. Fluid a on the left is transferring heat to the wall by convection; the heat is transferred through the wall by conduction, and fluid b on the right is removing heat from the wall by convection. The rates of heat flow by conduction and convection must be equal in the

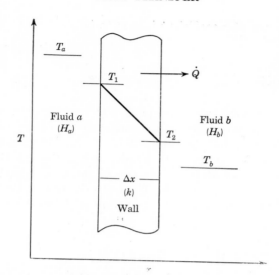

F<small>IG.</small> 14.5. D<small>IAGRAM FOR COMBINED CONVECTION AND CONDUCTION.</small>

steady state. Making use of Eqs. (14.7) and (14.3), the following relations may be written for the temperature differences:

$$T_a - T_1 = \frac{\dot{Q}}{A H_a} \tag{14.10a}$$

$$T_1 - T_2 = \frac{\dot{Q}\,\Delta x}{A k} \tag{14.10b}$$

$$T_2 - T_b = \frac{\dot{Q}}{A H_b} \tag{14.10c}$$

Taking the sum of these three equations and rearranging gives

$$\dot{Q} = \frac{A(T_a - T_b)}{(1/H_a) + (\Delta x/k) + (1/H_b)} \tag{14.10}$$

The heat balance for combined convection and conduction is frequently written in the form

$$\dot{Q} = U A(T_a - T_b) \tag{14.11}$$

where U is called the over-all heat transfer coefficient and has the same units as the film coefficient. For the simple case of convection on both sides of a plane wall, from Eqs. (14.10) and (14.11) the over-all heat transfer coefficient is seen to be

$$U = \left(\frac{1}{H_a} + \frac{\Delta x}{k} + \frac{1}{H_b}\right)^{-1} \quad \text{(Single plane wall)} \quad (14.12)$$

Example 14.6:

Heat is transferred through a plane wall with free convection on both sides of the wall. The thermal conductivity of the wall material is 0.040 B/hr-ft-F, and the wall is 1 in. thick. Air temperature on one side of the wall is 90F with a film coefficient of 2.5 B/hr-ft²-F. The air temperature on the other side of the wall is 30F, and the film coefficient is 2.0 B/hr-ft²-F. What are the rate of heat transfer per square foot of the wall and the over-all heat transfer coefficient?

Solution:

From Eq. (14.12) the over-all coefficient is

$$U = \left(\frac{1}{2.5} + \frac{1/12}{0.04} + \frac{1}{2}\right)^{-1}$$

$$= (0.40 + 2.08 + 0.5)^{-1}$$

$$= 0.335 \text{ B/hr-ft}^2\text{-F}$$

The rate of heat transfer per square foot from Eq. (14.11) is

$$\frac{\dot{Q}}{A} = 0.335(90 - 30) = 20.1 \text{ B/hr-ft}^2$$

14.8 Heat exchangers

Heat exchangers are a general class of devices, usually involving fluid flow through and around tubes or passages, whose purpose is to transfer heat from one fluid to another. Some examples of heat exchangers are power plant boilers and condensers, automobile radiators, aircraft oil coolers, and refrigeration coils. Five general classes of heat exchanger are:

1. Heat exchangers in which a fluid at constant temperature gives up heat to another fluid at a lower temperature. The temperature of the colder fluid increases as it passes through the exchanger. A steam condenser is an example of this type.

2. Heat exchangers in which a fluid at constant temperature receives heat from a fluid at a higher temperature. The temperature

of the hotter fluid decreases as it passes through the exchanger. A steam boiler is an example of this type.

3. Parallel flow heat exchangers in which both fluids pass through the device in the same direction and the temperature of the hotter fluid decreases while the temperature of the colder fluid increases from inlet to outlet.

4. Counterflow heat exchangers in which the fluids pass through the exchanger in opposite directions and the temperature of the hotter fluid decreases while the temperature of the colder fluid increases.

5. Crossflow heat exchangers in which one fluid flows at an angle to the other, usually at right angles, and the temperatures of both fluids change from inlet to outlet.

In all the above types of heat exchanger it will be noted that the temperature difference between the two fluids is not constant and the rate of heat transfer cannot be determined from Eq. (14.11) without some modification. This has led to the concept of the so-called "log mean temperature difference" which will be developed in the following article.

14.9 Log mean temperature difference

The log mean temperature difference can be der'ved for any of the first four classes of heat exchanger with the same result. The parallel flow heat exchanger will be chosen for the following derivation:

Consider a parallel flow heat exchanger in which heat is transferred from fluid a to fluid b through parallel tubes. Figure 14.6 is a schematic diagram of the variation of the fluid temperatures with surface area of the heat exchanger. The fluids enter on the left and leave on the right, and the area increases in the direction of flow.

From Eq. (14.11) the differential rate of heat flow at any location in the heat exchanger may be written

$$d\dot{Q} = U(T_a - T_b) \, dA \qquad (14.13a)$$

In terms of the heat energy removed from fluid a this same differential rate of heat flow is

$$d\dot{Q} = -\dot{w}_a c_{pa} \, dT_a \qquad (14.13b)$$

In terms of the heat energy added to fluid b this same differential rate of heat flow is

$$d\dot{Q} = \dot{w}_b c_{pb} \, dT_b \qquad (14.13c)$$

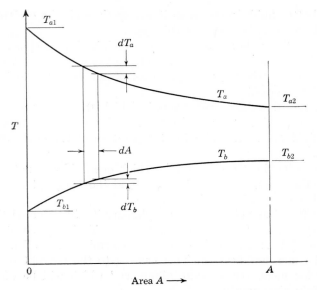

FIG. 14.6. TYPICAL TEMPERATURE DISTRIBUTION FOR PARALLEL FLOW HEAT EXCHANGER.

Combining Eqs. (14.13b) and (14.13c) and rearranging gives

$$dT_a - dT_b = d\dot{Q}\left(\frac{1}{\dot{w}_a c_{pa}} + \frac{1}{\dot{w}_b c_{pb}}\right) \tag{14.13d}$$

However, as shown in Fig. 14.6

$$dT_a - dT_b = d(T_a - T_b) \tag{14.13e}$$

Combining Eqs. (14.13a)–(14.13e) and rearranging results in

$$\frac{d(T_a - T_b)}{T_a - T_b} = \left(\frac{1}{\dot{w}_a c_{pa}} + \frac{1}{\dot{w}_b c_{pb}}\right) U \, dA \tag{14.13f}$$

This relation may be integrated between locations 1 and 2 to give

$$\ln\frac{(T_a - T_b)_2}{(T_a - T_b)_1} = \left(\frac{1}{\dot{w}_a c_{pa}} + \frac{1}{\dot{w}_b c_{pb}}\right) U_m A \tag{14.13g}$$

where U_m = mean value of U for the process
      A = total surface area

Integrating Eqs. (14.13b) and (14.13c) between locations 1 and 2 results in

$$\dot{Q} = -\dot{w}_a c_{pa}(T_{a2} - T_{a1}) \tag{14.13h}$$

$$\dot{Q} = w_b c_{pb}(T_{b2} - T_{b1}) \tag{14.13i}$$

Substituting Eqs. (14.13h) and (14.13i) in Eq. (14.13g) and rearranging gives

$$\dot{Q} = U_m A \frac{(T_a - T_b)_1 - (T_a - T_b)_2}{\ln \dfrac{(T_a - T_b)_1}{(T_a - T_b)_2}} \tag{14.13}$$

It is now possible to write Eq. (14.13) in the form

$$\dot{Q} = U_m A \, (\Delta T)_m \tag{14.14}$$

where the quantity $(\Delta T)_m$ is called the log mean temperature difference and is

$$(\Delta T)_m = \frac{(T_a - T_b)_1 - (T_a - T_b)_2}{\ln \dfrac{(T_a - T_b)_1}{(T_a - T_b)_2}} \tag{14.15}$$

One problem that arises in the use of Eq. (14.14) is the proper choice of the mean over-all heat transfer coefficient U_m. This coefficient will not in general be a constant for all locations in the heat exchanger but will depend on the fluid temperatures. The usual practice is to evaluate the film coefficients in the over-all heat transfer coefficient based on the average fluid temperatures. The values of U and $T_a - T_b$ will be most nearly constant in the case of counterflow heat exchangers.

Example 14.7:

A counterflow oil cooler has an average over-all heat transfer coefficient of 115 B/hr-ft²-F. Oil enters the cooler at 200F and leaves at 160F. The cooling air enters at 65F and leaves at 100F. What surface area is required to cool an oil flow of 140 lb_m/min if the specific heat of the oil is 0.8 B/lb_m F?

Solution:

The rate of heat flow is

$$\dot{Q} = 140(60)0.8(200 - 160)$$
$$= 268{,}800 \text{ B/hr}$$

The log mean temperature difference is

$$(\Delta T)_m = \frac{(200 - 100) - (160 - 65)}{\ln (100/95)}$$
$$= 113.1 \text{F}$$

The required area, from Eq. (14.11), is

$$A = \frac{268,800}{115(113.1F)} = 20.7 \text{ ft}^2$$

14.10 Radiation

Radiant heat transfer is an electromagnetic phenomenon similar to the transmission of light, X-rays, or radio waves. Radiant energy is transmitted at the speed of light (186,000 miles per second) and possesses some of the characteristics of wave motion although it may also be treated as though composed of particles of energy, called photons. Radiant heat transfer, unlike conduction, can pass through a medium such as air without heating it appreciably and is best transferred through a vacuum. It has been found that all substances emit radiant energy, and radiant heat transfer differs from light, X-rays, gamma-rays, and radio waves only in the wave length of the transmitted radiation.

In order to discuss the laws governing radiant heat transfer, it is necessary to define a "black body." A black body is a theoretical substance that will absorb without reflection all the radiant energy incident upon it in all wave lengths. Kirchhoff has shown that a black body is also a perfect emitter of radiant energy. While no true black body exists, it is possible to obtain "black" surfaces that will absorb up to 99 per cent of the incident radiation. The concept of a black body has been used to establish, both experimentally and theoretically, the Stefan-Boltzmann law of radiation. This law states that the rate of radiant energy per unit area emitted by a black body is equal to a constant times the fourth power of the absolute temperature of the body, that is,

$$\dot{Q} = A\sigma T^4 \qquad \text{(black body)} \qquad (14.16)$$

where σ is a physical constant equal to 0.174 $(10)^{-8}$ B/hr-ft^2-R^4, called the Stefan-Boltzmann constant.

While no true black body exists, the concept of a black body has been used to measure the radiating effectiveness of actual radiating surfaces. This radiating effectiveness is called the "emissivity" and is defined as the ratio of energy emitted from a body at a given temperature to the energy that would be emitted from a black body at the same temperature. In general, the emissivity of a surface is a function of temperature and wave length, but for many substances the emissivity is nearly constant at ordinary temperatures. Polished metallic surfaces have emissivities that increase roughly 100 per cent in the temperature range from 100 to 1000F, and the condition of the surface may greatly affect the emissivity. For example, smoothly polished steel at ordinary temperatures has an emissivity of approximately 0.07, while if the surface is oxidized, the emissivity may increase to as much as 0.80.

By making use of the definition of emissivity, the Stefan-Boltzmann law can be modified to account for the radiation actually emitted from a body as follows:

$$\dot{Q} = A \epsilon \sigma T^4 \tag{14.17}$$

where ϵ is the emissivity of the radiating body.

It can be shown that the percentage of the radiant energy incident upon a body that is absorbed by the body is equal to the emissivity of the absorbing surface.[†] That is, the absorptivity is equal to the emissivity for a body. A shiny surface, which reflects most of the energy incident upon it, therefore has a low absorptivity and emissivity.

14.11 Radiant heat transfer

The modified Stefan-Boltzmann law, Eq. (14.17), applies to the energy emitted by a body. The net heat transfer which takes place between two radiating bodies depends upon the ability of each body to emit and absorb radiation and upon the quantity of radiation emitted from each body that reaches the other body. Since radiation travels in straight lines and emanates equally in all unobstructed directions from all points on the radiating surface, the geometric factor involved in the net heat transfer between any two objects is extremely important. The determination of the geometrical factor for radiant heat transfer is often complicated, and only a few simple cases will be given here.

One of the simplest cases of net heat transfer by radiation is the idealized situation of two parallel black body surfaces that are infinite in extent and at different temperatures. Since the planes are assumed infinitely large, all the radiation emitted from each plane will be incident upon the other plane and the geometrical factor is

† See, for example, M. Jakob and G. A. Hawkins, *Elements of Heat Transfer and Insulation*, 2nd ed., John Wiley & Sons, Inc., New York, 1950, pp. 171–174.

unity. In this case the net heat transfer between the planes is the difference between the quantities of energy emitted by each plane and is

$$\dot{Q} = A\sigma(T_1^4 - T_2^4) \qquad \begin{array}{l}\text{(infinite black} \\ \text{parallel planes)}\end{array} \qquad (14.18)$$

If the planes are not black bodies but have different emissivities, ϵ_1 and ϵ_2, it has been shown that the interaction of the emissivities is such that the net heat transfer is

$$\dot{Q} = \frac{A\sigma(T_1^4 - T_2^4)}{(1/\epsilon_1) + (1/\epsilon_2) - 1} \qquad (14.19)$$

Example 14.8:

What is the radiant heat transfer per square foot between two large parallel planes whose emissivities are both 0.8 if the temperatures of the plates are 100 and 300F, respectively?

Solution:

From Eq. (14.19) the rate of heat transfer per square foot is

$$\frac{\dot{Q}}{A} = \frac{0.174(10)^{-8}(760^4 - 560^4)}{(1/0.8) + (1/0.8) - 1}$$

$$= 272 \text{ B/hr-ft}^2$$

A similar expression to Eq. (14.19) for concentric spheres or long coaxial cylinders is

$$\dot{Q} = \frac{A_1\sigma(T_1^4 - T_2^4)}{\dfrac{1}{\epsilon_1} + \dfrac{A_1}{A_2}\left(\dfrac{1}{\epsilon_2} - 1\right)} \qquad (14.20)$$

where A_1 and ϵ_1 apply to the interior sphere or cylinder. In the case where one sphere is much larger than the other the area ratio A_1/A_2 approaches zero, and the above expression becomes

$$\dot{Q} = A_1\epsilon_1\sigma(T_1^4 - T_2^4) \qquad (14.21)$$

Equation (14.21) may be used for any small convex object surrounded by a large concave enclosure.

Example 14.9:

An electric iron is at a temperature of 400F and has a surface area of 40 in.^{2} The iron is in a room whose walls are at a temperature of 70F. The emissivity of the iron is 0.1. What is the rate of radiant heat transfer between the iron and the room?

Solution:

From Eq. (14.21) the rate of heat transfer is

$$\dot{Q} = \frac{40}{144}\,(0.1)0.174(10)^{-8}(860^4 - 530^4)$$

$$= 20.4 \text{ B/hr}$$

PROBLEMS

1. What is the rate of heat transfer through a plane wall of mineral wool 8 ft $\times$ 16 ft $\times$ 3 in. if the surface temperatures are 80 and -5F?

2. What thickness of common brick has the insulating properties of 1 in. of white pine?

3. A composite wall is composed of $\frac{1}{2}$ in. of gypsum plaster, $3\frac{1}{2}$ in. of mineral wool, and $\frac{3}{4}$ in. of pine siding. What is the rate of heat transfer per square foot for a total temperature drop of 40F through the wall?

4. In Prob. 3, the inside plaster surface is 70F. What are the interface temperatures between the plaster and mineral wool and between the mineral wool and pine siding?

5. In Prob. 3, what thickness of mineral wool insulation would be required to reduce the heat flow by 50 per cent?

6. What is the rate of heat flow per foot through a 1-in. inside-diameter wrought-iron steam pipe whose outside diameter is 1.36 in. if the inner and outer wall temperatures are 186F and 185F?

7. A composite cylindrical wall has an inside diameter of 4 in. and an outside diameter of 6 in. The wall is composed of materials having conductivities of 10 and 0.1 B/hr-ft-F, with the higher conductivity on the inside. The inner and outer surface temperatures are 200F and 100F, and the rate of heat transfer is 342 B/hr-ft. What is the diameter at the interface between the two materials?

8. The wall in Prob. 1 is heated by natural convection of air at 85F; what is the film coefficient?

9. For turbulent flow in pipes, the constants C, a, and b in Eq. (14.9) are 0.023, 0.8, and 0.4, respectively. Determine the film coefficient for water flowing through a tube 1 in. in diameter if the following data apply:

Velocity	10 ft/sec
Density	1.94 slug/ft^3
Viscosity	0.078 slug/ft-hr
Specific heat	1 B/lb$_m$ F
Conductivity	0.34 B/hr-ft-F

10. Solve Prob. 9 if the tube diameter is $\frac{1}{2}$ in., all other data remaining unchanged.

11. A plane wall 6 in. thick has a conductivity of 1 B/hr-ft-F. Natural convection occurs on both sides of the wall and the film coefficients are 3 and 5, respectively, with corresponding temperatures of 60 and 20F. What is the over-all heat transfer coefficient?

12. What is the rate of heat transfer per square foot in Prob. 11?

13. Three inches of insulating material having a conductivity of 0.03 is added to the wall of Prob. 11. What is the rate of heat transfer per square foot?

14. A heat exchanger wall is made up of copper sheet $\frac{1}{8}$ in. thick. The film coefficients on each side are 500 and 1000 B/hr-ft^2-F. What is the over-all heat transfer coefficient?

15. What is the rate of heat transfer per square foot in Prob. 14 if the fluid temperatures are 200 and 60F, respectively?

16. Derive an expression for the over-all heat transfer coefficient based on the inner radius r_1 for heat transmission between two fluids, a and b, separated by a cylindrical wall of conductivity k and outer radius r_2 .

17. A parallel flow liquid-to-air heat exchanger is used to cool a hot liquid from 200F to 100F. Assuming cold air enters the exchanger at 30F and leaves at 85F, determine the log mean temperature difference for heat exchanger.

18. The mass rate of air flow through the heat exchanger of Prob. 17 is 10 lb$_m$/min, and the surface area is 10 ft^2. What is the over-all heat transfer coefficient?

19. What is the net radiant heat transfer per square foot between two large black parallel planes that are at temperatures of 100F and 300F?

20. Solve Prob. 19 if the emissivities of the plates are 0.85 and 0.7, respectively.

21. An oxidized iron pipe 2.3 in. in diameter passes through a room in which the room temperature is 72F. The surface temperature of the pipe is 274F, and the pipe is 20 ft long. What is the rate of radiant heat transfer between the pipe and the room?

APPENDIX

TABLE 1

Units

B   = British thermal unit
Cal = calorie
cm = centimeters
C   = degrees centigrade
ft   = feet
F   = degrees Fahrenheit
g   = grams
hr   = hours
in.   = inches
K   = degrees Kelvin
lb   = pounds force
lb_m = pounds mass
Mol = molar quantity
R   = degrees Rankine
sec = seconds

Symbols

		Units	American Standards Association Symbols
a	= acceleration	ft/sec^2	a
c	= speed of sound	ft/sec	a, c
c_n	= specific heat for general purposes	$B/lb_m\ F$	c_n
c_p	= specific heat at constant pressure	$B/lb_m\ F$	c_p
c_v	= specific heat at constant volume	$B/lb_m\ F$	c_v
C	= constant		C
F	= force		F, W
f	= friction coefficient (dimensionless)		f

Symbols (Con't)

			Units	*American Standards Association Symbols*
g	=	acceleration due to gravity	ft/sec^2	g
g_c	=	gravitational conversion factor	$lb_m ft/lb\ sec^2$	g_c
g_0	=	standard acceleration due to gravity	ft/sec^2	g_0
h	=	specific enthalpy	B/lb_m	h
$\bar{h}$	=	molar enthalpy	B/Mol	H, H_M
$\tilde{h}$	=	enthalpy	B	H, h
h_t	=	stagnation enthalpy	B/lb_m	
H	=	film coefficient	$B/hr\text{-}ft^2\text{-}F$	h
J	=	mechanical equivalent of heat	$ft\text{-}lb/B$	J
k	=	thermal conductivity	$B/ft\ sec\ F$	k, K
L	=	linear dimension	ft	l
m	=	mass	slugs	m, W
$\dot{m}$	=	mass rate	slugs/sec	w
M	=	molar quantity	lb_m/Mol	M
n	=	polytropic exponent (dimensionless)		n
N_M	=	Mach number (dimensionless)		M, N_M
P	=	pressure	lb/ft^2	p, P
P_t	=	stagnation pressure	lb/ft^2	
Q	=	heat per lb_m	B/lb_m	q, Q
$\bar{Q}$	=	molar heat	B/Mol	Q
$\tilde{Q}$	=	heat	B	Q
$\dot{Q}$	=	heat rate	B/sec	q
R	=	gas constant	$ft\text{-}lb/lb_m\ R$	R
$\bar{R}$	=	molar gas constant	$ft\text{-}lb/Mol\ R$	R_0
s	=	specific entropy	$B/lb_m\ R$	s
$\bar{s}$	=	molar entropy	$B/Mol\ R$	S, S_M
$\tilde{s}$	=	entropy	B/R	S
t	=	time	sec	t, τ, T
T	=	temperature	R	T, t
T_t	=	stagnation temperature	R	
u	=	specific internal energy	B/lb_m	u

Symbols (Con't)

			Units	*American Standards Association Symbols*
$\bar{u}$	=	molar internal energy	B/Mol	$U,\ U_M$
$\tilde{u}$	=	internal energy	B	U
U	=	overall heat transfer coefficient	B/hr-ft²-F	U
v	=	specific volume	ft³/lb$_m$	v
$\bar{v}$	=	molar volume	ft³/Mol	$V,\ V_M$
$\tilde{v}$	=	volume	ft³	$V,\ Q,\ v$
$\dot{v}$	=	volume rate	ft³/sec	$Q,\ q$
V	=	velocity	ft/sec	$v,\ u,\ V$
w	=	mass	lb$_m$	$W,\ m$
$\dot{w}$	=	mass rate	lb$_m$/sec	w
W	=	specific work	ft-lb/lb$_m$	$w,\ w_k$
$\overline{W}$	=	molar work	ft-lb/Mol	
$\tilde{W}$	=	work	ft-lb	W
$\dot{W}$	=	work rate, power	ft-lb/sec	P
x	=	distance	ft	$x,\ l$
X	=	quality (dimensionless)		x
y	=	elevation	ft	$y,\ h,\ z$
α	=	coefficient of thermal expansion	ft/ft-F	
β	=	coefficient of performance (dimensionless)		β
γ	=	specific heat ratio (dimensionless)		$\gamma,\ k$
ρ	=	density	slugs/ft³	$\rho,\ \gamma$
η	=	efficiency (dimensionless)		η
ϕ	=	entropy function	B/lb$_m$ R	
φ	=	relative humidity (dimensionless)		φ
σ	=	Stefan-Boltzmann constant	B/hr-ft²-R⁴	σ

TABLE 2. DRY SATURATED STEAM: TEMPERATURE TABLE*

Temp, F	Abs Press., Lb Sq In.	Specific Volume			Enthalpy			Entropy			Temp, F
		Sat. Liquid	Evap.	Sat. Vapor	Sat. Liquid	Evap.	Sat. Vapor	Sat. Liquid	Evap.	Sat. Vapor	
t	p	v_f	v_{fg}	v_g	h_f	h_{fg}	h_g	s_f	s_{fg}	s_g	t
32	0.08854	0.01602	3306	3306	0.00	1075.8	1075.8	0.0000	2.1877	2.1877	32
35	0.09995	0.01602	2947	2947	3.02	1074.1	1077.1	0.0061	2.1709	2.1770	35
40	0.12170	0.01602	2444	2444	8.05	1071.3	1079.3	0.0162	2.1435	2.1597	40
45	0.14752	0.01602	2036.4	2036.4	13.06	1068.4	1081.5	0.0262	2.1167	2.1429	45
50	0.17811	0.01603	1703.2	1703.2	18.07	1065.6	1083.7	0.0361	2.0903	2.1264	50
60	0.2563	0.01604	1206.6	1206.7	28.06	1059.9	1088.0	0.0555	2.0393	2.0948	60
70	0.3631	0.01606	867.8	867.9	38.04	1054.3	1092.3	0.0745	1.9902	2.0647	70
80	0.5069	0.01608	633.1	633.1	48.02	1048.6	1096.6	0.0932	1.9428	2.0360	80
90	0.6982	0.01610	468.0	468.0	57.99	1042.9	1100.9	0.1115	1.8972	2.0087	90
100	0.9492	0.01613	350.3	350.4	67.97	1037.2	1105.2	0.1295	1.8531	1.9826	100
110	1.2748	0.01617	265.3	265.4	77.94	1031.6	1109.5	0.1471	1.8106	1.9577	110
120	1.6924	0.01620	203.25	203.27	87.92	1025.8	1113.7	0.1645	1.7694	1.9339	120
130	2.2225	0.01625	157.32	157.34	97.90	1020.0	1117.9	0.1816	1.7296	1.9112	130
140	2.8886	0.01629	122.99	123.01	107.89	1014.1	1122.0	0.1984	1.6910	1.8894	140
150	3.718	0.01634	97.06	97.07	117.89	1008.2	1126.1	0.2149	1.6537	1.8685	150
160	4.741	0.01639	77.27	77.29	127.89	1002.3	1130.2	0.2311	1.6174	1.8485	160
170	5.992	0.01645	62.04	62.06	137.90	996.3	1134.2	0.2472	1.5822	1.8293	170
180	7.510	0.01651	50.21	50.23	147.92	990.2	1138.1	0.2630	1.5480	1.8109	180
190	9.339	0.01657	40.94	40.96	157.95	984.1	1142.0	0.2785	1.5147	1.7932	190
200	11.526	0.01663	33.62	33.64	167.99	977.9	1145.9	0.2938	1.4824	1.7762	200
210	14.123	0.01670	27.80	27.82	178.05	971.6	1149.7	0.3090	1.4508	1.7598	210
212	14.696	0.01672	26.78	26.80	180.07	970.3	1150.4	0.3120	1.4446	1.7566	212
220	17.186	0.01677	23.13	23.15	188.13	965.2	1153.4	0.3239	1.4201	1.7440	220
230	20.780	0.01684	19.365	19.382	198.23	958.8	1157.0	0.3387	1.3901	1.7288	230
240	24.969	0.01692	16.306	16.323	208.34	952.2	1160.5	0.3531	1.3609	1.7140	240
250	29.825	0.01700	13.804	13.821	216.48	945.5	1164.0	0.3675	1.3323	1.6998	250
260	35.429	0.01709	11.746	11.763	228.64	938.7	1167.3	0.3817	1.3043	1.6860	260
270	41.858	0.01717	10.044	10.061	238.84	931.8	1170.6	0.3958	1.2769	1.6727	270
280	49.203	0.01726	8.628	8.645	249.06	924.7	1173.8	0.4096	1.2501	1.6597	280
290	57.556	0.01735	7.444	7.461	259.31	917.5	1176.8	0.4234	1.2238	1.6472	290

t	p	v_f	v_fg	v_g	h_f	h_fg	h_g	s_f	s_fg	s_g	t
300	67.013	0.01745	6.449	6.466	269.59	910.1	1179.7	0.4369	1.1980	1.6350	300
310	77.68	0.01755	5.609	5.626	279.92	902.6	1182.5	0.4504	1.1727	1.6231	310
320	89.66	0.01765	4.896	4.914	290.28	894.9	1185.2	0.4637	1.1478	1.6115	320
330	103.06	0.01776	4.289	4.307	300.68	887.0	1187.7	0.4769	1.1233	1.6002	330
340	118.01	0.01787	3.770	3.788	311.13	879.0	1190.1	0.4900	1.0992	1.5892	340
350	134.63	0.01799	3.324	3.342	321.63	870.7	1192.3	0.5029	1.0754	1.5783	350
360	153.04	0.01811	2.939	2.957	332.18	862.2	1194.4	0.5158	1.0519	1.5677	360
370	173.37	0.01823	2.606	2.625	342.79	853.5	1196.3	0.5286	1.0287	1.5573	370
380	195.77	0.01836	2.317	2.335	353.45	844.6	1198.1	0.5413	1.0059	1.5471	380
390	220.37	0.01850	2.0651	2.0836	364.17	835.4	1199.6	0.5539	0.9832	1.5371	390
400	247.31	0.01864	1.8447	1.8633	374.97	826.0	1201.0	0.5664	0.9608	1.5272	400
410	276.75	0.01878	1.6512	1.6700	385.83	816.3	1202.1	0.5788	0.9386	1.5174	410
420	308.83	0.01894	1.4811	1.5000	396.77	806.3	1203.1	0.5912	0.9166	1.5078	420
430	343.72	0.01910	1.3308	1.3499	407.79	796.0	1203.8	0.6035	0.8947	1.4982	430
440	381.59	0.01926	1.1979	1.2171	418.90	785.4	1204.3	0.6158	0.8730	1.4887	440
450	422.6	0.0194	1.0799	1.0993	430.1	774.5	1204.6	0.6280	0.8513	1.4793	450
460	466.9	0.0196	0.9748	0.9944	441.4	763.2	1204.6	0.6402	0.8298	1.4700	460
470	514.7	0.0198	0.8811	0.9009	452.8	751.5	1204.3	0.6523	0.8083	1.4606	470
480	566.1	0.0200	0.7972	0.8172	464.4	739.4	1203.7	0.6645	0.7868	1.4513	480
490	621.4	0.0202	0.7221	0.7423	476.0	726.8	1202.8	0.6766	0.7653	1.4419	490
500	680.8	0.0204	0.6545	0.6749	487.8	713.9	1201.7	0.6887	0.7438	1.4325	500
520	812.4	0.0209	0.5385	0.5594	511.9	686.4	1198.2	0.7130	0.7006	1.4136	520
540	962.5	0.0215	0.4434	0.4649	536.6	656.6	1193.2	0.7374	0.6568	1.3942	540
560	1133.1	0.0221	0.3647	0.3868	562.2	624.2	1186.4	0.7621	0.6121	1.3742	560
580	1325.8	0.0228	0.2989	0.3217	588.9	588.4	1177.3	0.7872	0.5659	1.3532	580
600	1542.9	0.0236	0.2432	0.2668	617.0	548.5	1165.5	0.8131	0.5176	1.3307	600
620	1786.6	0.0247	0.1955	0.2201	646.7	503.6	1150.3	0.8398	0.4664	1.3062	620
640	2059.7	0.0260	0.1538	0.1798	678.6	452.0	1130.5	0.8679	0.4110	1.2789	640
660	2365.4	0.0278	0.1165	0.1442	714.2	390.2	1104.4	0.8987	0.3485	1.2472	660
680	2708.1	0.0305	0.0810	0.1115	757.3	309.9	1067.2	0.9351	0.2719	1.2071	680
700	3093.7	0.0369	0.0392	0.0761	823.3	172.1	995.4	0.9905	0.1484	1.1389	700
705.4	3206.2	0.0503	0	0.0503	902.7	0	902.7	1.0580	0	1.0580	705.4

* Abridged from *Thermodynamic Properties of Steam*, by Joseph H. Keenan and Frederick G. Keyes: John Wiley & Sons, Inc., New York, 1936.

TABLE 3. DRY SATURATED STEAM: PRESSURE TABLE*

Abs Press., Lb Sq In. p	Temp., F t	Specific Volume Sat. Liquid v_f	Specific Volume Sat. Vapor v_g	Enthalpy Sat. Liquid h_f	Enthalpy Evap h_{fg}	Enthalpy Sat. Vapor h_g	Entropy Sat. Liquid s_f	Entropy Evap s_{fg}	Entropy Sat. Vapor s_g	Internal Energy Sat. Liquid u_f	Internal Energy Sat. Vapor u_g	Abs Press., Lb Sq In. p
1.0	101.74	0.01614	333.6	69.70	1036.3	1106.0	0.1326	1.8456	1.9782	69.70	1044.3	1.0
2.0	126.08	0.01623	173.73	93.99	1022.2	1116.2	0.1749	1.7451	1.9200	93.98	1051.9	2.0
3.0	141.48	0.01630	118.71	109.37	1013.2	1122.6	0.2008	1.6855	1.8863	109.36	1056.7	3.0
4.0	152.97	0.01636	90.63	120.86	1006.4	1127.3	0.2198	1.6427	1.8625	120.85	1060.2	4.0
5.0	162.24	0.01640	73.52	130.13	1001.0	1131.1	0.2347	1.6094	1.8441	130.12	1063.1	5.0
6.0	170.06	0.01645	61.98	137.96	996.2	1134.2	0.2472	1.5820	1.8292	137.94	1065.4	6.0
7.0	176.85	0.01649	53.64	144.76	992.1	1136.9	0.2581	1.5586	1.8167	144.74	1067.4	7.0
8.0	182.86	0.01653	47.34	150.79	988.5	1139.3	0.2674	1.5383	1.8057	150.77	1069.2	8.0
9.0	188.28	0.01656	42.40	156.22	985.2	1141.4	0.2759	1.5203	1.7962	156.19	1070.8	9.0
10	193.21	0.01659	38.42	161.17	982.1	1143.3	0.2835	1.5041	1.7876	161.14	1072.2	10
14.696	212.00	0.01672	26.80	180.07	970.3	1150.4	0.3120	1.4446	1.7566	180.02	1077.5	14.696
15	213.03	0.01672	26.29	181.11	969.7	1150.8	0.3135	1.4415	1.7549	181.06	1077.8	15
20	227.96	0.01683	20.089	196.16	960.1	1156.3	0.3356	1.3962	1.7319	196.10	1081.9	20
25	240.07	0.01692	16.303	208.42	952.1	1160.6	0.3533	1.3606	1.7139	208.34	1085.1	25
30	250.33	0.01701	13.746	218.82	945.3	1164.1	0.3680	1.3313	1.6993	218.73	1087.8	30
35	259.28	0.01778	11.898	227.91	939.2	1167.1	0.3807	1.3063	1.6870	227.80	1090.1	35
40	267.25	0.01715	10.498	236.03	933.7	1169.7	0.3919	1.2844	1.6763	235.90	1092.0	40
45	274.44	0.01721	9.401	243.36	928.6	1172.0	0.4019	1.2650	1.6669	243.22	1093.7	45
50	281.01	0.01727	8.515	250.09	924.0	1174.1	0.4110	1.2474	1.6585	249.93	1095.3	50
55	287.07	0.01732	7.787	256.30	919.6	1175.9	0.4193	1.2316	1.6509	256.12	1096.7	55
60	292.71	0.01738	7.175	262.09	915.5	1177.6	0.4270	1.2168	1.6438	261.90	1097.9	60
65	297.97	0.01743	6.655	267.50	911.6	1179.1	0.4342	1.2032	1.6374	267.29	1099.1	65
70	302.92	0.01748	6.206	272.61	907.9	1180.6	0.4409	1.1906	1.6315	272.38	1100.2	70
75	307.60	0.01753	5.816	277.43	904.5	1181.9	0.4472	1.1787	1.6259	277.19	1101.2	75
80	312.03	0.01757	5.472	282.02	901.1	1183.1	0.4531	1.1676	1.6207	281.76	1102.1	80
85	316.25	0.01761	5.168	286.39	897.8	1184.2	0.4587	1.1571	1.6158	286.11	1102.9	85
90	320.27	0.01766	4.896	290.56	894.7	1185.3	0.4641	1.1471	1.6112	290.27	1103.7	90
95	324.12	0.01770	4.652	294.56	891.7	1186.2	0.4692	1.1376	1.6068	294.25	1104.5	95
100	327.81	0.01774	4.432	298.40	888.8	1187.2	0.4740	1.1286	1.6026	298.08	1105.2	100
110	334.77	0.01782	4.049	305.66	883.2	1188.9	0.4832	1.1117	1.5948	305.30	1106.5	110

Press	Temp	v_f	v_g	h_f	h_{fg}	h_g	s_f	s_{fg}	s_g	u_f	u_g	Press
120	341.25	0.01789	3.728	312.44	877.9	1190.4	0.4916	1.0962	1.5878	312.05	1107.6	120
130	347.32	0.01796	3.455	318.81	872.9	1191.7	0.4995	1.0817	1.5812	318.38	1108.6	130
140	353.02	0.01802	3.220	324.82	868.2	1193.0	0.5069	1.0682	1.5751	324.35	1109.6	140
150	358.42	0.01809	3.015	330.51	863.6	1194.1	0.5138	1.0556	1.5694	330.01	1110.5	150
160	363.53	0.01815	2.834	335.93	859.2	1195.1	0.5204	1.0436	1.5640	335.39	1111.2	160
170	368.41	0.01822	2.675	341.09	854.9	1196.0	0.5266	1.0324	1.5590	340.52	1111.9	170
180	373.06	0.01827	2.532	346.03	850.8	1196.9	0.5325	1.0217	1.5542	345.42	1112.5	180
190	377.51	0.01833	2.404	350.79	846.8	1197.6	0.5381	1.0116	1.5497	350.15	1113.1	190
200	381.79	0.01839	2.288	355.36	843.0	1198.4	0.5435	1.0018	1.5453	354.68	1113.7	200
250	400.95	0.01865	1.9438	376.00	825.1	1201.1	0.5675	0.9588	1.5263	375.14	1115.8	250
300	417.33	0.01890	1.5433	393.84	809.0	1202.8	0.5879	0.9225	1.5104	392.79	1117.1	300
350	431.72	0.01913	1.3260	409.69	794.2	1203.9	0.6056	0.8910	1.4966	408.45	1118.0	350
400	444.59	0.0193	1.1613	424.0	780.5	1204.5	0.6214	0.8630	1.4844	422.6	1118.5	400
450	456.28	0.0195	1.0320	437.2	767.4	1204.6	0.6356	0.8378	1.4734	435.5	1118.7	450
500	467.01	0.0197	0.9278	449.4	755.0	1204.4	0.6487	0.8147	1.4634	447.6	1118.6	500
550	476.94	0.0199	0.8424	460.8	743.1	1203.9	0.6608	0.7934	1.4542	458.8	1118.2	550
600	486.21	0.0201	0.7698	471.6	731.6	1203.2	0.6720	0.7734	1.4454	469.4	1117.7	600
650	494.90	0.0203	0.7083	481.8	720.5	1202.3	0.6826	0.7548	1.4374	479.4	1117.1	650
700	503.10	0.0205	0.6554	491.5	709.7	1201.2	0.6925	0.7371	1.4296	488.8	1116.3	700
750	510.86	0.0207	0.6092	500.8	699.2	1200.0	0.7019	0.7204	1.4223	498.0	1115.4	750
800	518.23	0.0209	0.5687	509.7	688.9	1198.6	0.7108	0.7045	1.4153	506.6	1114.4	800
850	525.26	0.0210	0.5327	518.3	678.8	1197.1	0.7194	0.6891	1.4085	515.0	1113.3	850
900	531.98	0.0212	0.5006	526.6	668.8	1195.4	0.7275	0.6744	1.4020	523.1	1112.1	900
950	538.43	0.0214	0.4717	534.6	659.1	1193.7	0.7355	0.6602	1.3957	530.9	1110.8	950
1000	544.61	0.0216	0.4456	542.4	649.4	1191.8	0.7430	0.6467	1.3897	538.4	1109.4	1000
1100	556.31	0.0220	0.4001	557.4	630.4	1187.8	0.7575	0.6205	1.3780	552.9	1106.4	1100
1200	567.22	0.0223	0.3619	571.7	611.7	1183.4	0.7711	0.5956	1.3667	566.7	1103.0	1200
1300	577.46	0.0227	0.3293	585.4	593.2	1178.6	0.7840	0.5719	1.3559	580.0	1099.4	1300
1400	587.10	0.0231	0.3012	598.7	574.7	1173.4	0.7963	0.5491	1.3454	592.7	1095.4	1400
1500	596.23	0.0235	0.2765	611.6	556.3	1167.9	0.8082	0.5269	1.3351	605.1	1091.2	1500
2000	635.82	0.0257	0.1878	671.7	463.4	1135.1	0.8619	0.4230	1.2849	662.2	1065.6	2000
2500	668.13	0.0287	0.1307	730.6	360.5	1091.1	0.9126	0.3197	1.2322	717.3	1030.6	2500
3000	695.36	0.0346	0.0858	802.5	217.8	1020.3	0.9731	0.1885	1.1615	783.4	972.7	3000
3206.2	705.40	0.0503	0.0503	902.7	0	902.7	1.0580		1.0580	872.9	872.9	3206.2

* Abridged from *Thermodynamic Properties of Steam*, by Joseph H. Keenan and Frederick G. Keyes; John Wiley & Sons, Inc., New York, 1936.

TABLE 4. PROPERTIES OF SUPERHEATED STEAM*

Abs Press, Lb Sq In. (Sat. Temp.)		Temperature—Degrees Fahrenheit												
		200	300	400	500	600	700	800	900	1000	1100	1200	1400	1600
1 (101.74)	v	392.6	452.3	512.0	571.6	631.2	690.8	750.4	809.9	869.5	929.1	988.7	1107.8	1227.0
	h	1150.4	1195.8	1241.7	1288.3	1335.7	1383.8	1432.8	1482.7	1533.5	1585.2	1637.7	1745.7	1857.5
	s	2.0512	2.1153	2.1720	2.2233	2.2702	2.3137	2.3542	2.3923	2.4283	2.4625	2.4952	2.5566	2.6137
5 (162.24)	v	78.16	90.25	102.26	114.22	126.16	138.10	150.03	161.95	173.87	185.79	197.71	221.6	245.4
	h	1148.8	1195.0	1241.0	1288.0	1335.4	1383.6	1432.7	1482.6	1533.4	1585.1	1637.7	1745.5	1857.4
	s	1.8718	1.9370	1.9942	2.0456	2.0927	2.1361	2.1767	2.2148	2.2509	2.2851	2.3178	2.3792	2.4363
10 (193.21)	v	38.85	45.00	51.04	57.05	63.03	69.01	74.98	80.95	86.92	92.88	98.84	110.77	122.69
	h	1146.6	1193.9	1240.6	1287.5	1335.1	1383.4	1432.5	1482.4	1533.2	1585.0	1637.6	1745.6	1857.3
	s	1.7927	1.8595	1.9172	1.9689	2.0160	2.0596	2.1002	2.1383	2.1744	2.2086	2.2413	2.3028	2.3598
14.696 (212.00)	v		30.53	34.68	38.78	42.86	46.94	51.00	55.07	59.13	63.19	67.25	75.37	83.48
	h		1192.8	1239.9	1287.1	1334.8	1383.2	1432.3	1482.3	1533.1	1584.8	1637.5	1745.5	1857.3
	s		1.8160	1.8743	1.9261	1.9734	2.0170	2.0576	2.0958	2.1319	2.1662	2.1989	2.2603	2.3174
20 (227.96)	v		22.36	25.43	28.46	31.47	34.47	37.46	40.45	43.44	46.42	49.41	55.37	61.34
	h		1191.6	1239.2	1286.6	1334.4	1382.9	1432.1	1482.1	1533.0	1584.7	1637.4	1745.4	1857.2
	s		1.7808	1.8396	1.8918	1.9392	1.9829	2.0235	2.0618	2.0978	2.1321	2.1648	2.2263	2.2834
40 (267.25)	v		11.040	12.628	14.168	15.688	17.198	18.702	20.20	21.70	23.20	24.69	27.68	30.66
	h		1186.8	1236.5	1284.8	1333.1	1381.9	1431.4	1481.4	1532.4	1584.3	1637.0	1745.1	1857.0
	s		1.6994	1.7608	1.8140	1.8619	1.9058	1.9467	1.9850	2.0212	2.0555	2.0883	2.1498	2.2069
60 (292.71)	v		7.259	8.357	9.403	10.427	11.441	12.449	13.452	14.454	15.453	16.451	18.446	20.44
	h		1181.6	1233.6	1283.0	1331.8	1380.9	1430.5	1480.8	1531.9	1583.8	1636.6	1744.8	1856.7
	s		1.6492	1.7135	1.7678	1.8162	1.8605	1.9015	1.9400	1.9762	2.0106	2.0434	2.1049	2.1621
80 (312.03)	v			6.220	7.020	7.797	8.562	9.322	10.077	10.830	11.582	12.332	13.830	15.325
	h			1230.7	1281.1	1330.5	1379.9	1429.7	1480.1	1531.3	1583.4	1636.2	1744.5	1856.5
	s			1.6791	1.7346	1.7836	1.8281	1.8694	1.9079	1.9442	1.9787	2.0115	2.0731	2.1303
100 (327.81)	v			4.937	5.589	6.218	6.835	7.446	8.052	8.656	9.259	9.860	11.060	12.258
	h			1227.6	1279.1	1329.1	1378.9	1428.9	1479.5	1530.8	1583.0	1635.7	1744.2	1856.2
	s			1.6518	1.7085	1.7581	1.8029	1.8443	1.8829	1.9193	1.9538	1.9867	2.0484	2.1056
120 (341.25)	v			4.081	4.636	5.165	5.683	6.195	6.702	7.207	7.710	8.212	9.214	10.213
	h			1224.4	1277.2	1327.7	1377.8	1428.1	1478.8	1530.2	1582.4	1635.3	1743.9	1856.0
	s			1.6287	1.6869	1.7370	1.7822	1.8237	1.8625	1.8990	1.9335	1.9664	2.0281	2.0854

P (t sat)														
140 (353.02)	v	.....	.....	3.468	3.954	4.413	4.861	5.301	5.738	6.172	6.604	7.035	7.895	8.752
	h	.....	.....	1221.1	1275.2	1326.4	1376.8	1427.3	1478.2	1529.7	1581.9	1634.9	1743.5	1855.7
	s	.....	.....	1.6087	1.6683	1.7190	1.7645	1.8063	1.8451	1.8817	1.9163	1.9493	2.0110	2.0683
160 (363.53)	v	.....	.....	3.008	3.443	3.849	4.244	4.631	5.015	5.396	5.775	6.152	6.906	7.656
	h	.....	.....	1217.6	1273.1	1325.0	1375.7	1426.6	1477.5	1529.1	1581.4	1634.5	1743.2	1855.5
	s	.....	.....	1.5908	1.6519	1.7033	1.7491	1.7911	1.8301	1.8667	1.9014	1.9344	1.9962	2.0535
180 (373.06)	v	.....	.....	2.649	3.044	3.411	3.764	4.110	4.452	4.792	5.129	5.466	6.136	6.804
	h	.....	.....	1214.0	1271.0	1323.5	1374.7	1425.6	1476.8	1528.6	1581.0	1634.1	1742.9	1855.2
	s	.....	.....	1.5745	1.6373	1.6894	1.7355	1.7776	1.8167	1.8534	1.8882	1.9212	1.9831	2.0404
200 (381.79)	v	.....	.....	2.361	2.726	3.060	3.380	3.693	4.002	4.309	4.613	4.917	5.521	6.123
	h	.....	.....	1210.3	1268.9	1322.1	1373.6	1424.8	1476.2	1528.0	1580.5	1633.7	1742.6	1855.0
	s	.....	.....	1.5594	1.6240	1.6767	1.7232	1.7655	1.8048	1.8415	1.8763	1.9094	1.9713	2.0287
220 (389.86)	v	.....	.....	2.125	2.465	2.772	3.066	3.352	3.634	3.913	4.191	4.467	5.017	5.565
	h	.....	.....	1206.5	1266.7	1320.7	1372.6	1424.0	1475.5	1527.5	1580.0	1633.3	1742.3	1854.7
	s	.....	.....	1.5453	1.6117	1.6652	1.7120	1.7545	1.7939	1.8308	1.8656	1.8987	1.9607	2.0181
240 (397.37)	v	.....	.....	1.9276	2.247	2.533	2.804	3.068	3.327	3.584	3.839	4.093	4.597	5.100
	h	.....	.....	1202.5	1264.5	1319.2	1371.5	1423.2	1474.8	1526.9	1579.6	1632.9	1742.0	1854.5
	s	.....	.....	1.5319	1.6003	1.6546	1.7017	1.7444	1.7839	1.8209	1.8558	1.8889	1.9510	2.0084
260 (404.42)	v	.....	.....	.....	2.063	2.330	2.582	2.827	3.067	3.305	3.541	3.776	4.242	4.707
	h	.....	.....	.....	1262.3	1317.7	1370.4	1422.3	1474.2	1526.3	1579.1	1632.5	1741.7	1854.2
	s	.....	.....	.....	1.5897	1.6447	1.6922	1.7332	1.7748	1.8118	1.8467	1.8799	1.9420	1.9995
280 (411.05)	v	.....	.....	.....	1.9047	2.156	2.392	2.621	2.845	3.066	3.286	3.504	3.938	4.370
	h	.....	.....	.....	1260.0	1316.2	1369.4	1421.5	1473.5	1525.8	1578.6	1632.1	1741.4	1854.0
	s	.....	.....	.....	1.5796	1.6354	1.6834	1.7265	1.7662	1.8033	1.8383	1.8716	1.9337	1.9912
300 (417.33)	v	.....	.....	.....	1.7675	2.005	2.227	2.442	2.652	2.859	3.065	3.269	3.674	4.078
	h	.....	.....	.....	1257.6	1314.7	1368.3	1420.6	1472.8	1525.2	1578.1	1631.7	1741.0	1853.7
	s	.....	.....	.....	1.5701	1.6268	1.6751	1.7184	1.7582	1.7954	1.8305	1.8638	1.9260	1.9835
350 (431.72)	v	.....	.....	.....	1.4923	1.7036	1.8980	2.084	2.266	2.445	2.622	2.798	3.147	3.493
	h	.....	.....	.....	1251.5	1310.9	1365.5	1418.5	1471.1	1523.8	1577.0	1630.7	1740.3	1853.1
	s	.....	.....	.....	1.5481	1.6070	1.6563	1.7002	1.7403	1.7777	1.8130	1.8463	1.9086	1.9663
400 (444.59)	v	.....	.....	.....	1.2851	1.4770	1.6508	1.8161	1.9767	2.134	2.290	2.445	2.751	3.055
	h	.....	.....	.....	1245.1	1306.9	1362.7	1416.4	1469.4	1522.4	1575.8	1629.6	1739.5	1852.5
	s	.....	.....	.....	1.5281	1.5594	1.6398	1.6842	1.7247	1.7623	1.7977	1.8311	1.8936	1.9513

* Abridged from *Thermodynamic Properties of Steam*, by Joseph H. Keenan and Frederick G. Keyes: John Wiley & Sons, Inc., New York, 1936.

TABLE 4. PROPERTIES OF SUPERHEATED STEAM (Cont'd)*

Abs Press. Lb Sq In. (Sat. Temp.)		500	550	600	620	640	669	680	700	800	900	1000	1200	1400	1600
450 (456.28)	v	1.1231	1.2155	1.3005	1.3332	1.3652	1.3967	1.4278	1.4584	1.6074	1.7516	1.8928	2.170	2.443	2.714
	h	1238.4	1272.0	1302.8	1314.6	1326.2	1337.5	1348.8	1359.9	1414.3	1467.7	1521.0	1628.6	1738.7	1851.9
	s	1.5095	1.5437	1.5735	1.5845	1.5961	1.6054	1.6153	1.6250	1.6699	1.7108	1.7486	1.8177	1.8803	1.9381
500 (467.01)	v	0.9927	1.0800	1.1591	1.1893	1.2188	1.2478	1.2763	1.3044	1.4405	1.5715	1.6996	1.9504	2.197	2.442
	h	1231.3	1266.8	1298.6	1310.7	1322.6	1334.2	1345.7	1357.0	1412.1	1466.0	1519.6	1627.6	1737.9	1851.3
	s	1.4919	1.5280	1.5588	1.5701	1.5810	1.5915	1.6016	1.6115	1.6571	1.6982	1.7363	1.8056	1.8683	1.9262
550 (476.94)	v	0.8852	0.9686	1.0431	1.0714	1.0989	1.1259	1.1523	1.1783	1.3038	1.4241	1.5414	1.7706	1.9957	2.219
	h	1223.7	1261.2	1294.3	1306.8	1318.9	1330.8	1342.5	1354.0	1409.9	1464.3	1518.2	1626.6	1737.1	1850.6
	s	1.4751	1.5131	1.5451	1.5568	1.5680	1.5787	1.5890	1.5991	1.6452	1.6868	1.7250	1.7946	1.8575	1.9155
600 (486.21)	v	0.7947	0.8753	0.9463	0.9729	0.9988	1.0241	1.0489	1.0732	1.1899	1.3013	1.4096	1.6208	1.8279	2.033
	h	1215.7	1255.5	1289.9	1302.7	1315.2	1327.4	1339.3	1351.1	1407.7	1462.5	1516.7	1625.5	1736.3	1850.0
	s	1.4586	1.4990	1.5323	1.5443	1.5558	1.5667	1.5773	1.5875	1.6343	1.6762	1.7147	1.7846	1.8476	1.9056
700 (503.10)	v		0.7277	0.7934	0.8177	0.8411	0.8639	0.8860	0.9077	1.0108	1.1082	1.2024	1.3853	1.5641	1.7405
	h		1243.2	1280.6	1294.3	1307.5	1320.3	1332.8	1345.0	1403.2	1459.0	1513.9	1623.5	1734.8	1848.8
	s		1.4722	1.5084	1.5212	1.5333	1.5449	1.5559	1.5665	1.6147	1.6573	1.6963	1.7666	1.8299	1.8881
800 (518.23)	v		0.6154	0.6779	0.7006	0.7223	0.7433	0.7635	0.7833	0.8763	0.9633	1.0470	1.2088	1.3662	1.5214
	h		1229.8	1270.7	1285.4	1299.4	1312.9	1325.9	1338.6	1398.6	1455.4	1511.0	1621.4	1733.2	1847.5
	s		1.4467	1.4863	1.5000	1.5129	1.5250	1.5366	1.5476	1.5972	1.6407	1.6801	1.7510	1.8146	1.8729
900 (531.98)	v		0.5264	0.5873	0.6089	0.6294	0.6491	0.6680	0.6863	0.7716	0.8506	0.9262	1.0714	1.2124	1.3509
	h		1215.0	1260.1	1275.9	1290.9	1305.1	1318.8	1332.1	1393.9	1451.8	1508.1	1619.3	1731.6	1846.3
	s		1.4216	1.4653	1.4800	1.4938	1.5066	1.5187	1.5303	1.5814	1.6257	1.6656	1.7371	1.8009	1.8595
1000 (544.61)	v		0.4533	0.5140	0.5350	0.5546	0.5733	0.5912	0.6084	0.6878	0.7604	0.8294	0.9615	1.0893	1.2146
	h		1198.3	1248.8	1265.9	1281.9	1297.0	1311.4	1325.3	1389.2	1448.2	1505.1	1617.3	1730.0	1845.0
	s		1.3961	1.4450	1.4610	1.4757	1.4893	1.5021	1.5141	1.5670	1.6121	1.6525	1.7245	1.7886	1.8474
1100 (556.31)	v			0.4532	0.4738	0.4929	0.5110	0.5281	0.5445	0.6191	0.6866	0.7503	0.8716	0.9885	1.1031
	h			1236.7	1255.3	1272.4	1288.5	1303.7	1318.3	1384.3	1444.5	1502.0	1615.2	1728.4	1843.8
	s			1.4251	1.4425	1.4583	1.4728	1.4862	1.4989	1.5535	1.5995	1.6405	1.7130	1.7775	1.8363
1200 (567.22)	v			0.4016	0.4222	0.4410	0.4586	0.4752	0.4909	0.5617	0.6250	0.6843	0.7967	0.9046	1.0101
	h			1223.5	1243.9	1262.4	1279.6	1295.7	1311.0	1379.3	1440.7	1499.2	1613.1	1726.9	1842.5
	s			1.4052	1.4243	1.4413	1.4568	1.4710	1.4843	1.5409	1.5879	1.6293	1.7025	1.7672	1.8263

Superheated-steam table (pressure in lb/in², saturation temperature in °F in parentheses; for each pressure the three property rows are v, h, s). Temperature columns (1–12) are unlabeled in this excerpt; "....." denotes a value omitted in the original table.

Pressure (sat. temp)	prop	1	2	3	4	5	6	7	8	9	10	11	12
1400 (587.10)	v	0.8640	0.7727	0.6789	0.5805	0.5281	0.4714	0.4062	0.3912	0.3753	0.3580	0.3390	0.3174
	h	1840.0	1723.7	1608.9	1493.2	1433.1	1369.1	1295.5	1278.5	1260.3	1240.4	1218.4	1193.0
	s	1.8083	1.7489	1.6836	1.6093	1.5666	1.5177	1.4567	1.4419	1.4258	1.4079	1.3877	1.3639
1600 (604.90)	v	0.7545	0.6738	0.5906	0.5027	0.4553	0.4034	0.3417	0.3271	0.3112	0.2936	0.2733	.....
	h	1837.5	1720.5	1604.6	1487.0	1425.3	1353.4	1278.7	1259.6	1238.7	1215.2	1187.8	.....
	s	1.7926	1.7328	1.6669	1.5914	1.5476	1.4964	1.4303	1.4137	1.3952	1.3741	1.3489	.....
1800 (621.03)	v	0.6693	0.5938	0.5218	0.4421	0.3986	0.3572	0.2907	0.2760	0.2597	0.2407	.....	.....
	h	1835.0	1717.3	1600.4	1480.8	1417.4	1347.2	1260.3	1238.5	1214.0	1185.1	.....	.....
	s	1.7786	1.7185	1.6520	1.5752	1.5301	1.4765	1.4041	1.3855	1.3638	1.3377	.....	.....
2000 (635.82)	v	0.6011	0.5352	0.4668	0.3935	0.3532	0.3074	0.2489	0.2337	0.2151	0.1936	.....	.....
	h	1832.5	1714.1	1596.1	1474.5	1409.2	1335.5	1240.0	1214.8	1184.9	1145.6	.....	.....
	s	1.7660	1.7055	1.6334	1.5603	1.5139	1.4576	1.3783	1.3564	1.3300	1.2945	.....	.....
2500 (668.13)	v	0.4784	0.4244	0.3678	0.3061	0.2710	0.2294	0.1686	0.1484	.....	.....	.....	.....
	h	1829.2	1701.1	1553.3	1453.4	1337.8	1303.6	1176.8	1132.3	.....	.....	.....	.....
	s	1.7389	1.6775	1.6098	1.5273	1.4772	1.4127	1.3073	1.2087	.....	.....	.....	.....
3000 (695.36)	v	0.3935	0.3535	0.3018	0.2476	0.2150	0.1730	0.0984	.....	.....	.....	.....	.....
	h	1819.9	1699.0	1574.3	1441.8	1325.0	1297.2	1060.7	.....	.....	.....	.....	.....
	s	1.7163	1.6540	1.5337	1.4984	1.4433	1.3600	1.1966	.....	.....	.....	.....	.....
3206.2 (705.40)	v	0.3703	0.3267	0.2806	0.2288	0.1981	0.1583	.....	.....	.....	.....	.....	.....
	h	1817.2	1694.6	1569.8	1434.7	1335.2	1250.5	.....	.....	.....	.....	.....	.....
	s	1.7030	1.6452	1.5742	1.4874	1.4303	1.3505	.....	.....	.....	.....	.....	.....
3500	v	0.3381	0.2977	0.2546	0.2058	0.1762	0.1364	0.0306	.....	.....	.....	.....	.....
	h	1813.6	1689.8	1583.3	1424.5	1340.7	1224.9	780.5	.....	.....	.....	.....	.....
	s	1.6968	1.6336	1.5515	1.4723	1.4127	1.3241	0.9515	.....	.....	.....	.....	.....
4000	v	0.2943	0.2581	0.2192	0.1743	0.1462	0.1052	0.0287	.....	.....	.....	.....	.....
	h	1807.2	1681.7	1552.1	1406.8	1314.4	1174.8	763.8	.....	.....	.....	.....	.....
	s	1.6795	1.6154	1.5417	1.4482	1.3827	1.2757	0.9347	.....	.....	.....	.....	.....
4500	v	0.2602	0.2273	0.1917	0.1500	0.1226	0.0798	0.0276	.....	.....	.....	.....	.....
	h	1800.9	1673.5	1540.8	1388.4	1286.5	1113.9	753.5	.....	.....	.....	.....	.....
	s	1.6640	1.5990	1.5235	1.4253	1.3529	1.2204	0.9235	.....	.....	.....	.....	.....
5000	v	0.2329	0.2027	0.1696	0.1303	0.1036	0.0593	0.0268	.....	.....	.....	.....	.....
	h	1794.5	1665.3	1529.5	1369.5	1256.5	1047.1	746.4	.....	.....	.....	.....	.....
	s	1.6499	1.5839	1.5066	1.4034	1.3231	1.1622	0.9152	.....	.....	.....	.....	.....
5500	v	0.2106	0.1825	0.1516	0.1143	0.0880	0.0463	0.0262	.....	.....	.....	.....	.....
	h	1788.1	1657.0	1518.2	1349.3	1224.1	985.0	741.3	.....	.....	.....	.....	.....
	s	1.6369	1.5699	1.4908	1.3821	1.2930	1.1093	0.9090	.....	.....	.....	.....	.....

* Abridged from *Thermodynamic Properties of Steam*, by Joseph H. Keenan and Frederick G. Keyes, John Wiley & Sons, Inc., 1936.

Table 5. Compressed Liquid

		32°	100°	200°	300°	400°	500°	600°	620°	640°	660°	680°	690°	700°	705.4°
Saturated Liquid	p	0.08854	0.9492	11.526	67.013	247.31	680.8	1542.9	1786.6	2059.7	2365.4	2708.1	2895.1	3093.7	3206.2
	v_f	0.016022	0.016132	0.016634	0.017449	0.018639	0.020432	0.023629	0.02466	0.02598	0.02777	0.03054	0.03277	0.03692	0.05030
	h_f	0	67.97	167.99	269.59	374.97	487.82	617.0	646.7	678.6	714.2	757.3	784.4	823.3	902.7
	s_f	0	0.12948	0.29382	0.43694	0.56638	0.68871	0.8131	0.8398	0.8679	0.8987	0.9351	0.9578	0.9905	1.0580

Abs. Press. Lb/Sq. In. (Sat. Temp.)

		32°	100°	200°	300°	400°	500°
200 (381.79)	$(v-v_f)\cdot 10^5$	−1.1	−1.1	−1.1	−1.1		
	$(h-h_f)$	+0.61	+0.54	+0.41	+0.23		
	$(s-s_f)\cdot 10^3$	+0.03	−0.05	−0.21	−0.21		
400 (444.59)	$(v-v_f)\cdot 10^5$	−2.3	−2.1	−2.2	−2.8	−2.1	
	$(h-h_f)$	+1.21	+1.09	+0.88	+0.61	+0.16	
	$(s-s_f)\cdot 10^3$	+0.04	−0.16	−0.47	−0.56	−0.40	
600 (486.21)	$(v-v_f)\cdot 10^5$	−3.5	−3.2	−3.4	−4.3	−4.4	
	$(h-h_f)$	+1.80	+1.67	+1.31	+0.97	+0.39	
	$(s-s_f)\cdot 10^3$	+0.07	−0.27	−0.74	−0.94	−0.96	
800 (518.23)	$(v-v_f)\cdot 10^5$	−4.6	−4.0	−4.4	−5.6	−6.5	−1.7
	$(h-h_f)$	+2.39	+2.17	+1.78	+1.35	+0.61	−0.05
	$(s-s_f)\cdot 10^3$	+0.10	−0.40	−0.97	−1.27	−1.48	−0.53
1000 (544.61)	$(v-v_f)\cdot 10^5$	−5.7	−5.1	−5.4	−6.9	−8.7	−6.4
	$(h-h_f)$	+2.99	+2.70	+2.21	+1.75	+0.84	−0.14
	$(s-s_f)\cdot 10^3$	+0.15	−0.53	−1.20	−1.64	−2.00	−1.41

1500 (506.23)	$(v-v_f)\cdot10^5$	-8.4	-7.5	-8.1	-10.4	-14.1	-17.3								
	$(h-h_f)$	$+4.48$	$+3.99$	$+3.36$	$+2.70$	$+1.44$	$+0.29$								
	$(s-s_f)\cdot10^3$	$+0.20$	-0.86	-1.79	-2.53	-3.32	-3.56								
2000 (635.82)	$(v-v_f)\cdot10^5$	-11.0	-9.9	-10.8	-13.8	-19.5	-27.8	-32.6							
	$(h-h_f)$	$+5.97$	$+5.31$	$+4.51$	$+3.64$	$+2.03$	-0.38	-2.5							
	$(s-s_f)\cdot10^3$	$+0.22$	-1.18	-2.39	-3.42	-4.57	-5.58	-4.3							
2500 (668.13)	$(v-v_f)\cdot10^5$	-13.7	-12.3	-13.4	-17.2	-24.8	-37.7	-61.9	-67	-48					
	$(h-h_f)$	$+7.49$	$+6.58$	$+5.63$	$+4.55$	$+2.66$	-0.41	-4.9	-5.4	-3.1					
	$(s-s_f)\cdot10^3$	$+0.25$	-1.48	-2.97	-4.25	-5.79	-7.54	-8.5	-6.9	-3.4					
3000 (695.36)	$(v-v_f)\cdot10^5$	-16.3	-14.7	-16.0	-20.7	-30.0	-47.1	-87.9	-101	-122	-146	-172	-166		
	$(h-h_f)$	$+9.00$	$+7.88$	$+6.76$	$+5.49$	$+3.33$	-0.41	-6.9	-8.7	-10.3	-11.8	-12.2	-8.9		
	$(s-s_f)\cdot10^3$	$+0.28$	-1.79	-3.56	-5.12	-7.03	-9.42	-12.4	-13.0	-13.4	-13.3	-12.0	-8.2		
3206.2 (705.40)	$(v-v_f)\cdot10^5$	-17.5	-15.7	-17.1	-22.2	-32.1	-51.0	-98.0	-114	-139	-177	-240	-299	-354	0
	$(h-h_f)$	$+9.61$	$+8.45$	$+7.25$	$+5.90$	$+3.62$	-0.40	-7.6	-9.8	-12.1	-14.6	-17.6	-19.4	-21.6	0
	$(s-s_f)\cdot10^3$	$+0.29$	-1.93	-3.80	-5.50	-7.54	-10.19	-14.0	-15.0	-16.0	-16.8	-17.8	-18.4	-19.2	0
3500	$(v-v_f)\cdot10^5$	-19.0	-16.9	-18.5	-24.2	-35.0	-56.1	-111.1	-133	-166	-215	-312	-407	-634	-1815
	$(h-h_f)$	$+10.44$	$+9.17$	$+7.90$	$+6.44$	$+4.01$	-0.34	-8.6	-11.2	-14.3	-17.8	-24.2	-29.7	-42.8	-104.1
	$(s-s_f)\cdot10^3$	$+0.30$	-2.08	-4.14	-5.97	-8.21	-11.24	-16.0	-17.4	-19.1	-20.9	-24.9	-28.7	-39.0	-91.0

Reprinted by permission from *Thermodynamic Properties of Steam*, by Joseph H. Keenan and Frederick G. Keyes: John Wiley & Sons, Inc., New York, 1936.

TABLE 6. THERMODYNAMIC PROPERTIES OF AIR AT LOW PRESSURE

(For One Pound)

(The properties given here are condensed by permission from *Gas Tables*, by J. H. Keenan
and J. Kaye, published by John Wiley and Sons, 1948.)

T, °R	T, °F	h, B/lb$_m$	p_r	u, B/lb$_m$	v_r	ϕ, B/lb$_m$ °R
100	−360	23.7	.00384	16.9	9640	.1971
120	−340	28.5	.00726	20.3	6120	.2408
140	−320	33.3	.01244	23.7	4170	.2777
160	−300	38.1	.01982	27.1	2990	.3096
180	−280	42.9	.0299	30.6	2230	.3378
200	−260	47.7	.0432	34.0	1717	.3630
220	−240	52.5	.0603	37.4	1352	.3858
240	−220	57.2	.0816	40.8	1089	.4067
260	−200	62.0	.1080	44.2	892	.4258
280	−180	66.8	.1399	47.6	742	.4436
200	−160	71.6	.1780	51.0	624	.4601
320	−140	76.4	.2229	54.5	532	.4755
340	−120	81.2	.2754	57.9	457	.4900
260	−100	86.0	.336	61.3	397	.5037
380	−80	90.8	.406	64.7	347	.5166
400	−60	95.5	.486	68.1	305	.5289
420	−40	100.3	.576	71.5	270	.5406
440	−20	105.1	.678	74.9	241	.5517
460	0	109.9	.791	78.4	215.3	.5624
480	20	114.7	.918	81.8	193.6	.5726
500	40	119.5	1.059	85.2	174.9	.5823
520	60	124.3	1.215	88.6	158.6	.5917
540	80	129.1	1.386	92.0	144.3	.6008
560	100	133.9	1.574	95.5	131.8	.6095
580	120	138.7	1.780	98.9	120.7	.6179
600	140	143.5	2.00	102.3	110.9	.6261
620	160	148.3	2.25	105.8	102.1	.6340
640	180	153.1	2.51	109.2	94.3	.6416
660	200	157.9	2.80	112.7	87.3	.6490
680	220	162.7	3.11	116.1	81.0	.6562
700	240	167.6	3.45	119.6	75.2	.6632
720	260	172.4	3.81	123.0	70.1	.6700
740	280	177.2	4.19	126.5	65.4	.6766
760	300	182.1	4.61	130.0	61.1	.6831
780	320	186.9	5.05	133.5	57.2	.6894

TABLE 6. THERMODYNAMIC PROPERTIES OF AIR AT LOW PRESSURE (*Cont'd.*)
(For One Pound)

T, °R	T, °F	h, B/lb$_m$	p_r	u, B/lb$_m$	v_r	ϕ, B/lb$_m$ °R
800	340	191.8	5.53	137.0	53.6	.6956
820	360	196.7	6.03	140.5	50.4	.7016
840	380	201.6	6.57	144.0	47.3	.7075
860	400	206.5	7.15	147.5	44.6	.7132
880	420	211.4	7.76	151.0	42.0	.7189
900	440	216.3	8.41	154.6	39.6	.7244
920	460	221.2	9.10	158.1	37.4	.7298
940	480	226.1	9.83	161.7	35.4	.7351
960	500	231.1	10.61	165.3	33.5	.7403
980	520	236.0	11.43	168.8	31.8	.7454
1000	540	241.0	12.30	172.4	30.1	.7504
1020	560	246.0	13.22	176.0	28.6	.7554
1040	580	251.0	14.18	179.7	27.2	.7602
1060	600	256.0	15.20	183.3	25.8	.7650
1080	620	261.0	16.28	186.9	24.6	.7696
1100	640	266.0	17.41	190.6	23.4	.7743
1120	660	271.0	18.60	194.2	22.3	.7788
1140	680	276.1	19.86	197.9	21.3	.7833
1160	700	281.1	21.2	201.6	20.29	.7877
1180	720	286.2	22.6	205.3	19.38	.7920
1200	740	291.3	24.0	209.0	18.51	.7963
1220	760	296.4	25.5	212.8	17.70	.8005
1240	780	301.5	27.1	216.5	16.93	.8047
1260	800	306.6	28.8	220.3	16.20	.8088
1280	820	311.8	30.6	224.0	15.52	.8128
1300	840	316.9	32.4	227.8	14.87	.8168
1320	860	322.1	34.3	231.6	14.25	.8208
1340	880	327.3	36.3	235.4	13.67	.8246
1360	900	332.5	38.4	239.2	13.12	.8285
1380	920	337.7	40.6	243.1	12.59	.8323
1400	940	342.9	42.9	246.9	12.10	.8360
1420	960	348.1	45.3	250.8	11.62	.8398
1440	980	353.4	47.8	254.7	11.17	.8434
1460	1000	358.6	50.3	258.5	10.74	.8470
1480	1020	363.9	53.0	262.4	10.34	.8506

TABLE 6. THERMODYNAMIC PROPERTIES OF AIR AT LOW PRESSURE (*Cont'd.*)

(For One Pound)

T, °R	T, °F	h, B/lb$_m$	$\Delta S = 0$ p_r	u, B/lb$_m$	$\Delta S = 0$ v_r	ϕ, B/lb$_m$ °R
1500	1040	369.2	55.9	266.3	9.95	.8542
1520	1060	374.5	58.8	270.3	9.58	.8568
1540	1080	379.8	61.8	274.2	9.23	.8611
1560	1100	385.1	65.0	278.1	8.89	.8646
1580	1120	390.4	68.3	282.1	8.57	.8679
1600	1140	395.7	71.7	286.1	8.26	.8713
1620	1160	401.1	75.3	290.0	7.97	.8746
1640	1180	406.4	79.0	294.0	7.69	.8779
1660	1200	411.8	82.8	298.0	7.42	.8812
1680	1220	417.2	86.8	302.0	7.17	.8844
1700	1240	422.6	91.0	306.1	6.92	.8876
1720	1260	428.0	95.2	310.1	6.69	.8907
1740	1280	433.4	99.7	314.1	6.46	.8939
1760	1300	438.8	104.3	318.2	6.25	.8970
1780	1320	444.3	109.1	322.2	6.04	.9000
1800	1340	449.7	114.0	326.3	5.85	.9031
1820	1360	455.2	119.2	330.4	5.66	.9061
1840	1380	460.6	124.5	334.5	5.48	.9091
1860	1400	466.1	130.0	338.6	5.30	.9120
1880	1420	471.6	135.6	342.7	5.13	.9150
1900	1440	477.1	141.5	346.8	4.97	.9179
1920	1460	482.6	147.6	351.0	4.82	.9208
1940	1480	488.1	153.9	355.1	4.67	.9236
1960	1500	493.6	160.4	359.3	4.53	.9264
1980	1520	499.1	167.1	363.4	4.39	.9293
2000	1540	504.7	174.0	367.6	4.26	.9320
2020	1560	510.3	181.2	371.8	4.13	.9348
2040	1580	515.8	188.5	376.0	4.01	.9376
2060	1600	521.4	196.2	380.2	3.89	.9403
2080	1620	527.0	204.0	384.4	3.78	.9430
2100	1640	532.6	212	388.6	3.67	.9456
2120	1660	538.2	220	392.8	3.56	.9483
2140	1680	543.7	229	397.0	3.46	.9509
2160	1700	549.4	238	401.3	3.36	.9535
2180	1720	555.0	247	405.5	3.27	.9561

TABLE 6. THERMODYNAMIC PROPERTIES OF AIR AT LOW PRESSURE (*Cont'd.*)
(For One Pound)

T, °R	T, °F	h, B/lb$_m$	$\Delta s = 0$ p_r	u, B/lb$_m$	$\Delta s = 0$ v_r	ϕ, B/lb$_m$ °R
2200	1740	560.6	257	409.8	3.18	.9587
2220	1760	566.2	266	414.0	3.09	.9612
2240	1780	571.9	276	418.3	3.00	.9638
2260	1800	577.5	287	422.6	2.92	.9663
2280	1820	583.2	297	426.9	2.84	.9688
2300	1840	588.8	308	431.2	2.76	.9712
2320	1860	594.5	319	435.2	2.69	.9737
2340	1880	600.2	331	439.8	2.62	.9761
2360	1900	605.8	343	444.1	2.55	.9785
2380	1920	611.5	355	448.4	2.48	.9809
2400	1940	617.2	368	452.7	2.42	.9833
2420	1960	622.9	380	457.0	2.36	.9857
2440	1980	628.6	394	461.4	2.30	.9880
2460	2000	634.3	407	465.7	2.24	.9904
2480	2020	640.0	421	470.0	2.18	.9927
2500	2040	645.8	436	474.4	2.12	.9950
2520	2060	651.5	450	478.8	2.07	.9972
2540	2080	657.2	466	483.1	2.02	.9995
2560	2100	663.0	481	487.5	1.971	1.0018
2580	2120	668.7	497	491.9	1.922	1.0040
2600	2140	674.5	514	496.3	1.876	1.0062
2620	2160	680.2	530	500.6	1.830	1.0084
2640	2180	686.0	548	505.0	1.786	1.0106
2660	2200	691.8	565	509.4	1.743	1.0128
2680	2220	697.6	583	513.8	1.702	1.0150
2700	2240	703.4	602	518.3	1.662	1.0171
2720	2260	709.1	621	522.7	1.623	1.0193
2740	2280	714.9	640	527.1	1.585	1.0214
2760	2300	720.7	660	531.5	1.548	1.0235
2780	2320	726.5	681	536.0	1.512	1.0256
2800	2340	732.3	702	540.4	1.478	1.0277
2820	2360	738.2	724	544.8	1.444	1.0297
2840	2380	744.0	746	549.3	1.411	1.0318
2860	2400	749.8	768	553.7	1.379	1.0338
2880	2420	755.6	791	558.2	1.348	1.0359

TABLE 6. THERMODYNAMIC PROPERTIES OF AIR AT LOW PRESSURE (*Cont'd.*)
(For One Pound)

T, °R	T, °F	h, B/lb$_m$	$\overset{\triangle s = 0}{p_r}$	u, B/lb$_m$	$\overset{\triangle s = 0}{v_r}$	ϕ, B/lb$_m$ °R
2900	2440	761.4	815	562.7	1.318	1.0379
2920	2460	767.3	839	567.1	1.289	1.0399
2940	2480	773.1	864	571.6	1.261	1.0419
2960	2500	779.0	889	576.1	1.233	1.0439
2980	2520	784.8	915	580.6	1.206	1.0458
3000	2540	790.7	941	585.0	1.180	1.0478
3020	2560	796.5	969	589.5	1.155	1.0497
3040	2580	802.4	996	594.0	1.130	1.0517
3060	2600	808.3	1025	598.5	1.106	1.0536
3080	2620	814.2	1054	603.0	1.083	1.0555
3100	2640	820.0	1083	607.5	1.060	1.0574
3120	2660	825.9	1114	612.0	1.038	1.0593
3140	2680	831.8	1145	616.6	1.016	1.0612
3160	2700	837.7	1176	621.1	.995	1.0630
3180	2720	843.6	1209	625.6	.975	1.0649
3200	2740	849.5	1242	630.1	.955	1.0668
3220	2760	855.4	1276	634.6	.935	1.0686
3240	2780	861.3	1310	639.2	.916	1.0704
3260	2800	867.2	1345	643.7	.898	1.0722
3280	2820	873.1	1381	648.3	.880	1.0740
3300	2840	879.0	1418	652.8	.862	1.0758
3320	2860	884.9	1455	657.4	.845	1.0776
3340	2880	890.9	1494	661.9	.828	1.0794
3360	2900	896.8	1533	666.5	.812	1.0812
3380	2920	902.7	1573	671.0	.796	1.0830
3400	2940	908.7	1613	675.6	.781	1.0847
3420	2960	914.6	1655	680.2	.766	1.0864
3440	2980	920.6	1697	684.8	.751	1.0882
3460	3000	926.5	1740	689.3	.736	1.0899
3480	3020	932.4	1784	693.9	.722	1.0916
3500	3040	938.4	1829	698.5	.709	1.0933
3520	3060	944.4	1875	703.1	.695	1.0950
3540	3080	950.3	1922	707.6	.682	1.0967
3560	3100	956.3	1970	712.2	.670	1.0984
3580	3120	962.2	2018	716.8	.657	1.1000
3600	3140	968.2	2068	721.4	.645	1.1017
3620	3160	974.2	2118	726.0	.633	1.1034
3640	3180	980.2	2170	730.6	.621	1.1050
3660	3200	986.1	2222	735.3	.610	1.1066
3680	3220	992.1	2276	739.9	.599	1.1083

TABLE 7

GAS PROPERTIES AT 60F

Gas	Specific Heat, B/lb_m F		Specific Heat Ratio, γ	Gas Constant R, ft-lb/lb_m R
	c_p	c_v		
Air........................	0.240	0.171	1.40	53.3
Carbon dioxide, CO_2..........	0.195	0.150	1.30	35.1
Carbon monoxide, CO........	0.248	0.177	1.40	55.2
Helium, H_e.................	1.251	0.754	1.66	386
Hydrogen, H_2................	3.41	2.42	1.41	767
Nitrogen, N_2................	0.248	0.177	1.40	55.2
Oxygen, O_2.................	0.219	0.157	1.39	48.3
Water Vapor, H_2O...........	0.451	0.339	1.33	85.7

TABLE 8. PROPERTIES OF SATURATED AMMONIA*

(Condensed from tables prepared by United States Bureau of Standards)

Pressure (abs) lb/sq in.	Temperature, °F.	Specific volume, cu ft/lb_m,	Enthalpy, B/lb_m			Entropy		
			Liquid	Evaporation	Vapor	Liquid	Evaporation	Vapor
p	t	v_g	h_f	h_{fg}	h_g	s_f	s_{fg}	s_g
10.0	−41.34	25.81	−1.4	598.5	597.1	−0.0034	1.4310	1.4276
20.0	−16.64	13.50	25.0	581.2	606.2	0.0578	1.3122	1.3700
30	− 0.57	9.236	42.3	569.3	611.6	0.0962	1.2402	1.3364
40	11.66	7.047	55.6	559.8	615.4	0.1246	1.1879	1.3125
50	21.67	5.710	66.5	551.7	618.2	0.1475	1.1464	1.2939
60	30.21	4.805	75.9	544.6	620.5	0.1668	1.1119	1.2787
70	37.70	4.151	84.2	538.2	622.4	0.1835	1.0823	1.2658
80	44.40	3.655	91.7	532.3	624.0	0.1982	1.0563	1.2545
90	50.47	3.266	98.4	526.9	625.3	0.2115	1.0330	1.2445
100	56.05	2.952	104.7	521.8	626.5	0.2237	1.0119	1.2356
110	61.21	2.693	110.5	517.0	627.5	0.2348	0.9927	1.2275
120	66.02	2.476	116.0	512.4	628.4	0.2452	0.9749	1.2201
130	70.53	2.291	121.1	508.1	629.2	0.2548	0.9584	1.2132
140	74.79	2.132	126.0	503.9	629.9	0.2638	0.9430	1.2068
150	78.81	1.994	130.6	499.9	630.5	0.2724	0.9285	1.2009
160	82.64	1.872	135.0	496.1	631.1	0.2804	0.9148	1.1952
170	86.29	1.764	139.3	492.3	631.6	0.2881	0.9019	1.1900
180	89.78	1.667	143.3	488.7	623.0	0.2954	0.8896	1.1850
190	93.13	1.581	147.2	485.2	632.4	0.3024	0.8778	1.1802
200	96.34	1.502	150.9	481.8	632.7	0.3090	0.8666	1.1756
225	103.87	1.336	159.7	473.6	633.3	0.3246	0.8405	1.1651
250	110.80	1.202	168.0	465.8	633.8	0.3388	0.8167	1.1555
275	117.22	1.091	175.6	458.4	634.0	0.3519	0.7947	1.1466
300	123.21	0.999	182.9	451.1	634.0	0.3642	0.7741	1.1383

* Taken from *Elements of Engineering Thermodynamics*, Moyer, Calderwood, and Potter: John Wiley and Sons. 1941.

TABLE 9. PROPERTIES OF SUPERHEATED AMMONIA*

(Condensed from tables prepared by United States Bureau of Standards)
v = specific volume in cubic feet per pound; h = enthalpy in Btu per pound;
s = total entropy.

Pressure (abs) lb per sq in. (p)	Temperature of saturated vapor, °F. (t)	Temperatures, degrees Fahrenheit								
		20	40	60	80	100	150	200	250	300
20	−16.6 v	14.78	15.45	16.12	16.78	17.43	19.05	20.66	....	....
	h	626.4	637.0	647.5	658.0	668.5	694.7	721.2	....	....
	s	1.4138	1.4356	1.4562	1.4760	1.4950	1.5399	1.5817	....	....
30	− 0.6 v	9.731	10.20	10.65	11.10	11.55	12.65	13.73	14.81	....
	h	623.5	634.6	645.5	656.2	666.9	693.5	720.3	747.5	....
	s	1.3618	1.3845	1.4059	1.4261	1.4456	1.4911	1.5334	1.5727	....
40	11.7 v	7.203	7.568	7.922	8.268	8.609	9.444	10.27	11.08	....
	h	620.4	632.1	643.4	654.4	665.3	962.3	719.4	746.8	....
	s	1.3231	1.3470	1.3692	1.3900	1.4098	1.4561	1.4987	1.5382	....
50	21.7 v	....	5.988	6.280	6.564	6.843	7.521	8.185	8.840	9.489
	h	....	629.5	641.2	652.6	663.7	691.1	718.5	746.1	774.0
	s	....	1.3169	1.3399	1.3613	1.3816	1.4286	1.4716	1.5118	1.5500
60	30.2 v	....	4.933	5.184	5.428	5.665	6.239	6.798	7.348	7.892
	h	....	626.8	639.0	650.7	662.1	689.9	717.5	745.3	773.3
	s	....	1.2913	1.3152	1.3373	1.3581	1.4058	1.4493	1.4897	1.5281
70	37.7 v	....	4.177	4.401	4.615	4.822	5.323	5.807	6.282	6.750
	h	....	623.9	636.6	648.7	660.4	688.7	716.6	744.5	772.7
	s	....	1.2688	1.2937	1.3166	1.3378	1.3863	1.4302	1.4710	1.5095
80	44.4 v	....	....	3.812	4.005	4.190	4.635	5.063	5.481	5.894
	h	....	....	634.3	646.7	658.7	687.5	715.6	743.7	772.1
	s	....	....	1.2745	1.2981	1.3199	1.3692	1.4136	1.4547	1.4933
90	50.5 v	....	....	3.353	3.529	3.698	4.100	4.484	4.859	5.288
	h	....	....	631.8	644.7	657.0	686.3	714.7	743.0	771.5
	s	....	....	1.2571	1.2814	1.3038	1.3539	1.3988	1.4401	1.4789
100	56.1 v	....	....	2.985	3.149	3.304	3.672	4.021	4.361	4.695
	h	....	....	629.3	642.6	655.2	685.0	713.7	742.2	770.8
	s	....	....	1.2409	1.2661	1.2891	1.3401	1.3854	1.4271	1.4660

* Taken from *Elements of Engineering Thermodynamics*, by J. A. Moyer, J. P. Calderwood, and A. A. Potter: John Wiley & Sons, Inc., 1941.

TABLE 9. PROPERTIES OF SUPERHEATED AMMONIA (*Cont'd.*)

Pressure (abs) lb per sq in. (p)	Temperature of saturated vapor, °F. (t)	Temperatures, degrees Fahrenheit								
		20	40	60	80	100	150	200	250	300
110	61.2 v	....	....	....	2.837	2.981	3.321	3.642	3.954	4.259
	H	....	....	....	640.5	653.4	683.7	712.8	741.5	770.2
	S	....	....	....	1.2519	1.2755	1.3274	1.3732	1.4151	1.4543
120	66.0 v	....	....	....	2.576	2.712	3.029	3.326	3.614	3.895
	H	....	....	....	638.3	651.6	682.5	711.8	740.7	769.6
	S	....	....	....	1.2386	1.2628	1.3157	1.3620	1.4042	1.4435
130	70.5 v	....	....	....	2.355	2.484	2.781	3.059	3.326	3.587
	H	....	....	....	636.0	649.7	681.2	710.9	739.9	769.0
	S	....	....	....	1.2260	1.2509	1.3048	1.3516	1.3941	1.4336
140	74.8 v	....	....	....	2.166	2.288	2.569	2.830	3.080	3.323
	H	....	....	....	633.8	647.8	679.9	709.9	739.2	768.3
	S	....	....	....	1.2140	1.2396	1.2945	1.3418	1.3846	1.4243
150	78.8 v	....	....	....	....	2.118	2.385	2.631	2.866	3.095
	H	....	....	....	....	645.9	678.6	708.9	738.4	767.7
	S	....	....	....	....	1.2289	1.2849	1.3327	1.3758	1.4157
160	82.6 v	....	....	....	....	1.969	2.224	2.457	2.679	2.895
	H	....	....	....	....	643.9	677.2	707.9	737.6	767.1
	S	....	....	....	....	1.2186	1.2757	1.3240	1.3675	1.4076
180	89.8 v	....	....	....	....	1.720	1.955	2.167	2.367	2.561
	H	....	....	....	....	639.9	674.5	705.9	736.1	765.8
	S	....	....	....	....	1.1992	1.2586	1.3081	1.3521	1.3926
200	96.3 v	....	....	....	....	1.520	1.740	1.935	2.118	2.295
	H	....	....	....	....	635.6	671.8	703.9	734.5	764.5
	S	....	....	....	....	1.1809	1.2429	1.2935	1.3382	1.3791
220	102.4 v	....	....	....	....	....	1.564	1.745	1.914	2.076
	H	....	....	....	....	....	669.0	701.9	732.9	763.2
	S	....	....	....	....	....	1.2281	1.2801	1.3255	1.3668
240	108.1 v	....	....	....	....	....	1.416	1.587	1.745	1.895
	H	....	....	....	....	....	666.1	699.8	731.3	762.0
	S	....	....	....	....	....	1.2145	1.2677	1.3137	1.3554

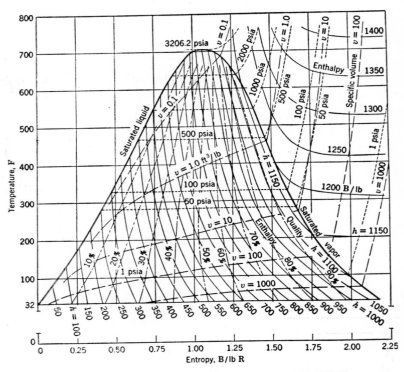

Chart II. temperature-entropy diagram for steam.
(Data from J. H. Keenan and F. G. Keyes, *Thermodynamic Properties of Steam*, John Wiley & Sons, Inc., 1936.)

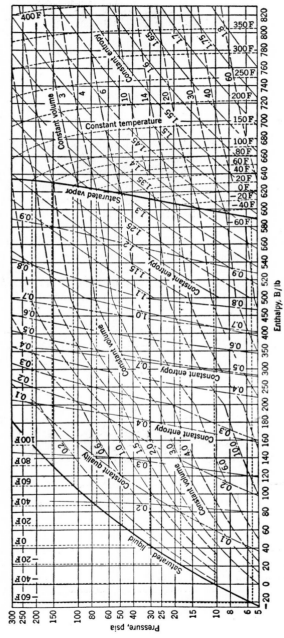

CHART III. PRESSURE-ENTHALPY DIAGRAM FOR AMMONIA.
(Data from "Tables of Thermodynamic Properties
of Ammonia," Bureau of Standards, U. S. Department of Commerce.)

Glossary of Thermodynamic Terms

INTRODUCTION

The material in the text has been presented primarily to acquaint the student with the fundamentals of engineering thermodynamics. Brief mention has been made of many thermodynamic devices and measurements but always in relation to the application of thermodynamic fundamentals to the devices or measurements. Since the practicing engineer should have a vocabulary of the tools of his profession that is more inclusive than that given in the text, a descriptive glossary of several important thermodynamic terms is presented here as a basis for such a vocabulary. The material is divided into two sections—those terms relating to machinery, and those terms relating to measurements. Some repetition has been made in the interest of completeness. The material for this glossary was suggested by the staff of the Department of Mechanics at the U. S. Military Academy, West Point, N. Y.

Section I: Machinery

1. POSITIVE DISPLACEMENT DEVICES

Mechanisms that absorb work from a fluid or perform work on a fluid that is trapped temporarily within a compartment are called positive displacement devices. *Piston machines* are the most common type of positive displacement device. In these machines the fluid is trapped in a cylinder under the action of a piston. The translational motion of the piston is usually changed to or derived from the rotation of a *crankshaft* by means of a *connecting rod* and *crank*. Examples of piston engines are automobile and aircraft engines, steam engines, hydraulic presses, and air compressors. An air compressor is shown in Fig. 1 and is typical of piston machines.

Gear pumps and *rotary vane compressors* are positive displacement devices that do not employ pistons to transmit work. A rotary vane compressor is shown in Fig. 2.

Fig. 1. Piston compressor, showing components of typical piston machine: (1) piston, (2) cylinder, (3) crankshaft, (4) connecting rod. (Courtesy Worthington Corp.)

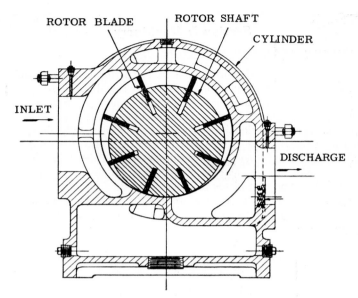

ROTOR BLADE   ROTOR SHAFT

CYLINDER

INLET

DISCHARGE

Fig. 2. Sectional view of rotary vane positive displacement compressor
(Courtesy Allis-Chalmers Manufacturing Co.)

2. *PISTON MACHINE TERMINOLOGY*

Piston machines constitute an important class of thermodynamic devices. The most frequently used terminology is given here.

The *head end* is that end of the cylinder opposite the crankshaft. The *crank end* is that end of the cylinder nearest the crankshaft. *Top* (dead) *center* is the position of the piston at the instant it has stopped at the head end and its direction of motion is reversing. *Bottom* (dead) *center* is the position of the piston at the instant it has stopped at the crank end and its direction of motion is reversing.

Bore and stroke: The bore is the diameter of the piston. The stroke is the movement or distance of movement of the piston from one end of the cylinder to the other. Bore and stroke distances are normally expressed in inches. Example: A "3 × 5" piston has a 3 in. diameter and travels 5 in.

Single-acting and double-acting: If the working fluid pushes only one face of the piston, the machine is single-acting. If the working fluid pushes both faces, the machine is double-acting. In the latter case, the cylinder is completely enclosed and the thermodynamic medium is admitted to both ends of the cylinder.

The *camshaft* is an auxiliary shaft, powered off the crankshaft, and has cams which activate *valves* for controlling fluid flow. *The intake and exhaust ports* are holes with valves which are used to admit and expel the thermodynamic medium. In multicylinder engines, the intake ports are joined together by an *intake manifold*. The exhaust ports are joined together by an *exhaust manifold*.

EXPANSION AND COMPRESSION: A gas or vapor expands or is compressed depending upon the change in its specific volume. If the specific volume increases, then the gas is expanding regardless of what happens to the pressure of the gas.

The *displacement volume* is the volume which the piston displaces as it moves from top center position to bottom center position. It is found by multiplying the area of the piston by its stroke. The *clearance volume* is the volume in the head end of the cylinder when the piston is in the top center position (for single-acting engines). The *cutoff volume* is a term which is normally applied only to diesel engines. It is the volume in the head end of the cylinder when combustion of the fuel has been completed.

VOLUME RATIOS: When dealing with characteristics of piston machines it is convenient to analyze volume changes which occur as the various processes take place within the cylinder (see page 156). These changes are usually expressed as the ratio of the largest volume to the smallest volume of the fluid during the process. Expressed as a fraction, the ratio would always be greater than one. A *compression ratio* would then be the ratio of the initial to the final volume of a compression process. An expansion ratio would be the ratio of final to initial volume in an expansion process. A *cutoff ratio* would be the ratio of the cutoff volume to the clearance volume during the combustion process in a diesel engine. Note that these are volume ratios. Pressure ratios are seldom used except when dealing with turbomachinery.

The *power stroke* is the stroke of an internal combustion engine during which the burned gases do work in expanding. A *two-stroke* engine is one in which power is delivered every other stroke. This corresponds to one power stroke per revolution of the crankshaft. A *four-stroke* engine is one in which each fourth stroke is a power stroke. This corresponds to one power stroke per two revolutions of the crankshaft.

3. *TURBOMACHINERY*

Mechanisms that absorb work from a fluid or perform work on a fluid under steady-flow conditions by means of impulse or reaction forces are called *turbomachines*. The fluid forces act on blades mounted on a central spindle shaft and rotary motion results. Flow of the fluid may be perpendicular to the rotating shaft in which case the machine is termed *radial-flow* or *centrifugal-flow*. If the flow is parallel to the rotating shaft the machine is termed

FIG. 3. TYPICAL TURBINE (GAS OR STEAM) COMPONENTS: AT LEFT, TURBINE CASING AND STATOR ASSEMBLY; AT RIGHT, TURBINE ROTOR ASSEMBLY.

axial-flow. If the flow is a combination of radial and axial the machine is termed *mixed-flow.* Examples of turbomachines are fans, blowers, centrifugal compressors or pumps, propellers, steam and gas turbines. A turbine element from an aircraft gas turbine is shown in Fig. 3.

4. *TURBOMACHINERY TERMINOLOGY*

Although turbomachine terminology tends to be more specialized than that for piston machines, several of the more frequently occurring terms are given here.

The pressure ratio is the ratio of stagnation pressures acting across the machine—outlet to inlet in the case of a compressor, inlet to outlet in the case of a turbine. The pressure ratio for a turbine is frequently called the *expansion ratio,* which should not be confused with the expansion ratio defined for piston machines.

The *wheel* or *disk* is the solid section of the rotating element.

The *blades* are the vanes through which the working fluid passes. They may be either stationary or moving. In the case of turbine rotors the blades are sometimes called *buckets.* The stationary blades decrease the kinetic energy and increase the enthalpy in the case of compressors, or decrease the enthalpy and increase the kinetic energy in the case of turbines.

The *rotor* is the rotating element consisting of the wheel and moving blades. The *stator* is the ring assembly of stationary blades. In the case of turbines it is sometimes called the *nozzle ring* or *nozzle diaphragm*. In the case of centrifugal compressors it is called the *diffuser* since it slows down the flow.

A *stage* is the combination of a rotor and stator. A multistage unit consists of two or more stages in series.

5. COMPRESSOR OR PUMP

A compressor or pump is a thermodynamic device in which shaft work is utilized to increase the energy (and pressure) stored in a stream of fluid. A *compressor* handles gases or vapors while a *pump* handles liquids. When liquids are pumped the ideal process is considered to be at constant volume; that is, the fluid is thought of as being incompressible. When gases or vapors are compressed the ideal process may be isentropic (no heat transferred as a result of very rapid compression), polytropic, or isothermal (perfect cooling, approached by intercooling between stages in a multistage compressor), or at constant temperature, depending upon the quantity of heat rejected during compression. Compressors or pumps may be either positive displacement or turbo types. An exception to the above definition is the *vacuum pump*, which utilizes shaft work to decrease the energy (and pressure) of a gas (air) below its ambient level. Vacuum pumps are usually positive displacement devices.

A piston compressor is shown in Fig. 1. Figure 4 shows an axial-flow compressor and a centrifugal flow compressor, both of the turbo type.

6. TURBINE OR EXPANDER

A *turbine* or *expander* is a thermodynamic device in which shaft work is obtained from energy previously stored in a stream of fluid. A turbine is a turbomachine and an expander is normally considered to be a piston machine. While turbines may be of the radial-flow type, most turbines are of the axial-flow type, such as that shown in Fig. 3. The ideal expansion process may be isentropic (rapid expansion), polytropic, or isothermal, although the latter finds little application to practical heat engines.

7. EXPANSION VALVE

An *expansion valve* is a valve (normally insulated) used to increase the volume of a flowing fluid. No shaft work occurs during the process and the expansion is normally rapid enough to assume no transfer of heat even though the valve is not insulated. The process occurs with constant stagnation enthalpy, but the entering and leaving kinetic energies are usually small, allowing the approximation that the entering enthalpy is equal to the leaving enthalpy. The process is irreversible and is called a *throttling process*. Such throttling valves are sometimes called *Joule-Thompson* valves. An example

(a)   (b)

(c)

FIG. 4. TYPICAL TURBO-COMPRESSORS: (a) AXIAL-FLOW COMPRESSOR ROTOR AS-
SEMBLY; (b) AXIAL-FLOW CASE HALF WITH STATOR BLADES; (c) CENTRIFUGAL-FLOW
IMPELLER.

of an expansion valve is the valve in the vapor refrigeration cycle used to expand the saturated liquid at high pressure to wet vapor at low pressure, with a corresponding drop in temperature.

8. *HEAT EXCHANGER*

A *heat exchanger* is any device used to transfer heat from one medium to another. Frequently heat is extracted from one fluid and absorbed by another fluid by circulating both fluids through a heat exchanger where the fluids are separated by tube walls of a heat-conducting metal, such as copper. Several classifications of heat exchangers are given in Chapter XIV. No shaft work is done in steady-flow heat exchangers and the ideal process occurs at constant stagnation pressure.

Examples of heat exchangers are oil radiators; preheaters; compressor intercoolers and aftercoolers; and steam boilers, superheaters, and condensers. A steam boiler plant is shown in Fig. 5.

Combustion chambers, such as oil burners, jet engine combustors, and afterburners may also be classed as heat exchangers in which air and fuel are mixed and the chemical energy of combustion is absorbed by the combustion products. A gas turbine combustor is shown in Fig. 6.

Nuclear reactors are another class of heat exchanger in which the energy of atomic fission generated within the reactor is removed by the circulation of a fluid coolant. A typical nuclear reactor is shown in Fig. 7.

9. *POWERPLANTS*

Powerplants are thermodynamic systems whose purpose is to produce rotary shaft power. They may be classed as piston or turbine types. The essential processes of all powerplants are compression, heat addition, expansion, and heat rejection. Several of the most common powerplants will be mentioned in the following paragraphs.

One of the most familiar types of piston powerplants is the conventional *spark ignition internal combustion* engine used to power automobiles as shown in Fig. 8. For more rugged duty and for stationary powerplants the *diesel* or *compression ignition* internal combustion engine is used.

The *steam engine*, which is becoming obsolete except for special applications, is another example of a piston engine that has been widely used as the prime mover of a thermodynamic system.

In the field of turbine powerplants the *steam turbine* is almost universally used for the production of electric power and for marine propulsion. A multi-stage steam turbine is shown in Fig. 9. Steam cycles are described in Chapter IX.

Recent improvements in *gas turbines* have led to their use in the petroleum and natural gas industries. Gas turbine cycles are described in Chapter VIII.

Fig. 5. Steam boiler installation, showing typical components: (1) pulverizers, (2) burners, (3) furnace, (4) steam drum, (5) suspension frame, (6) superheater, (7) economizer, (8) air heater. (Courtesy Babcock & Wilcox Co.)

10. *PROPULSION SYSTEMS*

Propulsion systems are a combination of thermodynamic devices whose purpose is to propel craft through air, space, or water. Until recent years the most common propulsion system consisted of a shaft-power engine driving a *propeller* for either marine or aircraft. The propeller develops propulsive

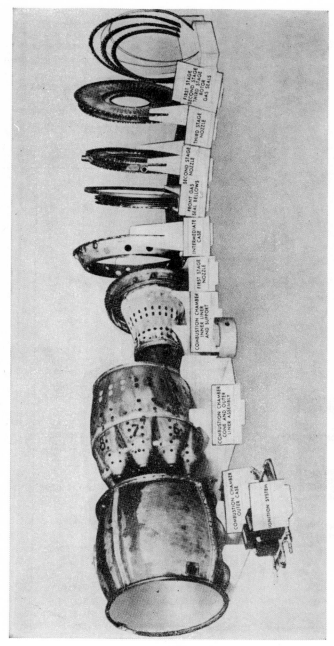

Labels visible in figure:

FIRST STAGE SECOND STAGE THIRD STAGE ROTOR GAS SEALS

THIRD STAGE NOZZLE

SECOND STAGE NOZZLE

FRONT GAS SEAL BELLOWS

INTERMEDIATE CASE

FIRST STAGE NOZZLE

COMBUSTION CHAMBER INNER LINER AND SUPPORT

COMBUSTION CHAMBER CONE AND OUTER LINER ASSEMBLY

COMBUSTION CHAMBER OUTER CASE

IGNITION SYSTEM

FIG. 6. GAS TURBINE COMBUSTOR. (Courtesy Pratt & Whitney Division, United Aircraft Corp.)

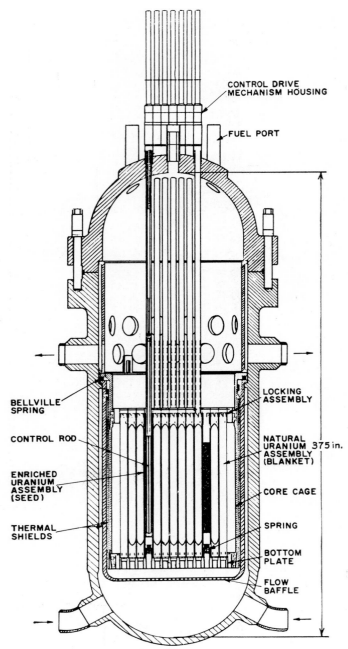

CONTROL DRIVE
MECHANISM HOUSING

FUEL PORT

BELLVILLE
SPRING

CONTROL ROD

ENRICHED
URANIUM
ASSEMBLY
(SEED)

THERMAL
SHIELDS

LOCKING
ASSEMBLY

NATURAL
URANIUM 375 in.
ASSEMBLY
(BLANKET)

CORE CAGE

SPRING

BOTTOM
PLATE

FLOW
BAFFLE

FIG. 7. SECTIONAL VIEW OF TYPICAL NUCLEAR REACTOR.
(Courtesy Western Electric Corp.)

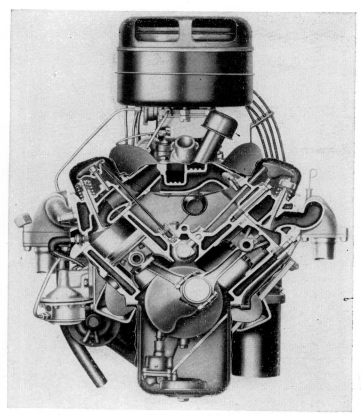

Fig. 8. Cutaway view of v-8 automotive engine.
(Courtesy Chevrolet Division, General Motors Corp.)

thrust by increasing the momentum of the fluid passing through it by accelerating a large mass of fluid a relatively small amount. The propellers for aircraft propulsion systems are driven by both spark ignition piston engines and gas turbines. A *turbopropeller* engine is shown in Fig. 10. The propellers for marine propulsion systems are driven by spark ignition and compression ignition piston engines as well as by steam turbines, and in some cases by steam engines.

In the field of jet propulsion three types of system are widely used, *turbojet*, *ramjet*, and *rocket*. Two types of airbreathing jet propulsion systems are turbojets and ramjets. Figure 11 shows a turbojet engine and Fig. 12 shows a typical supersonic ramjet engine. Both turbojet and ramjet develop pro-

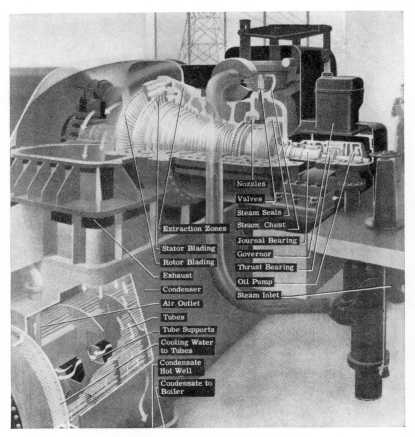

FIG. 9. STEAM TURBINE AND CONDENSER.
(Courtesy Westinghouse Electric Corp.)

pulsive thrust by accelerating a relatively small amount of air (compared to a propeller) to a high velocity relative to the air velocity entering the system. Turbojets are generally used for man-carrying aircraft while ramjets are used for supersonic guided missiles. Ramjets fly at such high speed that the necessary compression is obtained by slowing down the incoming air. Turbojets, which usually operate at lower speeds than ramjets, have mechanical compressors that are driven by gas turbines.

The third type of jet propulsion system, the rocket, carries its entire propellant mass with it and is capable of extreme thrusts and the ability

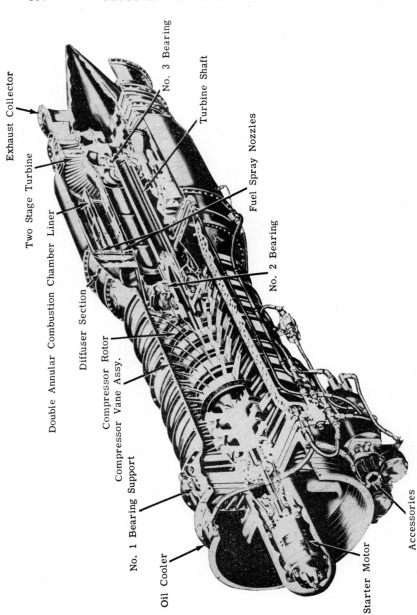

FIG. 11. CUTAWAY VIEW OF TURBOJET ENGINE. (Courtesy Westinghouse Electric Corp.)

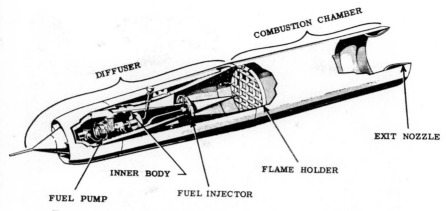

FIG. 12. SCHEMATIC VIEW OF TYPICAL SUPERSONIC RAMJET ENGINE.
(Courtesy Marquardt Aircraft.)

to produce thrust outside the earth's atmosphere. Rockets are broadly classed as *liquid propellant* and *solid propellant*. Liquid propellant systems require either a *turbo-pump* or tank pressurization by inert gas to force the propellant into the combustion chamber. Solid propellant systems are simpler since they depend for pressure on the extreme volume increase the propellant undergoes within a confined space in changing from a solid to a gas during combustion. Liquid propellant systems are basically more efficient since they develop more thrust per unit propellant mass flow rate. The largest application of rockets is in missiles, both guided and unguided. Turbojet, ramjet, and rocket cycles are described in Chapter XI.

11. *REFRIGERATION SYSTEMS*

Refrigeration systems are a combination of thermodynamic devices whose purpose is to maintain the temperature of a confined space below that of its surroundings. They require the same component processes as powerplants, but the fluid flows in the reverse manner, with the heat addition and expansion taking place at lower temperature than the heat rejection and compression processes.

Refrigeration systems may be either piston or turbo devices and are classified as *open cycle* or *closed cycle*. Open cycle units are usually of the turbo type such as that shown in Fig. 13, which is used for aircraft cooling requirements. Closed cycle units may be either positive displacement or turbo type and usually employ expansion valves for the expansion process.

FIG. 13. OPEN CYCLE REFRIGERATION MACHINE SHOWING (1) COMPRESSOR, (2) TURBINE. (Courtesy The Garrett Corp.)

Section II: Measurements

Many measurements are necessary to determine the effectiveness of thermodynamic devices from the engineering standpoint. In research and development work many specialized measurements and instruments are used. No attempt will be made here to describe such specialized instrumentation, but rather a brief description will be presented of the more common measurement devices and measurements encountered in the testing of thermodynamic components and systems.

Two basic quantities to be measured in thermodynamic testing are *pressure* and *temperature*. The instruments used to measure these quantities are mentioned in Chapter I.

12. *PRESSURE MEASUREMENT*

Pressure can be measured by a variety of instruments such as *differential manometers* or *U-tubes, Bourdon gages,* and *aneroid* or *bellows units.* Manometers indicate pressure by the difference in liquid level of the two legs. In the case of Bourdon gages the pressure to be measured is introduced into a curved, closed-end tube of noncircular cross section whose closed end is free to move. The effect of the pressure is to increase the radius of curvature of the curved tube, thus displacing the closed end. The displacement of the closed end is proportional to the applied pressure and is translated to the hand of a circular dial by a mechanical linkage.

In the case of aneroid units, pressure is introduced into a closed-end bellows and displaces the closed end, which is free to move. The displacement of the end of the bellows is translated to a dial by a suitable linkage.

13. TEMPERATURE MEASUREMENT

Temperature is commonly measured by the familiar *liquid column thermometer, vapor pressure thermometer,* and *thermoelectric pyrometer* (thermocouple). The upper temperature limit for commercial thermocouples is approximately 3000F. In the case of high temperatures in the range of the visible spectrum temperatures may be measured by *optical pyrometers* and *total radiation pyrometers,* sometimes called *bolometers.*

Optical pyrometers compare the brightness of the surface whose temperature is to be measured with the brightness of a tungsten filament within the instrument, whose temperature is known in terms of a variable electric current supplied by the instrument.

Total radiation pyrometers focus the radiation from the surface to be measured on a thermopile (several thermocouples in series) through a system of lenses. The voltage output of the thermopile is a function of the radiation intensity of the surface, and hence the temperature.

The measurement of fluid stagnation temperature has been discussed in Chapter VI.

14. FLOW MEASUREMENT

The measurement of mass and volume flow rates is necessary in the analysis of steady-flow thermodynamic devices. Instruments used to measure mass flow rates and volume flow rates are called *flowmeters.* The most basic method of measuring liquid flow rates is to determine the time required to collect a measured volume or weight of liquid in a tank. The rate of flow is determined by dividing the time into the measured quantity. Such a direct method is usually not practical for the measurement of gas flows. Several types of *positive displacement* gas meters are available for measuring gas volume flow rates when the flowing gas is at or near atmospheric pressure. A number of other laboratory flow meters are described in the following paragraphs.

Orifice and *Venturi* meters: These devices measure pressure differences occurring in a closed-channel flow when the area is reduced with a corresponding fluid velocity increase. Using these pressure differences and the area of the restriction, the volume flow rate can be determined; and when the fluid density is also known, the mass flow rate can be calculated. Venturi meters employ a gradual reduction and increase in the flow channel area, while

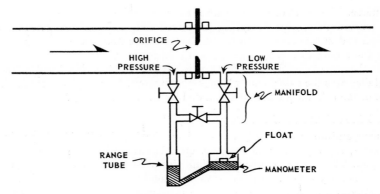

FIG. 14. TYPICAL ORIFICE METER. (Courtesy Fischer & Porter Co.)

orifice meters have an abrupt area reduction. Figure 14 shows a typical orifice meter installation.

VARIABLE-AREA, FLOAT-TYPE METERS: In these flowmeters the fluid flows vertically upward through a transparent, graduated tube having a tapered internal bore flaring upward. A metal float is suspended in the tube and held in equilibrium by the upward force of the fluid moving past it and the downward force of its weight. The position of the float indicates directly the volume or mass rate of flow. Figure 15 is a diagram of a variable-area meter.

TURBINE-TYPE FLOWMETERS: Another type of flowmeter widely used for the measurement of liquids is the turbine flowmeter shown in Fig. 16. The fluid flows through a small turbine wheel causing it to rotate. A permanent magnet is mounted with the rotor which sends a pulse through the sensing pickup on every revolution. The flow rate is proportional to the frequency of current transmitted by the pickup and is indicated or recorded remotely.

15. *ROTATIONAL SPEED*

Rotational speed is another quantity that is measured in testing thermodynamic components with rotating shafts. Instruments used to measure rotational speed are called *tachometers*. Tachometers may be either electrical or mechanical.

16. *POWER*

Power is an important measurement in the testing of a large number of thermodynamic devices. Devices that measure shaft power are called *dynamometers*. A dynamometer resists the turning of the shaft by electrical, mechanical, or hydraulic means. The amount of resistance in terms of torque

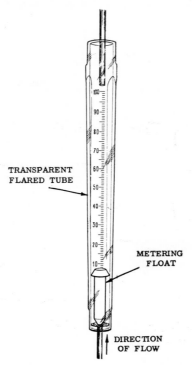

TRANSPARENT
FLARED TUBE

METERING
FLOAT

DIRECTION
OF FLOW

FIG. 15. VARIABLE-AREA FLOAT-TYPE METER.
(Courtesy Potter Aeronautical Co.)

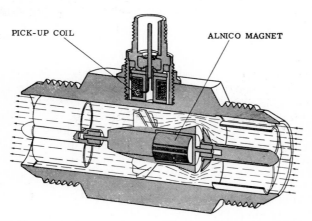

PICK-UP COIL

ALNICO MAGNET

FIG. 16. TURBINE-TYPE FLOWMETER. (Courtesy Potter Aeronautical Co.)

and the rotational speed is measured and from these measurements the power is determined.

One of the simplest dynamometers is the *prony brake*, illustrated schematically by Fig. 17. The prony brake is clamped to the rotating shaft and friction is developed to any desired quantity by tightening the brake. The resulting frictional force tends to turn the brake with the shaft, but turning is prevented by a lever arm that bears on a weighing device. The power measured by a dynamometer is frequently called the *brake power* and is usually measured in horsepower.

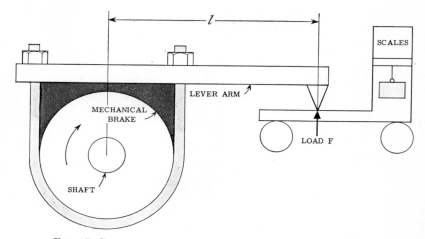

Fig. 17. Schematic diagram of prony brake dynamometer.

The brake or shaft horsepower measured is given by the relation:

$$\text{bhp} = \frac{2\pi N L F}{33,000}$$

where L = lever arm (ft), N = rotational speed of the shaft (rpm), and F = load on scales (lb).

In electrical dynamometers the braking action is produced when lines of magnetic flux are cut by an electrical rotor placed on the shaft.

Hydraulic dynamometers employ fluid couplings to produce the braking action with one half of the coupling attached to the shaft and the other half attached to the casing and prevented from rotating by the weighing device. Such devices are sometimes called *water brakes*. Both electric and hydraulic dynamometers are more suited to testing high-speed machines than the prony brake. Since the work done in all these devices is converted into heat, some provision must be made for cooling them.

In addition to shaft or brake power, several other classifications of power are used in thermodynamic devices. The *ideal power* is the power which would be developed by an ideal (frictionless) engine operating with all processes reversible. The actual power is always less than the ideal, of course.

In piston engines, the power developed by the thermodynamic medium acting on the face of the piston is called the *indicated power*. It can be measured by a device called an *indicator* attached to the cylinder that traces out to scale a plot of fluid pressure vs. volume within the cylinder. The areas of these plots, called *indicator cards* or *indicator diagrams*, are measured with instruments called *planimeters*. By dividing the product of the area and a scale factor called the spring constant by the length of the diagram, an average pressure exerted on the piston is obtained. This pressure is called the indicated mean effective pressure. An indicator diagram is shown in Fig. 18.

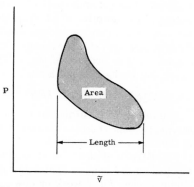

Fig. 18. Typical indicator diagram.

Indicated horsepower is computed from the *indicated mean effective pressure* by the relation:

$$\text{ihp} = \frac{P_m LAN}{33,000}$$

where P_m = mean effective pressure (lb/ft²), L = length of stroke (ft), A = piston area (ft²), and N = number of power strokes per minute.

The *friction power* for a piston engine is the difference between the indicated power and the brake power. It is sometimes measured by running electric dynamometers as motors and finding the power required to rotate the engine with no fuel flow or combustion.

17. TORQUE

Torque is a quantity frequently used in the analysis of engines producing shaft power. In the dynamometer power formula torque is given by the product LF. The torque developed by an engine is a measure of its ability to overcome resistance, and by itself is not a measure of efficiency of an engine or the power developed. For example, an engine with large torque may be quite inefficient and have a low power. The common units for torque are ft-lb.

18. *THRUST*

The output of a jet engine is not measured in terms of power but in terms of *thrust*. The common unit of thrust is lb. Jet engines are mounted for testing in frameworks called *thrust stands*, in which the framework to which the engine is mounted is restrained by a force-measuring device called a *thrust meter*. Thrust is the reactive linear force produced by a jet or propeller engine. It is a measure of the ability of the engine to overcome resisting forces and by itself is not a measure of the thermal efficiency of the engine.

19. *MEASURED EFFICIENCIES*

A number of performance characteristics are determined from tests of thermodynamic components and systems. Several of these will be mentioned in the following paragraphs.

The *thermal efficiency* of an engine is the ratio of the work or power developed to the heat or heat rate supplied, and is normally applied only to engine cycles. Since work or power may be ideal, indicated, or brake, it is possible to have three different thermal efficiencies for the same engine, depending on the power used. For internal combustion engines and gas turbines the *specific fuel consumption* is often used as an indicator of thermal efficiency. The specific fuel consumption (sfc) is the mass (lb_m) of fuel consumed per hour in developing one horsepower, either indicated or brake. For jet engines the specific fuel consumption is defined as the mass (lb_m) of fuel consumed in developing one pound of thrust for one hour. In comparing similar engines operating under similar conditions the specific fuel consumption varies inversely as the thermal efficiency. When thermal efficiency is a maximum, specific fuel consumption is a minimum.

An indicator of the performance of steam engines and steam turbines is the *steam rate*. It is the number of pounds-mass of steam supplied per hour to develop one horsepower. It is simple to measure and compute but is useful only when comparing steam engines or turbines operating under similar inlet and exhaust conditions. It may be based on either the ideal, indicated, or brake power.

The *mechanical efficiency* of an engine is the ratio of the brake power to the indicated power. Expressed in per cent it is always less than 100 and is not only a measure of the efficiency of converting translation motion of piston to rotary motion of crankshaft, but a rough measure of engine wear.

Volumetric efficiency is a measure of the pumping effectiveness of a piston machine. It is the ratio of the mass of air actually inducted into the cylinder per intake stroke to the mass of ambient air required to fill the displacement volume. In general, it is less than 100 per cent, but may be greater than 100 per cent by the above definition for a supercharged engine.

INDEX